MATHEMATICS

Its Content, Methods, and Meaning

VOLUME TWO

MATHEMATICS

Its Content, Methods, and Meaning

EDITED BY

A. D. Aleksandrov, A. N. Kolmogorov, M. A. Lavrent'ev

TRANSLATED BY

S. H. Gould

 THE M.I.T. PRESS
Massachusetts Institute of Technology
Cambridge, Massachusetts

МАТЕМАТИКА

ЕЕ СОДЕРЖАНИЕ, МЕТОДЫ И ЗНАЧЕНИЕ

Издательство Академии Наук СССР

Москва 1956

Fourth printing, 1984

First MIT Press paperback edition, 1969

Translation aided by grant NSF–G 16422 from the National Science Foundation

PREFACE TO
THE RUSSIAN EDITION

Mathematics, which originated in antiquity in the needs of daily life, has developed into an immense system of widely varied disciplines. Like the other sciences, it reflects the laws of the material world around us and serves as a powerful instrument for our knowledge and mastery of nature. But the high level of abstraction peculiar to mathematics means that its newer branches are relatively inaccessible to nonspecialists. This abstract character of mathematics gave birth even in antiquity to idealistic notions about its independence of the material world.

In preparing the present volume, the authors have kept in mind the goal of acquainting a sufficiently wide circle of the Soviet intelligentsia with the various mathematical disciplines, their content and methods, the foundations on which they are based, and the paths along which they have developed.

As a minimum of necessary mathematical knowledge on the part of the reader, we have assumed only secondary-school mathematics, but the volumes differ from one another with respect to the accessibility of the material contained in them. Readers wishing to acquaint themselves for the first time with the elements of higher mathematics may profitably read the first few chapters, but for a complete understanding of the subsequent parts it will be necessary to have made some study of corresponding textbooks. The book as a whole will be understood in a fundamental way only by readers who already have some acquaintance with the applications of mathematical analysis; that is to say, with the differential and integral calculus. For such readers, namely teachers of mathematics and instructors in engineering and the natural sciences, it will be particularly important to read those chapters which introduce the newer branches of mathematics.

Naturally it has not been possible, within the limits of one book, to exhaust all the riches of even the most fundamental results of mathematical research; a certain freedom in the choice of material has been inevitable here. But along general lines, the present book will give an idea of the present state of mathematics, its origins, and its probable future development. For this reason the book is also intended to some extent for persons already acquainted with most of the factual material in it. It may perhaps help to remove a certain narrowness of outlook occasionally to be found in some of our younger mathematicians.

The separate chapters of the book are written by various authors, whose names are given in the Contents. But as a whole the book is the result of collaboration. Its general plan, the choice of material, the successive versions of individual chapters, were all submitted to general discussion, and improvements were made on the basis of a lively exchange of opinions. Mathematicians from several cities in the Soviet Union were given an opportunity, in the form of organized discussion, to make many valuable remarks concerning the original version of the text. Their opinions and suggestions were taken into account by the authors.

The authors of some of the chapters also took a direct share in preparing the final version of other chapters: The introductory part of Chapter II was written essentially by B. N. Delone, while D. K. Faddeev played an active role in the preparation of Chapter IV and Chapter XX.

A share in the work was also taken by several persons other than the authors of the individual chapters: §4 of Chapter XIV was written by L. V. Kantorovič, §6 of Chapter VI by O. A. Ladyženskaja, §5 of Chapter 10 by A. G. Postnikov; work was done on the text of Chapter V by O. A. Oleĭnik and on Chapter XI by Ju. V. Prohorov.

Certain sections of Chapters I, II, VII, and XVII were written by V. A. Zalgaller. The editing of the final text was done by V. A. Zalgaller and V. S. Videnskiĭ with the cooperation of T. V. Rogozkinaja and A. P. Leonovaja.

The greater part of the illustrations were prepared by E. P. Sen′kin.

Moscow
1956   EDITORIAL BOARD

FOREWORD BY THE
EDITOR OF THE TRANSLATION

Mathematics, in view of its abstractness, offers greater difficulty to the expositor than any other science. Yet its rapidly increasing role in modern life creates both a need and a desire for good exposition.

In recent years many popular books about mathematics have appeared in the English language, and some of them have enjoyed an immense sale. But for the most part they have contained little serious mathematical instruction, and many of them have neglected the twentieth century, the undisputed "golden age" of mathematics. Although they are admirable in many other ways, they have not yet undertaken the ultimate task of mathematical exposition, namely the large-scale organization of modern mathematics in such a way that the reader is constantly delighted by the obvious economizing of his own time and effort. Anyone who reads through some of the chapters in the present book will realize how well this task has been carried out by the Soviet authors, in the systematic collaboration they have described in their preface.

Such a book, written for "a wide circle of the intelligentsia," must also discuss the general cultural importance of mathematics and its continuous development from the earliest beginnings of history down to the present day. To form an opinion of the book from this point of view the reader need only glance through the first chapter in Part 1 and the introduction to certain other chapters; for example, Analysis, or Analytic Geometry.

In translating the passages on the history and cultural significance of mathematical ideas, the translators have naturally been aware of even greater difficulties than are usually associated with the translation of scientific texts. As organizer of the group, I express my profound gratitude to the other two translators, Tamas Bartha and Kurt Hirsch, for their skillful cooperation.

The present translation, which was originally published by the American Mathematical Society, will now enjoy a more general distribution in its new format. In thus making the book more widely available the Society has been influenced by various expressions of opinion from American mathematicians. For example, ". . . the book will contribute materially to a better understanding by the public of what mathematicians are up to. . . . It will be useful to many mathematicians, physicists and chemists, as well as to laymen. . . . Whether a physicist wishes to know what a Lie algebra is and how it is related to a Lie group, or an undergraduate would like to begin the study of homology, or a crystallographer is interested in Fedorov groups, or an engineer in probability, or any scientist in computing machines, he will find here a connected, lucid account."

In its first edition this translation has been widely read by mathematicians and students of mathematics. We now look forward to its wider usefulness in the general English-speaking world.

August, 1964

S. H. GOULD
Editor of Translations
American Mathematical Society
Providence, Rhode Island

CONTENTS

ix

PART 4

PART 3

CHAPTER VI

PARTIAL
DIFFERENTIAL EQUATIONS

§1. Introduction

In the study of the phenomena of nature, partial differential equations are encountered just as often as ordinary ones. As a rule this happens in cases where an event is described by a function of several variables. From the study of nature there arose that class of partial differential equations that is at the present time the most thoroughly investigated and probably the most important in the general structure of human knowledge, namely the equations of mathematical physics.

Let us first consider oscillations in any kind of medium. In such oscillations every point of the medium, occupying in equilibrium the position (x, y, z), will at time t be displaced along a vector $u(x, y, z, t)$, depending on the initial position of the point (x, y, z) and on the time t. In this case the process in question will be described by a vector field. But it is easy to see that knowledge of this vector field, namely the field of displacements of points of the medium, is not sufficient in itself for a full description of the oscillation. It is also necessary to know, for example, the density $\rho(x, y, z, t)$ at each point of the medium, the temperature $T(x, y, z, t)$, and the internal stress, i.e., the forces exerted on an arbitrarily chosen volume of the body by the entire remaining part of it.

Physical events and processes occuring in space and time always consist of the changes, during the passage of time, of certain physical magnitudes related to the points of the space. As we saw in Chapter II these quantities can be described by functions with four independent variables, x, y, z, and t, where x, y, and z are the coordinates of a point of the space, and and t is the time.

Physical quantities may be of different kinds. Some are completely characterized by their numerical values, e.g., temperature, density, and the like, and are called scalars. Others have direction and are therefore vector quantities: velocity, acceleration, the strength of an electric field, etc. Vector quantities may be expressed not only by the length of the vector and its direction but also by its "components" if we decompose it into the sum of three mutually perpendicular vectors, for example parallel to the coordinate axes.

In mathematical physics a scalar quantity or a scalar field is presented by one function of four independent variables, whereas a vector quantity defined on the whole space or, as it is called, a vector field is described by three functions of these variables. We can write such a quantity either in the form

$$\mathbf{u}(x, y, z, t),$$

where the bold face type indicates the $\mathbf{u}$ is a vector, or in the form of three functions

$$u_x(x, y, z, t), \quad u_y(x, y, z, t), \quad u_z(x, y, z, t),$$

where u_x, u_y, and u_z denote the projections of the vector on the coordinate axes.

In addition to vector and scalar quantities, still more complicated entities occur in physics, for example the state of stress of a body at a given point. Such quantities are called tensors; after a fixed choice of coordinate axes, they may be characterized everywhere by a set of functions of the same four independent variables.

In this manner, the description of widely different kinds of physical phenomena is usually given by means of several functions of several variables. Of course, such a description cannot be absolutely exact.

For example, when we describe the density of a medium by means of one function of our independent variables, we ignore the fact that at a given point we cannot have any density whatsoever. The bodies we are investigating have a molecular structure, and the molecules are not contiguous but occur at finite distances from one another. The distances between molecules are for the most part considerably larger than the dimensions of the molecules themselves. Thus the density in question is the ratio of the mass contained in some small, but not extremely small, volume to this volume itself. The density at a point we usually think of as the limit of such ratios for decreasing volumes. A still greater simplification and idealization is introduced in the concept of the temperature of a medium. The heat in a body is due to the random motion of its molecules.

The energy of the molecules differs, but if we consider a volume containing a large collection of molecules, then the average energy of their random motions will define what is called temperature.

Similarly, when we speak of the pressure of a gas or a liquid on the wall of a container, we should not think of the pressure as though a particle of the liquid or gas were actually pressing against the wall of the container. In fact, these particles, in their random motion, hit the wall of the container and bounce off it. So what we describe as pressure against the wall is actually made up of a very large number of impulses received by a section of the wall that is small from an everyday point of view but extremely large in comparison with the distances between the molecules of the liquid or gas. It would be easy to give dozens of examples of a similar nature. The majority of the quantities studied in physics have exactly the same character. Mathematical physics deals with idealized quantities, abstracting them from the concrete properties of the corresponding physical entities and considering only the average values of these quantities.

Such an idealization may appear somewhat coarse but, as we will see, it is very useful, since it enables us to make an excellent analysis of many complicated matters, in which we consider only the essential elements and omit those features which are secondary from our point of view.

The object of mathematical physics is to study the relations existing among these idealized elements, these relations being described by sets of functions of several independent variables.

§2. The Simplest Equations of Mathematical Physics

The elementary connections and relations among physical quantities are expressed by the laws of mechanics and physics. Although these relations are extremely varied in character, they give rise to more complicated ones, which are derived from them by mathematical argument and are even more varied. The laws of mechanics and physics may be written in mathematical language in the form of partial differential equations, or perhaps integral equations, relating unknown functions to one another. To understand what is meant here, let us consider some examples of the equations of mathematical physics.

Equations of conservation of mass and of heat energy. Let us express in mathematical form the basic physical laws governing the motions of a medium.

1. First of all we express the law of conservation of the matter contained in any volume Ω which we mentally mark off in a space and keep fixed.

For this purpose we must calculate the mass of the matter contained in this volume. The mass $M_\Omega(t)$ is expressed by the integral

$$M_\Omega(t) = \iiint\limits_\Omega \rho(x, y, z, t) \, dx \, dy \, dz.$$

This mass will not, of course, be constant; in an oscillatory process the density at each point will be changing in view of the fact that the particles of matter in their oscillations will at one time enter this volume and at another leave it. The rate of change of the mass can be found by differentiation with respect to time and is given by the integral

$$\frac{dM_\Omega}{dt} = \iiint\limits_\Omega \frac{\partial \rho}{\partial t} \, dx \, dy \, dz.$$

This rate of change of the mass contained in the volume may also be calculated in another way. We may express the amount of matter which passes through the surface S, bounding our volume Ω, at each second of time, where the matter leaving Ω must be taken with a minus sign. To this end we consider an element ds of the surface S sufficiently small that it may be assumed to be plane and have the same displacement for all its points. We will follow the displacement of points on this segment of the surface during the interval of time from t to $t + dt$. First of all we compute the vector

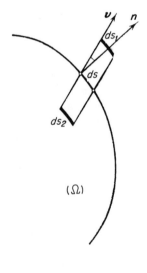

$$\boldsymbol{v} = \frac{du}{dt},$$

which represents the velocity of each particle. In the time dt the particles on ds move along the vector $\boldsymbol{v} \, dt$, and take up a position ds_1, while the position ds will now be occupied by the particles which were formerly at the position ds_2 (figure 1). So during this time the column of matter leaving the volume Ω will be that which was earlier contained between ds_2 and ds_1. The altitude of this small column is equal to $v \, dt \cos (\boldsymbol{n}, \boldsymbol{v})$, where $\boldsymbol{n}$ denotes the exterior normal to the surface; the volume of the small column will thus be equal to

FIG. 1. $v \cos (\boldsymbol{n}, \boldsymbol{v}) \, ds \, dt,$

and the mass equal to

$$\rho v \cos (\boldsymbol{n}, \boldsymbol{v}) \, ds \, dt.$$

Adding together all these small pieces, we get for the amount of matter leaving the volume during the time dt the expression

$$\iint\limits_{S} \rho v \cos (\boldsymbol{n}, \boldsymbol{v}) \, ds \, dt.$$

At those points where the velocity is directed toward the interior of Ω the sign of the cosine will be negative, which means that in this integral the matter entering Ω is taken with a minus sign. The product of the velocity of motion of the medium with its density is called its flux. The flux vector of the mass is $\boldsymbol{q} = \rho \boldsymbol{v}$.

In order to find the rate of flow of matter out of the volume Ω it is sufficient to divide this expression by dt, so that for the rate of flow we have

$$\iint\limits_{S} \rho v_n \, ds = \iint\limits_{S} q_n \, ds,$$

where

$$v_n = v \cos (\boldsymbol{n}, \boldsymbol{v}), \quad q_n = q \cos (\boldsymbol{n}, \boldsymbol{q}).$$

The normal component of the vector $\boldsymbol{v}$ may be replaced by its expression in terms of the components of the vectors $\boldsymbol{v}$ and $\boldsymbol{n}$ along the coordinate axes. From analytic geometry we know that

$$v_n = v \cos (\boldsymbol{n}, \boldsymbol{v}) = v_x \cos (\boldsymbol{n}, \boldsymbol{x}) + v_y \cos (\boldsymbol{n}, \boldsymbol{y}) + v_z \cos (\boldsymbol{n}, \boldsymbol{z}),$$

hence we can rewrite the expression for the rate of flow in the form

$$\iint\limits_{S} \rho(v_x \cos (\boldsymbol{n}, \boldsymbol{x}) + v_y \cos (\boldsymbol{n}, \boldsymbol{y}) + v_z \cos (\boldsymbol{n}, \boldsymbol{z})) \, ds.$$

From the law of conservation of matter, these two methods of computing the change in the amount of matter must give the same result, since all change in the mass included in Ω can occur only as a result of the entering or leaving of mass through the surface S.

Hence, equating the rate of change of the amount of matter contained in the volume with the rate of flow of matter into the volume, we get

$$\iiint\limits_{\Omega} \frac{\partial \rho}{\partial t} \, dx \, dy \, dz$$

$$= - \iint\limits_{S} [\rho v_x \cos (\boldsymbol{n}, \boldsymbol{x}) + \rho v_y \cos (\boldsymbol{n}, \boldsymbol{y}) + \rho v_z \cos (\boldsymbol{n}, \boldsymbol{z})] \, ds$$

$$= - \iint\limits_{S} [q_x \cos (\boldsymbol{n}, \boldsymbol{x}) + q_y \cos (\boldsymbol{n}, \boldsymbol{y}) + q_z \cos (\boldsymbol{n}, \boldsymbol{z})] \, ds.$$

This integral relation, as we have said, is true for any volume Ω. It is called "the equation of continuity."

The integral occurring on the right side of the last equation may be transformed into a volume integral by using Ostrogradskiĭ's formula. This formula, derived in Chapter II gives

$$\iint_S (\rho v_x \cos(n, x) + \rho v_y \cos(n, y) + \rho v_z \cos(n, z))\, ds$$
$$= \iiint_\Omega \left[\frac{\partial(\rho v_x)}{\partial x} + \frac{\partial(\rho v_y)}{\partial y} + \frac{\partial(\rho v_z)}{\partial z} \right] d\Omega.$$

Hence it follows that

$$\iiint_\Omega \left[\frac{\partial \rho}{\partial t} + \frac{\partial(\rho v_x)}{\partial x} + \frac{\partial(\rho v_y)}{\partial y} + \frac{\partial(\rho v_z)}{\partial z} \right] d\Omega = 0.$$

So we get the following result; the integral of the function

$$\frac{\partial \rho}{\partial t} + \frac{\partial(\rho v_x)}{\partial x} + \frac{\partial(\rho v_y)}{\partial y} + \frac{\partial(\rho v_z)}{\partial z} \quad \text{or} \quad \frac{\partial \rho}{\partial t} + \frac{\partial q_x}{\partial x} + \frac{\partial q_y}{\partial y} + \frac{\partial q_z}{\partial z}$$

over any volume Ω is equal to zero. But this is possible only if the function is identically zero. We thus obtain the equation of continuity in differential form

$$\frac{\partial \rho}{\partial t} + \frac{\partial(\rho v_x)}{\partial x} + \frac{\partial(\rho v_y)}{\partial y} + \frac{\partial(\rho v_z)}{\partial z} = 0. \tag{1}$$

Equation (1) is a typical example of the formulation of a physical law in the language of partial differential equations.

2. Let us consider another such problem, namely the problem of heat conduction.

In any medium whose particles are in motion on account of heat, the heat flows from some points to others. This flow of heat will occur through every element of surface ds lying in the given medium. It can be shown that the process may be described numerically by a single vector quantity, the heat-conduction vector, which we denote by τ. Then the amount of heat flowing per second through an element of area ds will be expressed by $\tau_n\, ds$, in the same way as $q_n\, ds$ earlier expressed the amount of material passing per second through an area ds. In place of the flux of liquid $q = \rho v$ we have the heat flow vector τ.

In the same way as we obtained the equation of continuity, which for the motion of a liquid expresses the law of conservation of mass, we may obtain a new partial differential equation expressing the law of conservation of energy, as follows.

The volume density of heat energy Q at a given point may be expressed by the formula

$$Q = CT,$$

where C is the heat capacity and T is the temperature.

Here it is easy to establish the equation

$$C \frac{\partial T}{\partial t} + \frac{\partial \tau_x}{\partial x} + \frac{\partial \tau_y}{\partial y} + \frac{\partial \tau_z}{\partial z} = 0. \tag{2}$$

The derivation of this equation is identical with the derivation of the equation of continuity, if we replace "density" by "density of heat energy" and flow of mass by flow of heat. Here we have assumed that the heat energy in the medium never increases. But if there is a source of heat present in the medium, equation (2) for the balance of heat energy must be modified. If q is the productivity density of the source, that is the amount of heat energy produced per unit of volume in one second, then the equation of conservation of heat energy has the following more complicated form:

$$C \frac{\partial T}{\partial t} + \frac{\partial \tau_x}{\partial x} + \frac{\partial \tau_y}{\partial y} + \frac{\partial \tau_z}{\partial z} = q. \tag{3}$$

3. Still another equation of the same type as the equation of continuity may be derived by differentiating equation (1) with respect to time. Let us do this for the equation of small oscillations of a gas near a position of equilibrium. We will assume that for such oscillations changes of the density are not great and the quantities $\partial \rho/\partial x$, $\partial \rho/\partial y$, $\partial \rho/\partial z$, and $\partial \rho/\partial t$ are sufficiently small that their products with v_x, v_y, and v_z may be ignored. Then

$$\frac{\partial \rho}{\partial t} + \rho \left(\frac{\partial v_x}{\partial x} + \frac{\partial v_y}{\partial y} + \frac{\partial v_z}{\partial z} \right) = 0.$$

Differentiating this equation with respect to time and ignoring the products of $\partial \rho/\partial t$ with $\partial v_x/\partial x$, $\partial v_y/\partial y$, and $\partial v_z/\partial z$, we obtain

$$\frac{\partial^2 \rho}{\partial t^2} + \rho \left[\frac{\partial \left(\frac{dv_x}{dt} \right)}{\partial x} + \frac{\partial \left(\frac{dv_y}{dt} \right)}{\partial y} + \frac{\partial \left(\frac{dv_z}{dt} \right)}{\partial z} \right] = 0. \tag{4}$$

Equation of motion.

1. An important example of the expression of a physical law by a differential equation occurs in the equations of equilibrium or of motion of a medium. Let the medium consist of material particles, moving with

various velocities. As in the first example, we mentally mark off in space a volume Ω, bounded by the surface S and filled with particles of matter of the medium, and write Newton's second law for the particles in this volume. This law states that for every motion of the medium the rate of change of momentum, summed up for all particles, in the volume is equal to the sum of all the forces acting on the volume. The momentum, as is known from mechanics, is represented by the vector quantity

$$\boldsymbol{P} = \iiint\limits_{\Omega} \rho \boldsymbol{v}\, d\Omega.$$

The particles occupying a small volume $d\Omega$ with density ρ will, after time $\varDelta t$, fill a new volume $d\Omega'$ with density ρ', although the mass will be unchanged

$$\rho'\, d\Omega' = \rho\, d\Omega.$$

If velocity $\boldsymbol{v}$ changes during this time to a new value $\boldsymbol{v}'$, i.e., by the amount $\varDelta\boldsymbol{v} = \boldsymbol{v}' - \boldsymbol{v}$, the corresponding change of momentum will be

$$\rho'\boldsymbol{v}'\, d\Omega' - \rho\boldsymbol{v}\, d\Omega = \rho\boldsymbol{v}'\, d\Omega - \rho\boldsymbol{v}\, d\Omega = \rho\, \varDelta\boldsymbol{v}\, d\Omega,$$

or in the unit of time:

$$\rho\, \frac{\varDelta\boldsymbol{v}}{\varDelta t}\, d\Omega \approx \rho\, \frac{d\boldsymbol{v}}{dt}\, d\Omega.$$

Adding over all particles in the volume Ω, we find that the rate of change of momentum is equal to

$$\iiint\limits_{\Omega} \rho\, \frac{d\boldsymbol{v}}{dt}\, d\Omega$$

or, in other words

$$\iiint\limits_{\Omega} \rho\, \frac{dv_x}{dt}\, d\Omega, \quad \iiint\limits_{\Omega} \rho\, \frac{dv_y}{dt}\, d\Omega, \quad \iiint\limits_{\Omega} \rho\, \frac{dv_z}{dt}\, d\Omega.$$

(Here the derivatives dv_x/dt, dv_y/dt, and dv_z/dt denote the rate of change of the components of $\boldsymbol{v}$ not at a given point of the space but for a given particle. This is what is meant by the notation d/dt instead of $\partial/\partial t$. As is well known, $d/dt = \partial/\partial t + v_x(\partial/\partial x) + v_y(\partial/\partial y) + v_z(\partial/\partial z)$.)

The forces acting on the volume may be of two kinds: volume forces acting on every particle of the body, and surface forces or stresses on the surface S bounding the volume. The former are long-range forces, while the latter are short-range.

To illustrate these remarks, let us assume that the medium under consideration is a fluid. The surface forces acting on an element of the surface ds will in this case have the value $p\,ds$, where p is the pressure on the fluid, and will be exerted in a direction opposite to that of the exterior normal.

If we denote the unit vector in the direction of the normal to the surface S by $\mathbf{n}$, then the forces acting on the section ds will be equal to

$$-p\mathbf{n}\,ds.$$

If we let $\mathbf{F}$ denote the vector of the external forces acting on a unit of volume, our equation takes the form

$$\iiint_\Omega \rho\,\frac{d\mathbf{v}}{dt}\,d\Omega = \iiint_\Omega \mathbf{F}\,d\Omega - \iint_S p\mathbf{n}\,ds.$$

This is the equation of motion in integral form. Like the equation of continuity, this equation also may be transformed into differential form. We obtain the system:

$$\rho\,\frac{dv_x}{dt} + \frac{\partial p}{\partial x} = F_x,\ \rho\,\frac{dv_y}{dt} + \frac{\partial p}{\partial y} = F_y,\ \rho\,\frac{dv_z}{dt} + \frac{\partial p}{\partial z} = F_z. \qquad (5)$$

This system is the differential form of Newton's second law.

2. Another characteristic example of the application of the laws of mechanics in differential form is the equation of a vibrating string. A string is a long, very slender body of elastic material that is flexible because of its extreme thinness, and is usually tightly stretched. If we imagine the string divided at any point x into two parts, then on each of the parts there is exerted a force equal to the tension in the direction of the tangent to the curve of the string.

Let us examine a short segment of the string. We will denote by $u(x, t)$ the displacement of a point of the string from its position of equilibrium. We assume that the oscillation of the string occurs in one plane and consists of displacements perpendicular to the axis Ox, and we represent the displacement $u(x, t)$ graphically at some instant of time (figure 2). We will investigate the behavior of the segment of the string between the points x_1 and x_2. At these points there are two forces acting, which are equal to the tension T in the direction of the corresponding tangent to $u(x, t)$.

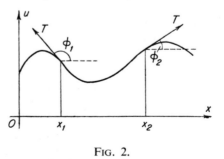

FIG. 2.

If the segment is curved, the resolvent of these two forces will not be equal to zero. This resolvent, from the laws of mechanics, must be equal to the rate of change of momentum of the segment.

Let the mass contained in each centimeter of length of the string be equal to ρ. Then the rate of change of momentum will be

$$\rho \int_{x_1}^{x_2} \frac{d^2u}{dt^2}\, dx.$$

If the angle between the tangent to the string and the axis Ox is denoted by ϕ, we will have

$$T \sin \phi_2 - T \sin \phi_1 = \int_{x_1}^{x_2} \rho \frac{\partial^2 u}{\partial t^2}\, dx.$$

This is the usual equation expressing the second law of mechanics in integral form. It is easy to transform it into differential form. We have obviously

$$\rho \frac{\partial^2 u}{\partial t^2} = \frac{\partial}{\partial x}(T \sin \phi).$$

From well-known theorems of differential calculus, it is easy to relate $T \sin \phi$ to the unknown function u. We get

$$\tan \phi = \frac{\partial u}{\partial x}, \quad \sin \phi = \frac{\tan \phi}{\sqrt{1 + \tan^2 \phi}} = \frac{\partial u/\partial x}{\sqrt{1 + (\partial u/\partial x)^2}}$$

and under the assumption that $(\partial u/\partial x)^2$ is small, we have

$$\sin \phi \approx \frac{\partial u}{\partial x}.$$

Then

$$T \frac{\partial^2 u}{\partial x^2} = \rho \frac{\partial^2 u}{\partial t^2}. \tag{6}$$

This last equation is the *equation of the vibrating string* in differential form.

Basic forms of equations of mathematical physics. As mentioned previously, the various partial differential equations describing physical phenomena usually form a system of equations in several unknown variables. But in the great majority of cases it is possible to replace this system by one equation, as may easily be shown by very simple examples.

For instance, let us turn to the equations of motion considered in the preceding paragraph. It is required to solve these equations along with the equation of continuity. The actual methods of solution we will consider somewhat later.

1. We begin with the equation for steady flow of an idealized fluid.

All possible motions of a fluid can be divided into rotational and irrotational, the latter also being called *potential.* Although irrotational motions are only special cases of motion and, generally speaking, the motion of a liquid or a gas is always more or less rotational, nevertheless experience shows that in many cases the motion is irrotational to a high degree of exactness. Moreover, it may be shown from theoretical considerations that in a fluid with viscosity equal to zero a motion which is initially irrotational will remain so.

For a potential motion of a fluid, there exists a scalar function $U(x, y, z, t)$, called the *velocity potential,* such that the velocity vector $\boldsymbol{v}$ is expressed in terms of this function by the formulas

$$v_x = \frac{\partial U}{\partial x}, \quad v_y = \frac{\partial U}{\partial y}, \quad v_z = \frac{\partial U}{\partial z}.$$

In all the cases we have studied up to now, we have had to deal with systems of four equations in four unknown functions or, in other words, with one scalar and one vector equation, containing one unknown scalar function and one unknown vector field. Usually these equations may be combined into one equation with one unknown function, but this equation will be of the second order. Let us do this, beginning with the simplest case.

For potential motion of an incompressible fluid, for which $\partial \rho / \partial t = 0$, we have two systems of equations: the equation of continuity

$$\rho \left(\frac{\partial v_x}{\partial x} + \frac{\partial v_y}{\partial y} + \frac{\partial v_z}{\partial z} \right) = 0$$

and the equations of potential motion

$$v_x = \frac{\partial U}{\partial x}, \quad v_y = \frac{\partial U}{\partial y}, \quad v_z = \frac{\partial U}{\partial z}.$$

Substituting in the first equation the values of the velocity as given in the second we have

$$\frac{\partial^2 U}{\partial x^2} + \frac{\partial^2 U}{\partial y^2} + \frac{\partial^2 U}{\partial z^2} = 0. \tag{7}$$

2. The vector field of "heat flow" can also be expressed, by means of differential equations, in terms of one scalar quantity, the temperature.

It is well known that heat "flows" in the direction from a hot body to a cold one. Thus the vector of the flow of heat lies in the direction opposite to that of the so-called temperature-gradient vector. It is also natural to assume, as is justified by experience, that to a first approximation the length of this vector is directly proportional to the temperature gradient.

The components of the temperature gradient are

$$\frac{\partial T}{\partial x}, \frac{\partial T}{\partial y}, \frac{\partial T}{\partial z}.$$

Taking the coefficient of proportionality to be k, we get three equations

$$\tau_x = -k \frac{\partial T}{\partial x}, \ \tau_y = -k \frac{\partial T}{\partial y}, \ \tau_z = -k \frac{\partial T}{\partial z}.$$

These are to be solved, together with the equation for the conservation of heat energy

$$C \frac{\partial T}{\partial t} + \frac{\partial \tau_x}{\partial x} + \frac{\partial \tau_y}{\partial y} + \frac{\partial \tau_z}{\partial z} = q.$$

Replacing τ_x, τ_y, and τ_z by their values in terms of T, we get

$$C \frac{\partial T}{\partial t} = k \left(\frac{\partial^2 T}{\partial x^2} + \frac{\partial^2 T}{\partial y^2} + \frac{\partial^2 T}{\partial z^2} \right) + q. \tag{8}$$

3. Finally, for small vibrations in a gaseous medium, for example the vibrations of sound, the equation

$$\frac{\partial^2 \rho}{\partial t^2} + \rho \frac{\partial}{\partial x} \left(\frac{dv_x}{dt} \right) + \rho \frac{\partial}{\partial y} \left(\frac{dv_y}{dt} \right) + \rho \frac{\partial}{\partial z} \left(\frac{dv_z}{dt} \right) = 0$$

and the equations of dynamics (5), give

$$\rho \frac{dv_x}{dt} + \frac{\partial p}{\partial x} = F_x, \ \rho \frac{dv_y}{dt} + \frac{\partial p}{\partial y} = F_y, \ \rho \frac{dv_z}{dt} + \frac{\partial p}{\partial z} = F_z,$$

and, assuming the absence of external forces ($F_x = F_y = F_z = 0$) we get

$$\frac{\partial^2 p}{\partial t^2} = a^2 \left(\frac{\partial^2 p}{\partial x^2} + \frac{\partial^2 p}{\partial y^2} + \frac{\partial^2 p}{\partial z^2} \right) \tag{9}$$

(to obtain this equation it is sufficient to substitute the expression for the accelerations in the equation of continuity and to eliminate the density ρ by using the Boyle-Mariotte law: $p = a^2\rho$).

Equations (7), (8), and (9) are typical for many problems of mathematical physics in addition to the ones considered here. The fact that they have been investigated in detail enables us to gain an understanding of many physical situations.

§3. Initial-Value and Boundary-Value Problems; Uniqueness of a Solution

With partial differential equations as with ordinary ones, it is the case, with rare exceptions, that every equation has infinitely many particular solutions. Thus to solve a concrete physical problem, i.e., to find an unknown function satisfying some equation, we must know how to choose the required solution from an infinite set of solutions. For this purpose it is usually necessary to know not only the equation itself but a certain number of supplementary conditions. As we saw previously, partial differential equations are the expression of elementary laws of mechanics or physics, referring to small particles situated in a medium. But it is not enough to know only the laws of mechanics, if we wish to predict the course of some process. For example, to predict the motion of the heavenly bodies, as is done in astronomy, we must know not only the general formulation of Newton's laws but also, assuming that the masses of these bodies are known, we must know the initial state of the system, i.e., the position of the bodies and their velocities at some initial instant of time. Supplementary conditions of this kind are always encountered in solving the problems of mathematical physics.

Thus, the problems of mathematical physics consist of finding solutions of partial differential equations that satisfy certain supplementary conditions.

The equations (7), (8), (9) differ in structure among themselves. Correspondingly different are the physical problems that may be solved by means of these equations.

The Laplace and Poisson equations; harmonic functions and uniqueness of solution of boundary-value problems for them. Let us analyze these problems a little more in detail. We begin with the Laplace and Poisson equations. The *Poisson equation* is*

$$\Delta u = -4\pi\rho,$$

where ρ is usually the density. In particular, ρ may vanish. For $\rho \equiv 0$ we get the *Laplace equation*

$$\Delta u = 0.$$

---

* The symbol Δu is an abbreviation for the expression $\partial^2 u/\partial x^2 + \partial^2 u/\partial y^2 + \partial^2 u/\partial z^2$ and is called the *Laplacian* of the function u.

It is not difficult to see that the difference between any two particular solutions u_1 and u_2 of the Poisson equation is a function satisfying the Laplace equation, or in other words is a *harmonic function*. The entire manifold of solutions of the Poisson equation is thus reduced to the manifold of harmonic functions.

If we have been able to construct even one particular solution u_0 of the Poisson equation, and if we define a new unknown function w by

$$u = u_0 + w,$$

we see that w must satisfy the Laplace equation; and in exactly the same way, we determine the corresponding boundary conditions for w. Thus it is particularly important to investigate boundary value problems for the Laplace equation.

As is most often the case with mathematical problems, the proper statement of the problem for an equation of mathematical physics is immediately suggested by the practical situation. The supplementary conditions arising in the solution of the Laplace equation come from the physical statement of the problem.

Let us consider, for example, the establishment of a steady temperature in a medium, i.e., the propagation of heat in a medium where the sources of heat are constant and are situated either inside or outside the medium. Under these conditions, with the passage of time the temperature attained at any point of the medium will be independent of the time. Thus to find the temperature T at each point, we must find that solution of the equation

$$\frac{\partial T}{\partial t} = \Delta T + q,$$

where q is the density of the sources of heat distribution, which is independent of t. We get

$$\Delta T + q = 0.$$

Thus the temperature in our medium satisfies the Poisson equation. If the density of heat sources q is zero, then the Poisson equation becomes the Laplace equation.

In order to find the temperature inside the medium, it is necessary, from simple physical considerations, to know also what happens on the boundary of the medium.

Obviously the physical laws previously considered for interior points of a body call for quite another formulation at boundary points.

In the problem of establishing the steady-state temperature, we can prescribe either the distribution of temperature on the boundary, or the rate of flow of heat through a unit area of the surface, or finally, a law connecting the temperature with the flow of heat.

Considering the temperature in a volume Ω, bounded by the surface S, we can write these three conditions as:

$$T\,|_S = \phi(Q), \tag{10}$$

or

$$\frac{\partial T}{\partial n}\,\Big|_S = \psi(Q), \tag{10'}$$

or finally, in the most general case

$$\alpha \frac{\partial T}{\partial n}\,\Big|_S + \beta T\,|_S = \chi(Q), \tag{10''}$$

where Q denotes an arbitrary point of the surface S. Conditions of the form (10) are called *boundary conditions*. Investigation of the Laplace or Poisson equation under boundary conditions of one of these types will show that as a rule the solution is uniquely determined.

Thus, in our search for a solution of the Laplace or Poisson equation it will usually be necessary and sufficient to be given one arbitrary function on the boundary of the domain.* Let us examine the Laplace equation a little more in detail. We will show that a harmonic function u, i.e., a function satisfying the Laplace equation, is completely determined if we know its values on the boundary of the domain.

First of all we establish the fact that a harmonic function cannot take on values inside the domain that are larger than the largest value on the boundary. More precisely, we show that the absolute maximum, as well as the absolute minimum of a harmonic function are attained on the boundary of the domain.

From this it will follow at once that if a harmonic function has a constant value on the boundary of a domain Ω, then in the interior of this domain it will also be equal to this constant. For if the maximum and minimum value of a function are both the same constant, then the function will be everywhere equal to this constant.

We now establish the fact that the absolute maximum and minimum of a harmonic function cannot occur inside the domain. First of all, we note that if the Laplacian Δu of the function $u(x, y, z)$ is positive for the whole domain, then this function cannot have a maximum inside the domain, and if it is negative, then the function cannot have a minimum inside the

---

* The words "arbitrary function" here and in what follows mean that no special conditions, other than certain requirements of regularity, are imposed on the functions.

domain. For at a point where the function u attains its maximum it must have a maximum as a function of each variable separately for fixed values of the other variables. Thus it follows that every partial derivative of second order with respect to each variable must be nonpositive. This means that their sum will be nonpositive, whereas the Laplacian is positive, which is impossible. Similarly it may be shown that if the function has a minimum at some interior point, then its Laplacian cannot be negative at this point. This means that if the Laplacian is negative everywhere in the domain, then the function cannot have a minimum in this domain.

If a function is harmonic, it may always be changed by an arbitrarily small amount in such a way that it will have a positive or negative Laplacian; to this end it is sufficient to add to it the quantity

$$\pm \eta r^2 = \pm \eta(x^2 + y^2 + z^2),$$

where η is an arbitrarily small constant:

The addition of a sufficiently small quantity cannot change the property that the function has an absolute maximum or absolute minimum within the domain. If a harmonic function were to have a maximum inside the domain, then by adding $+ \eta r^2$ to it, we would get a function with a positive Laplacian which, as was shown above, could not have a maximum inside the domain. This means that a harmonic function cannot have an absolute maximum inside the domain. Similarly, it can be shown that a harmonic function cannot have an absolute minimum inside the domain.

This theorem has an important corollary. Two harmonic functions that agree on the boundary of a domain must agree everywhere inside the domain. For then the difference of these functions (which itself will be a harmonic function) vanishes on the boundary of the domain and thus is everywhere equal to zero in the interior of the domain.

So we see that the values of a harmonic function on the boundary completely determine the function. It may be shown (although we cannot give the details here) that for arbitrarily preassigned values on the boundary one can always find a harmonic function that assumes these values.

It is somewhat more complicated to prove that the steady-state temperature established in a body is completely determined, if we know the rate of flow of heat through each element of the surface of the body or a law connecting the flow of heat with the temperature. We will return to some aspects of this question when we discuss methods of solving the problems of mathematical physics.

The boundary-value problem for the heat equation. A completely different situation occurs in the problem of the heat equation in the nonstationary case. It is physically clear that the values of the temperature on the boundary or of the rate of the flow of heat through the boundary are not sufficient in themselves to define a unique solution of the problem. But if in addition we know the temperature distribution at some initial instant of time, then the problem is uniquely determined. Thus to determine the solution of the equation of heat conduction (8) it is usually necessary and sufficient to assign one arbitrary function $T_0(x, y, z)$ describing the initial distribution of temperature and also one arbitrary function on the boundary of the domain. As before, this may be either the temperature on the surface of the body, or the rate of heat flow through each element of the surface, or a law connecting the flow of heat with the temperature.

In this manner, the problem may be stated as follows. We seek a solution of equation (8) under the condition

$$T\,|_{t=0} = T_0(x, y, z) \tag{11}$$

and one of three following conditions

$$T\,|_S = \phi(Q), \tag{12}$$

$$\frac{\partial T}{\partial n}\bigg|_S = \psi(Q), \tag{12'}$$

$$\alpha \frac{\partial T}{\partial n}\bigg|_S + \beta T\,|_S = \chi(Q), \tag{12''}$$

where Q is any point of the surface S.

Condition (11) is called an *initial condition*, while conditions (12) are *boundary conditions*.

We will not prove in detail that every such problem has a unique solution but will establish this fact only for the first of these problems; moreover, we will consider only the case where there are no heat sources in the interior of the medium. We show that the equation

$$\Delta T = \frac{1}{a^2} \frac{\partial T}{\partial t}$$

under the conditions

$$T\,|_{t=0} = T_0(x, y, z),$$

$$T\,|_S = \phi(Q)$$

can have only one solution.

The proof of this statement is very similar to the previous proof for the uniqueness of the solution of the Laplace equation. We show first of all that if

$$\Delta T - \frac{1}{a^2}\frac{\partial T}{\partial t} < 0,$$

then the function T, as a function of four variables, x, y, z, and $t(0 \leqslant t \leqslant t_0)$, assumes its minimum either on the boundary of the domain Ω or else inside Ω, but in the latter case necessarily at the initial instant of time, $t = 0$.

For if not, then the minimum would be attained at some interior point. At this point all the first derivatives, including $\partial T/\partial t$, will then be equal to zero, and if this minimum were to occur for $t = t_0$, then $\partial T/\partial t$ would be nonpositive. Also, at this point all second derivatives with respect to the variables x, y, and z will be nonnegative. Consequently $\Delta T - (1/a^2)$ $(\partial T/\partial t)$ will be nonnegative, which in our case is impossible.

In exactly the same way we can establish that if $\Delta T - (1/a^2)(\partial T/\partial t) > 0$, then inside Ω for $0 < t \leqslant t_0$ there cannot exist a maximum for the function T.

Finally, if $\Delta T - (1/a^2)(\partial T/\partial t) = 0$, then inside Ω for $0 < t \leqslant t_k$ the function T cannot attain its absolute maximum nor its absolute minimum, since if the function T were to have, for example, such an absolute minimum, then by adding to it the term $\eta(t - t_0)$ and considering the function $T_1 = T + \eta(t - t_0)$, we would not destroy the absolute minimum if η were sufficiently small, and then $\Delta T_1 - (1/a^2)(\partial T_1/\partial t)$ would be negative, which is impossible.

In the same way we can also show the absence of an absolute maximum for T in the domain under consideration.

However, an absolute maximum, as well as an absolute minimum of temperature may occur either at the initial instant $t = 0$ or on the boundary S of the medium. If $T = 0$ both at the initial instant and on the boundary, then we have the identity $T = 0$ throughout the interior of the domain for all $t \leqslant t_0$. If any two temperature distributions T_1 and T_2 have identical values for $t = 0$ and on the boundary then their difference $T_1 - T_2 = \text{T}$ will satisfy the heat equation and will vanish for $t = 0$ and on the boundary. This means that $T_1 - T_2$ will be everywhere equal to zero, so that the two temperature distributions T_1 and T_2 will be everywhere identical.

In the investigation given later of methods of solving the equations of mathematical physics we will see that the value of T for $t = 0$ and the right side of one of the equations (12) may be given arbitrarily, i.e., that the solution of such a problem will exist.

The energy of oscillations and the boundary-value problem for the equation of oscillation. We now consider the conditions under which the third of the basic differential equations has a unique solution, namely equation (9).

For simplicity we will consider the equation for the vibrating string $\partial^2 u/\partial x^2 = (1/a^2)\,(\partial^2 u/\partial t^2)$, which is very similar to equation (9), differing from it only in the number of space variables. On the right side of this equation there is the quantity $\partial^2 u/\partial t^2$ expressing the acceleration of an arbitrary point of the string. The motion of any mechanical system for which the forces, and consequently the accelerations, are expressed by the coordinates of the moving bodies, is completely determined if we are given the initial positions and velocities of all the points of the system. Thus for the equation of the vibrating string, it is natural to assign the positions and velocities of all points at the initial instant.

$$u\,|_{t=0} = u_0(x)$$

$$\frac{\partial u}{\partial t}\bigg|_{t=0} = u_1(x).$$

But as was pointed out earlier, at the ends of the string the formulas expressing the laws of mechanics for interior points cease to apply. Thus at both ends we must assign supplementary conditions. If, for example, the string is fixed in a position of equilibrium at both ends, then we will have

$$u\,|_{x=0} = u\,|_{x=l} = 0.$$

These conditions can sometimes be replaced by more general ones, but a change of this sort is not of basic importance.

The problem of finding the necessary solutions of equation (9) is analogous. In order that such a solution be well defined, it is customary to assign the conditions

$$p\,|_{t=0} = \phi_0(x, y, z),$$

$$\frac{\partial p}{\partial t}\bigg|_{t=0} = \phi_1(x, y, z), \tag{13}$$

and also one of the "boundary conditions"

$$p\,|_S = \phi(Q), \tag{14}$$

$$\frac{\partial p}{\partial n}\bigg|_S = \psi(Q), \tag{14'}$$

$$\alpha\frac{\partial p}{\partial n}\bigg|_S + \beta p|_S = \chi(Q).^* \tag{14''}$$

---

* If the right-hand sides in conditions (13) and (14) are equal to zero, such conditions are called "homogeneous."

The difference from the preceding case is simply that instead of the one initial condition in equation (11) we have the two conditions (13).

Equations (14) obviously express the physical laws for the particles on the boundary of the volume in question.

The proof that in the general case the conditions (13) together with an arbitrary one of the conditions (14) uniquely define a solution of the problem will be omitted. We will show only that the solution can be unique for one of the conditions in (14).

Let it be known that a function u satisfies the equation

$$\frac{\partial^2 u}{\partial x^2} = \frac{1}{a^2} \frac{\partial^2 u}{\partial t^2},$$

with initial conditions

$$u\big|_{t=0} = 0, \; \frac{\partial u}{\partial t}\bigg|_{t=0} = 0$$

and boundary condition

$$\frac{\partial u}{\partial n}\bigg|_{S} = 0.$$

(It would be just as easy to discuss the case in which $u\big|_S = 0$.)

We will show that under these conditions the function u must be identically zero.

To prove this property it will not be sufficient to use the arguments introduced earlier to establish the uniqueness of the solution of the first two problems. But here we may make use of the physical interpretation.

We will need just one physical law, the "law of conservation of energy." We restrict ourselves again for simplicity to the vibrating string, the displacement of whose points $u(x, t)$ satisfies the equation

$$T \frac{\partial^2 u}{\partial x^2} = \rho \frac{\partial^2 u}{\partial t^2}.$$

The kinetic energy of each particle of the string oscillating from x to $x + dx$ is expressed in the form

$$\frac{1}{2}\left(\frac{\partial u}{\partial t}\right)^2 \rho \, dx.$$

Along with its kinetic energy, the string in its displaced position also possesses potential energy created by its increase of length in comparison with the straight-line position. Let us compute this potential energy. We concern ourselves with an element of the string between the points x and

$x + dx$. This element has an inclined position with respect to the axis Ox, such that its length is approximately equal to

$$\sqrt{(dx)^2 + \left(\frac{\partial u}{\partial x} dx\right)^2} \; ;$$

so its elongation is

$$\sqrt{1 + \left(\frac{\partial u}{\partial x}\right)^2} \, dx - dx \approx \frac{1}{2} \left(\frac{\partial u}{\partial x}\right)^2 dx.$$

Multiplying this elongation by the tension T, we find the potential energy of the elongated element of the string

$$\frac{1}{2} T \left(\frac{\partial u}{\partial x}\right)^2 dx.$$

The total energy of the string of length l is obtained by summing the kinetic and potential energies over all of the points of the string. We get

$$E = \frac{1}{2} \int_0^l \left[T \left(\frac{\partial u}{\partial x}\right)^2 + \rho \left(\frac{\partial u}{\partial t}\right)^2 \right] dx.$$

If the forces acting on the end of the string do no work, in particular if the ends of the string are fixed, then the total energy of the string must be constant.

$$E = \text{const.}$$

Our expression for the law of conservation of energy is a mathematical corollary of the basic equations of mechanics and may be derived from them. Since we have already written the laws of motion in the form of the differential equation of the vibrating string with conditions on the ends, we can give the following mathematical proof of the law of conservation of energy in this case. If we differentiate E with respect to time, we have, from basic general rules,

$$\frac{dE}{dt} = \int_0^l \left(T \frac{\partial u}{\partial x} \frac{\partial^2 u}{\partial x \, \partial t} + \rho \frac{\partial u}{\partial t} \frac{\partial^2 u}{\partial t^2} \right) dx.$$

Using the wave equation (6) and replacing $\rho(\partial^2 u/\partial t^2)$ by $T(\partial^2 u/\partial x^2)$, we get dE/dt in the form

$$\frac{dE}{dt} = \int_0^l T \left[\left(\frac{\partial u}{\partial x} \frac{\partial^2 u}{\partial x \, \partial t}\right) + \frac{\partial u}{\partial t} \frac{\partial^2 u}{\partial x^2} \right] dx$$

$$= \int_0^l T \frac{\partial}{\partial x} \left(\frac{\partial u}{\partial x} \frac{\partial u}{\partial t}\right) dx = T \frac{\partial u}{\partial x} \frac{\partial u}{\partial t} \Big|_{x=l} - T \frac{\partial u}{\partial x} \frac{\partial u}{\partial t} \Big|_{x=0}.$$

If $(\partial u/\partial x)|_{x=0}$ or $u|_{x=0}$ vanishes, and also $(\partial u/\partial x)|_{x=l}$ or $u|_{x=l}$ vanishes, then

$$\frac{dE}{dt} = 0,$$

which shows that E is constant.

The wave equation (9) may be treated in exactly the same way to prove that the law of conservation of energy holds here also. If p satisfies equation (9) and the condition

$$p\,|_S = 0 \quad \text{or} \quad \frac{\partial p}{\partial n}\bigg|_S = 0,$$

then the quantity

$$E = \iiint \left[\left(\frac{\partial p}{\partial x}\right)^2 + \left(\frac{\partial p}{\partial y}\right)^2 + \left(\frac{\partial p}{\partial z}\right)^2 + \frac{1}{a^2}\left(\frac{\partial p}{\partial t}\right)^2 \right] dx\, dy\, dz$$

will not depend on t.

If, at the initial instant of time, the total energy of the oscillations is equal to zero, then it will always remain equal to zero, and this is possible only in the case that no motion occurs. If the problem of integrating the wave equation with initial and boundary conditions had two solutions p_1 and p_2, then $v = p_1 - p_2$ would be a solution of the wave equation satisfying the conditions with zero on the right-hand side, i.e., homogeneous conditions.

In this case, when we calculated the "energy" of such an oscillation, described by the function v, we would discover that the energy $E(v)$ is equal to zero at the initial instant of time. This means that it is always equal to zero and thus that the function v is identically equal to zero, so that the two solutions p_1 and p_2 are identical. Thus the solution of the problem is unique.

In this way we have convinced ourselves that all three problems are correctly posed.

Incidentally, we have been able to discover some very simple properties of the solutions of these equations. For example, solutions of the Laplace equation have the following maximum property: Functions satisfying this equation have their largest and smallest values on the boundaries of their domains of definition.

Functions describing the distribution of heat in a medium have a maximum property of a different form. Every maximum or minimum of temperature occuring at any point gradually disperses and decreases with time. The temperature at any point can rise or fall only if it is lower or higher than at nearby points. The temperature is smoothed out with the passage of time. All unevennesses in it are leveled out by the passage of heat from hot places to cold ones.

But no smoothing-out process of this kind occurs in the propagation of the oscillations considered here. These oscillations do not decrease or level out, since the sum of their kinetic and potential energies must remain constant for all time.

§4. The Propagation of Waves

The properties of oscillations can be very clearly demonstrated by the simplest examples. Let us consider two characteristic cases.

Our first example is the equation of the vibrating string

$$\frac{\partial^2 u}{\partial x^2} = \frac{1}{a^2} \frac{\partial^2 u}{\partial t^2}.$$

(15)

This equation, as may be proved, has two particular solutions of the form

$$u_1 = \phi_1(x - at), \quad u_2 = \phi_2(x + at),$$

where ϕ_1 and ϕ_2 are arbitrary twice-differentiable functions.

By direct differentiation it is easy to show that the functions u_1 and u_2 satisfy equation (15). It may be shown that

$$u = u_1 + u_2$$

is a general solution of this equation.

The general form of the oscillations described by the functions u_1 and u_2 is of considerable interest. To consider it in the most convenient fashion, we mentally carry out the following experiment. Let the observer of the vibrating string himself be not stationary but moving along the axis Ox with velocity a. For such an observer the position of a point on the string will be defined not by a stationary coordinate system but by a moving one. Let ξ denote the x-coordinate of this system. Then $\xi = 0$ will obviously correspond at each instant of time to the value $x = at$. Hence it is clear that

$$\xi = x - at.$$

We can represent an arbitrary function $u(x, t)$ in the form

$$u(x, t) = \phi(\xi, t).$$

For the solution u_1 we will have

$$u_1(x, t) = \phi_1(\xi),$$

so that in this coordinate system the solution $u_1(x, t)$ turns out to be independent of time. Consequently, for an observer moving with velocity a, the string looks like a stationary curve. For a stationary observer, however, the string appears to have a wave flowing along the axis Ox with velocity a.

In exactly the same way the solution $u_2(x, t)$ may be considered as a wave travelling in the opposite direction with velocity a. With an infinite string both waves will be propagated infinitely far. Moving in different directions they may, by their superposition, produce quite strange shapes in the string. The resultant displacement may be increasing at certain times and decreasing at others.

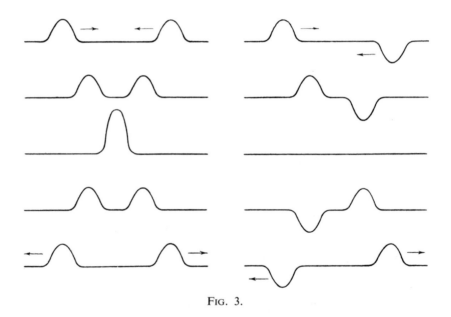

FIG. 3.

If u_1 and u_2, as they arrive at a given point from opposite sides, have the same sign, then they augment each other, but if they have opposite signs, they counteract each other. Figure 3 shows several successive positions of the string for two particular displacements. Initially the waves move independently toward each other, and then begin to interact. In the second case in figure 3 there will be an instant of complete annihilation of the oscillations, after which the waves again separate.

Another example that easily lends itself to qualitative investigation is the propagation of waves in space.

The equation

$$\Delta u = \frac{1}{a^2} \frac{\partial^2 u}{\partial t^2} \tag{16}$$

derived earlier, has two particular solutions of the form

$$u_1 = \frac{1}{r} \phi_1(r - at), \quad u_2 = \frac{1}{r} \phi_2(r + at), \tag{17}$$

where r denotes the distance of a given point from the origin of the coordinate system $r^2 = x^2 + y^2 + z^2$, and ϕ_1 and ϕ_2 are arbitrary, twice-differentiable functions.

The proof that u_1 and u_2 are solutions would take considerable time and is omitted here.

The form of the waves described by these solutions is in general the same as for the string. If we pay no attention to the factor $1/r$ occuring on the right, then the first solution represents a wave travelling in the direction of increasing r. This wave is spherically symmetric; it is identical at all points that have the same value of r.

The factor $1/r$ produces the result that the amplitude of the wave is inversely proportional to the distance from the origin. Such an oscillation is called a diverging spherical wave. A good picture of it is given by the circles that spread out over the surface of the water when a stone is thrown into it, except that in this case the waves are circular rather than spherical.

This second solution of (17) is also of great interest; it is called a converging wave, travelling in the direction of the origin. Its amplitude grows with time to infinity as it approaches the origin. We see that such a concentration of the disturbance at one point may lead, even though the initial oscillations are small, to an immense upheaval.

§5. Methods of Constructing Solutions

On the possibility of decomposing any solution into simpler solutions. Solutions of the problems of mathematical physics formulated previously may be derived by various devices, which are different specific problems. But at the basis of these methods there is one general idea. As we have seen, all the equations of mathematical physics are, for small values of the unknown functions, linear with respect to the functions and their derivatives. The boundary conditions and initial conditions are also linear.

If we form the difference between any two solutions of the same equation, this difference will also be a solution of the equation with the right-hand terms equal to zero. Such an equation is called the corresponding homogeneous equation. For example, for the Poisson equation $\Delta u = -4\pi\rho$, the corresponding homogeneous equation is the Laplace equation $\Delta u = 0$.

If two solutions of the same equation also satisfy the same boundary conditions, then their difference will satisfy the corresponding homogeneous condition: The values of the corresponding expression on the boundary will be equal to zero.

Hence the entire manifold of the solutions of such an equation, for given boundary conditions, may be found by taking any particular solution that satisfies the given nonhomogeneous condition together with all possible solutions of the homogeneous equation satisfying homogeneous boundary conditions (but not, in general, satisfying the initial conditions).

Solutions of homogeneous equations, satisfying homogeneous boundary conditions may be added, or multiplied by constants, without ceasing to be solutions.

If a solution of a homogeneous equation with homogeneous conditions is a function of some parameter, then integrating with respect to this parameter will also give us such a solution. These facts form the basis of the most important method of solving linear problems of all kinds for the equations of mathematical physics, the method of superposition.

The solution of the problem is sought in the form

$$u = u_0 + \sum_k u_k \,,$$

where u_o is a particular solution of the equation satisfying the boundary conditions but not satisfying the initial conditions, and the u_k are solutions of the corresponding homogeneous equation satisfying the corresponding homogeneous boundary conditions. If the equation and the boundary conditions were originally homogeneous, then the solution of the problem may be sought in the form

$$u = \sum_k u_k \,.$$

In order to be able to satisfy arbitrary initial conditions by the choice of particular solutions u_k of the homogeneous equation, we must have available a sufficiently large arsenal of such solutions.

The method of separation of variables. For the construction of the necessary arsenal of solutions there exists a method called *separation of variables* or *Fourier's method.*

Let us examine this method, for example, for solving the problem

$$\Delta u = \frac{\partial^2 u}{\partial t^2}, \tag{18}$$

$$u\,|_S = 0, \quad u\,|_{t=0} = f_0(x, y, z), \quad u_t|_{t=0} = f_1(x, y, z).$$

In looking for any particular solution of the equation, we first of all assume that the desired function u satisfies the boundary condition $u\,|_S = 0$ and can be expressed as the product of two functions, one of which depends only on the time t and the other only on the space variables:

$$u(x, y, z, t) = U(x, y, z)\, T(t).$$

Substituting this assumed solution into our equation, we have

$$T(t)\,\Delta U = T''(t)\, U.$$

Dividing both sides by TU gives

$$\frac{T''}{T} = \frac{\Delta U}{U}.$$

The right side of this equation is a function of the space variables only and the left is independent of the space coordinates. Hence it follows that the given equation can be true only if the left and right sides have the same constant value. We are led to a system of two equations

$$\frac{T''}{T} = -\lambda_k^2, \quad \frac{\Delta U}{U} = -\lambda_k^2.$$

The constant quantity on the right is denoted here by $-\lambda_k^2$ in order to emphasize that it is negative (as may be rigorously proved). The subscript k is used here to note that there exist infinitely many possible values of $-\lambda_k^2$, where the solutions corresponding to them form a system of functions complete in a well-known sense.

Cross-multiplying in both equations, we get

$$T'' + \lambda_k^2 T = 0; \quad \Delta U + \lambda_k^2 U = 0.$$

The first of these equations has, as we know, the simple solution

$$T = A_k \cos \lambda_k t + B_k \sin \lambda_k t,$$

where A_k and B_k are arbitrary constants. This solution may be further simplified by introducing the auxiliary angle ϕ. We have

$$\frac{A_k}{\sqrt{A_k^2 + B_k^2}} = \sin \phi_k, \quad \frac{B_k}{\sqrt{A_k^2 + B_k^2}} = \cos \phi_k, \quad \sqrt{A_k^2 + B_k^2} = M_k.$$

Then

$$T = \sqrt{A_k^2 + B_k^2}\, \sin\,(\lambda_k t + \phi_k) = M_k \sin\,(\lambda_k t + \phi_k).$$

The function T represents a harmonic oscillation with frequency λ_k, shifted in phase by the angle ϕ_k.

More difficult and more interesting is the problem of finding a solution of the equation

$$\Delta U + \lambda_k^2 U = 0 \tag{19}$$

for given homogeneous boundary conditions; for example, for the conditions

$$U\,|_S = 0$$

(where S is the boundary of the volume Ω under consideration), or for any other homogeneous condition. The solution of this problem is not always easy to construct as a finite combination of known functions, although it always exists and can be found to any desired degree of accuracy.

The equation $\Delta U + \lambda_k^2 U = 0$ for the condition $U\,|_S = 0$ has first of all the obvious solution $U \equiv 0$. This solution is trivial and completely useless for our purposes. If the λ_k are any randomly chosen numbers, then in general there will not be any other solution to our problem. However, there usually exist values of λ_k for which the equation does have a nontrivial solution.

All possible values of the constant λ_k^2 are determined by the requirement that equation (19) have a nontrivial solution, i.e., distinct from the identically vanishing function, which satisfies the condition $U\,|_S = 0$. From this it also follows that the numbers denoted by $-\lambda_k^2$ must be negative.

For each of the possible values of λ_k in equation (19), we can find at least one function U_k. This allows us to construct a particular solution of the wave equation (18) in the form

$$u_k = M_k \sin\,(\lambda_k t + \phi_k)\, U_k(x, y, z).$$

Such a solution is called a *characteristic oscillation* (or *eigenvibration*) of the volume under consideration. The constant λ_k is the frequency of the characteristic oscillation, and the function $U_k(x, y, z)$ gives us its form. This function is usually called an *eigenfunction* (*characteristic function*). For all instants of time, the function u_k, considered as a function of the variables x, y, and z, will differ from the function $U_k(x, y, z)$ only in scale.

We do not have space here for a detailed proof of the many remarkable properties of characteristic oscillations and of eigenfunctions; therefore we will restrict ourselves merely to listing some of them.

The first property of the characteristic oscillations consists of the fact that for any given volume there exists a countable set of characteristic frequencies. These frequencies tend to infinity with increasing k.

Another property of the characteristic oscillations is called *orthogonality*. It consists of the fact that the integral over the domain Ω of the product of eigenfunctions corresponding to different values of λ_k is equal to zero.*

$$\iiint\limits_{\Omega} U_k(x, y, z)\, U_j(x, y, z)\, dx\, dy\, dz = 0 \quad (j \neq k).$$

For $j = k$ we will assume

$$\iiint\limits_{\Omega} U_k(x, y, z)^2\, dx\, dy\, dz = 1.$$

This can always be arranged by multiplying the functions $U_k(x, y, z)$ by an appropriate constant, the choice of which does not change the fact that the function satisfies equation (19) and the condition $U \mid_S = 0$.

Finally, a third property of the characteristic oscillations consists of the fact that, if we do not omit any value of λ_k, then by means of the eigenfunctions $U_k(x, y, z)$, we can represent with any desired degree of exactness a completely arbitrary function $f(x, y, z)$, provided only that it satisfies the boundary condition $f \mid_S = 0$ and has continuous first and second derivatives. Any such function $f(x, y, z)$ may be represented by the convergent series

$$f(x, y, z) = \sum_{k=1}^{\infty} C_k U_k(x, y, z). \tag{20}$$

The third property of the eigenfunctions provides us in principle with the possibility of representing any function $f(x, y, z)$ in a series of eigenfunctions of our problem, and from the second property we can find all

---

* If to one and the same value of λ there correspond several essentially different (linearly independent) functions U, then this value of λ is considered as occurring a corresponding number of times in the set of eigenvalues λ_k. The condition of orthogonality for functions corresponding to the same value of λ_k may be ensured by proper choice of these functions.

the coefficients of this series. In fact, if we multiply both sides of equation (20) by $U_j(x, y, z)$ and integrate over the domain Ω, we get

$$\iiint\limits_\Omega f(x, y, z)\, U_j(x, y, z)\, dx\, dy\, dz$$

$$= \sum_{k=1}^{\infty} C_k \iiint U_k(x, y, z)\, U_j(x, y, z)\, dx\, dy\, dz.$$

In the sum on the right, all the terms in which $k \neq j$ disappear because of the orthogonality, and the coefficient of C_j is equal to one. Consequently we have

$$C_j = \iiint\limits_\Omega f(x, y, z)\, U_j(x, y, z)\, dx\, dy\, dz.$$

These properties of the characteristic oscillations now allow us to solve the general problem of oscillation for any initial conditions.

For this we assume that we have a solution of the problem in the form

$$u = \sum U_k(x, y, z)\, (A_k \cos \lambda_k t + B_k \sin \lambda_k t) \tag{21}$$

and try to choose the constants A_k and B_k so that we have

$$u\,|_{t=0} = f_0(x, y, z),$$

$$\frac{\partial u}{\partial t}\bigg|_{t=0} = f_1(x, y, z).$$

Putting $t = 0$ in the right side of (21), we see that the sine terms disappear and $\cos \lambda_k t$ becomes equal to one, so that we will have

$$f_0(x, y, z) = \sum_{k=1}^{\infty} A_k U_k(x, y, z).$$

From the third property, the characteristic oscillations can be used for such a representation, and from the second property, we have

$$A_k = \iiint\limits_\Omega f_0(x, y, z)\, U_k(x, y, z)\, dx\, dy\, dz.$$

In the same way, differentiating formula (21) with respect to t and putting $t = 0$, we will have

$$\frac{\partial u}{\partial t}\bigg|_{t=0} = f_1(x, y, z) = \sum_{k=1}^{\infty} \lambda_k(B_k \cos \lambda_k t - A_k \sin \lambda_k t)\,|_{t=0} U_k(x, y, z)$$

$$= \sum_{k=1}^{\infty} \lambda_k B_k U_k(x, y, z).$$

Hence, as before, we obtain the values of B_k as

$$B_k = \frac{1}{\lambda_k} \iiint\limits_{\Omega} f_1(x, y, z) \, U_k(x, y, z) \, dx \, dy \, dz.$$

Knowing A_k and B_k, we in fact know both the phases and the amplitudes of all the characteristic oscillations.

In this way we have shown that by addition of characteristic oscillations it is possible to obtain the most general solution of the problem with homogeneous boundary conditions.

Every solution thus consists of characteristic oscillations, whose amplitude and phase we can calculate if we know the initial conditions.

In exactly the same way, we may study oscillations with a smaller number of independent variables. As an example let us consider the vibrating string, fixed at both ends. The equation of the vibrating string has the form

$$\frac{\partial^2 u}{\partial t^2} = a^2 \frac{\partial^2 u}{\partial x^2}.$$

Let us suppose that we are looking for a solution of the problem for a string of length l, fixed at the ends

$$u \mid_{x=0} = u \mid_{x=l} = 0.$$

We will look for a collection of particular solutions

$$u_k = T_k(t) \, U_k(x).$$

We obviously obtain, just as before,

$$T_k'' U_k = a^2 U_k'' T_k ,$$

or

$$\frac{T_k''}{T_k} = a^2 \frac{U_k''}{U_k} = -\lambda_k^2 .$$

Hence

$$T_k = A_k \cos \lambda_k t + B_k \sin \lambda_k t,$$

$$U_k = M_k \cos \frac{\lambda_k}{a} x + N_k \sin \frac{\lambda_k}{a} x.$$

We use the boundary conditions in order to find the values of λ_k. For general λ_k it is not possible to satisfy both the boundary conditions. From the condition $U_k|_{x=0} = 0$ we get $M_k = 0$, and this means that $U_k = N_k$ sin $(\lambda_k/a)\, x$. Putting $x = l$, we get sin $(\lambda_k l/a) = 0$. This can only happen if $\lambda_k l/a = k\pi$, where k is an integer. This means that

$$\lambda_k = \frac{ak\pi}{l}.$$

The condition $\int_0^l U_k^2\, dx = 1$ shows that $N_k = \sqrt{\frac{2}{l}}$. Finally

$$U_k(x) = \sqrt{\frac{2}{l}} \sin \frac{k\pi x}{l}, \quad T_k = A_k \cos \frac{ak\pi t}{l} + B_k \sin \frac{ak\pi t}{l}.$$

In this manner the characteristic oscillations of the string, as we see, have sinusoidal form with an integral number of half waves on the entire string. Every oscillation has its own frequency, and the frequencies may be arranged in increasing order

$$\frac{a\pi}{l}, 2\frac{a\pi}{l}, 3\frac{a\pi}{l}, \cdots, k\frac{a\pi}{l}, \cdots.$$

It is well known that these frequencies are exactly those that we hear in the vibrations of a sounding string. The frequency is called the *fundamental frequency*, and the remaining frequencies are *overtones*. The eigenfunctions $\sqrt{2/l} \sin (k\pi x/l)$ on the interval $0 \leqslant x \leqslant l$ change sign $k - 1$ times, since $k\pi x/l$ runs through values from 0 to $k\pi$, which means that its sine changes sign $k - 1$ times. The points where the eigenfunctions U_k vanish are called *nodes* of the oscillations.

If we arrange in some way that the string does not move at a point corresponding to a node, for example of the first overtone, then the fundamental tone will be suppressed, and we will hear only the sound of the first overtone, which is an octave higher. Such a device, called stopping, is made use of on instruments played with a bow: the violin, viola, and violoncello.

We have analyzed the method of separating variables as applied to the problem of finding characteristic oscillations. But the method can be applied much more widely, to problems of heat flow and to a whole series of other problems.

For the equation of heat flow

$$\Delta T = \frac{\partial T}{\partial t}$$

with the condition

$$T|_S = 0$$

we will have, as before,

$$T = \Sigma F_k(t) \, U_k(x, y, z).$$

Here

$$\frac{F'_k(t)}{F_k(t)} = -\lambda_k^2, \quad \Delta U_k + \lambda_k^2 U_k = 0.$$

The solution is obtained in the form

$$T = \sum_{k=1}^{\infty} e^{-\lambda_k^2 t} \, U_k(x, y, z).$$

This method has also been used with great success to solve some other equations. Consider, for example, the Laplace equation

$$\Delta u = 0$$

in the circle

$$x^2 + y^2 \leqslant 1,$$

and assume that we have to construct a solution satisfying the condition

$$u \mid_{r=1} = f(\vartheta),$$

where r and ϑ denote the polar coordinates of a point in the plane.

The Laplace equation may be easily transformed into polar coordinates. It then has the form

$$\frac{\partial^2 u}{\partial r^2} + \frac{1}{r} \frac{\partial u}{\partial r} + \frac{1}{r^2} \frac{\partial^2 u}{\partial \vartheta^2} = 0.$$

We want to find a solution of this equation in the form

$$u = \sum_{k=1}^{\infty} R_k(r) \, \theta_k(\vartheta).$$

If we require that every term of the series individually satisfy the equation, we have

$$\left[R''_k(r) + \frac{1}{r} R'_k(r) \right] \theta_k(\vartheta) + \frac{1}{r^2} \theta''_k(\vartheta) R_k(r) = 0.$$

Dividing the equation by $R_k(r) \, \theta_k(\vartheta)/r^2$, we get

$$\frac{r^2 \left[R''_k(r) + \dfrac{1}{r} R'_k(r) \right]}{R_k(r)} = -\frac{\theta'_k(\vartheta)}{\theta_k(\vartheta)}.$$

Again setting

$$\frac{\theta_k''(\vartheta)}{\theta_k(\vartheta)} = -\lambda_k^2 \,,$$

we have

$$r^2 \left[R_k'' + \frac{1}{r} R_k' \right] - \lambda_k^2 R_k = 0.$$

It is easy to see that the function $\theta_k(\vartheta)$ must be a periodic function of ϑ with period 2π. Integrating the equation $\theta_k''(\vartheta) + \lambda_k^2 \theta_k(\vartheta) = 0$, we get

$$\theta_k = a_k \cos \lambda_k \vartheta + b_k \sin \lambda_k \vartheta.$$

This function will be periodic with the required period only if λ_k is an integer. Putting $\lambda_k = k$, we have

$$\theta_k = a_k \cos k\vartheta + b_k \sin k\vartheta.$$

The equation for R_k has a general solution of the form

$$R_k = Ar^k + \frac{B}{r^k} \,.$$

Retaining only the term that is bounded for $r \to 0$, we get the general solution of the Laplace equation in the form

$$u = a_0 + \sum_{k=1}^{\infty} (a_k \cos k\vartheta + b_k \sin k\vartheta) \, r^k.$$

This method may often be used to find nontrivial solutions of the equation $\varDelta U_k + \lambda_k^2 \, U_k = 0$ that satisfy homogeneous boundary conditions. In case the problem can be reduced to problems of solving ordinary differential equations, we say that it allows a complete separation of variables. This complete separation of variables by the Fourier method can be carried out, as was shown by the Soviet mathematician V. V. Stepanov, only in certain special cases. The method of separation of variables was known to mathematicians a long time ago. It was used essentially by Euler, Bernoulli, and d'Alembert. Fourier used it systematically for the solution of problems of mathematical physics, particularly in heat conduction. However, as we have mentioned, this method is often inapplicable; we must use other methods, which we will now discuss.

The method of potentials.   The essential feature of this method is, as before, the superposition of particular solutions for the construction of a solution in general form. But this time for the particular fundamental solutions, we use functions that become infinite at one point. Let us illustrate with the Laplace and Poisson equations.

Let M_0 be a point of our space. We denote by $r(M, M_0)$ the distance from the point M_0 to a variable point M. The function $1/r(M, M_0)$ for a fixed M_0 is a function of the variable point M. It is easy to establish the fact that this function is a harmonic function of the point M in the entire space,* except of course, at the point M_0, where the function becomes infinite, together with its derivatives.

The sum of several functions of this form

$$\sum_{i=1}^{N} A_i \frac{1}{r(M, M_i)},$$

where the points M_1, M_2, $\cdots$, M_N are any points in the space, is again a harmonic function of the point M. This function will have singularities at all the points M_i. If we choose the points M_1, M_2, $\cdots$, M_N as densely distributed as we please in some volume Ω, and at the same time multiply by coefficients A_i, we may pass to the limit in this expression and get a new function

$$U = \lim \sum_{i=1}^{N} \frac{A_i}{r(M, M_i)} = \iiint_{\Omega} \frac{A(M')}{r(M, M')} \, d\Omega,$$

where the points M' range over all of the volume Ω. The integral in this form is called a *Newtonian potential*. It may be shown, although we will not do it here, that the function U thus constructed satisfies the equation $\Delta U = -4\pi A$.

The Newtonian potential has a simple physical meaning. To understand it, we will begin with the function $A_i/r(M, M_i)$.

The partial derivatives of this function with respect to the coordinates are

$$A_i \frac{x_i - x}{r^3} = X, \quad A_i \frac{y_i - y}{r^3} = Y, \quad A_i \frac{z_i - z}{r^3} = Z.$$

At the point M_i we place a mass A_i, which will attract all bodies with a force directed toward the point M_i and inversely proportional to the square of the distance from M_i. We decompose this force into its components along the coordinate axes. If the magnitude of the force acting on a material point of unit mass is A_i/r^2, the cosines of the angles between the direction of this force and the coordinate axis will be $(x_i - x)/r$, $(y_i - y)/r$, $(z_i - z)/r$. Thus the components of the force exerted on a unit mass at the point M by an attracting center M_i will be equal to X, Y, and Z, the partial derivatives of the function A_i/r with respect to the coordinates. If

---

* That is, the function satisfies the Laplace equation.

we place attracting masses at points M_1, M_2, $\cdots$, M_N, then every material point with unit mass placed at a point M will be acted on by a force equal to the resultant of all the forces acting on it from the given points M_i. In other words

$$X = \frac{\partial}{\partial x} \sum \frac{A_i}{r(M, M_i)}, \quad Y = \frac{\partial}{\partial y} \sum \frac{A_i}{r(M, M_i)}, \quad Z = \frac{\partial}{\partial z} \sum \frac{A_i}{r(M, M_i)}.$$

Passing to the limit and replacing the sum by an integral, we get

$$\bar{X} = \frac{\partial U}{\partial x}, \quad \bar{Y} = \frac{\partial U}{\partial y}, \quad \bar{Z} = \frac{\partial U}{\partial z}, \quad \text{where} \quad U = \iiint_\Omega \frac{A}{r} \, d\Omega.$$

The function U, with partial derivatives equal to the components of the force acting on a point, is called the *potential* of the force. Thus the function $A_i/r(M, M_i)$ is the potential of the attraction exerted by the point M_i, the function $\sum [A_i/r(M, M_i)]$ is the potential of the attraction exerted by the group of points M_1, M_2, $\cdots$, M_N, and the function $U = \iiint_\Omega (A/r) \, d\Omega$ is the potential of the attraction exerted by the masses continuously distributed in the volume Ω.

Instead of distributing the masses in a volume, we may place the points M_1, M_2, $\cdots$, M_N on a surface S. Again increasing the number of these points, we get in the limit the integral

$$V = \iint_S \frac{A(Q)}{r} \, ds, \tag{22}$$

where Q is a point on the surface S.

It is not difficult to see that this function will be harmonic everywhere inside and outside the surface S. On the surface itself the function is continuous, as can be proved, although its partial derivatives of the first order have finite discontinuities.

The functions $\partial(1/r)/\partial x_i$, $\partial(1/r)/\partial y_i$, and $\partial(1/r)/\partial z_i$ also are harmonic functions of the point M for fixed M_i. From these functions in turn, we may form the sums

$$\sum A_i \frac{\partial \frac{1}{r}}{\partial x_i} + \sum B_i \frac{\partial \frac{1}{r}}{\partial y_i} + \sum C_i \frac{\partial \frac{1}{r}}{\partial z_i},$$

which will be harmonic functions everywhere except perhaps at the points M_1, M_2, $\cdots$, M_N.

Of particular importance is the integral

$$W = \iint\limits_{S} \mu(Q) \left[\frac{\partial \frac{1}{r}}{\partial x'} \cos(n, x) + \frac{\partial \frac{1}{r}}{\partial y'} \cos(n, y) + \frac{\partial \frac{1}{r}}{\partial z'} \cos(n, z) \right] ds$$

$$= \iint\limits_{S} \mu(Q) \, K(Q, M) \, ds, \tag{23}$$

in which x', y', and z' are the coordinates of a variable point Q on the surface S, n is the direction of the normal to the surface S at the point Q while x, y, and z are the directions of the coordinate axes, and r is the distance from Q to the point M at which the value of the function W is defined.

The integral (22) is called the *potential of a simple layer*, and the integral (23) the *potential of a double layer*.* The potential of a double layer and the potential of a simple layer represent a function harmonic inside and outside of the surface S.

Many problems in the theory of harmonic functions may be solved by using potentials. By using the potential of a double layer, we may solve the problem of constructing, in a given domain, a harmonic function u, having given values $2\pi\phi(Q)$ on the boundary S of the domain. In order to construct such a function, we only need to choose the function $\mu(Q)$ in a suitable way.

This problem is somewhat reminiscent of the similar problem of finding the coefficients in the series

$$\phi = \sum a_k U_k$$

so that it may represent the function on the left side.

A remarkable property of the integral W consists of the fact that its limiting value as the point M approaches Q_o from the inner side of the surface has the form

$$\lim_{M \to Q_0} W = 2\pi\mu(Q_0) + \iint\limits_{S} K(Q, Q_0) \, \mu(Q) \, ds.$$

---

* The names of these potentials are connected with the following physical fact. We assume that on the surface S, we have introduced electrical charges. They create in the space an electric field. The potential of this field will be represented by the integral (22), which is therefore called the potential of a simple layer.

We now assume that the surface S is a thin nonconducting film. On one side of it we distribute, according to some law, electric charges of one sign (for example, positive). On the other side of S we distribute, with the same law, electric charges of opposite sign. The action of these two electric layers also generates in the space an electric field. As can be calculated, the potential of this field will be represented by the integral (23).

Equating this expression to the given function $2\pi\phi(Q_0)$, we get the equation

$$\mu(Q_0) + \frac{1}{2\pi} \iint\limits_S K(Q, Q_0)\, \mu(Q)\, ds = \phi(Q_0).$$

This equation is called an *integral equation of the second kind*. The theory of such equations has been developed by many mathematicians. If we can solve this equation by any method, we obtain a solution of our original problem.

In exactly the same way, we may find a solution of other problems in the theory of harmonic functions. After choice of a suitable potential, the density, i.e., the value of an arbitrary function appearing in it, is defined in such a way that all the prescribed conditions are fulfilled.

From a physical point of view, this means that every harmonic function may be represented as the potential of a double electric layer, if we distribute this layer over a surface S with appropriate density.

Approximate construction of solutions; Galerkin's method and the method of nets. 1. We have discussed two methods for solving equations of mathematical physics: the method of complete separation of variables and the method of potentials. These methods were developed by scientists of the 18th and 19th centuries, Fourier, Poisson, Ostrogradskiĭ, Ljapunov, and others. In the 20th century they were augmented by a series of other methods. We will examine two of them, Galerkin's method and the method of finite differences, or the method of nets.

The first method was proposed by the Academician B. G. Galerkin for the solution of equations of the form

$$\sum \sum \sum \sum A_{ijkl} \frac{\partial^4 U}{\partial x_i\, \partial x_j\, \partial x_k\, \partial x_l} + \sum \sum \sum B_{ijk} \frac{\partial^3 U}{\partial x_i\, \partial x_j\, \partial x_k}$$
$$+ \sum \sum C_{ij} \frac{\partial^2 U}{\partial x_i\, \partial x_j} + \sum D_i \frac{\partial U}{\partial x_i} + EU + \lambda U = 0,$$

containing an unknown parameter λ, where the indices i, j, k, and l independently take on the values 1, 2, and 3. These equations are derived from equations containing an independent variable t, by using the method of separation of variables in the same way as the wave equation

$$\varDelta u = \frac{\partial^2 u}{\partial t^2}$$

leads to the equation $\varDelta U + \lambda^2 U = 0$. The problem consists of finding those values of λ for which the homogeneous boundary-value problem has a nonzero solution and then constructing that solution.

The essence of Galerkin's method is as follows. The unknown function is sought in the approximate form

$$U \approx \sum_{m=1}^{N} a_m \omega_m(x_1, x_2, x_3),$$

where the $\omega_m(x_1, x_2, x_3)$ are arbitrary functions satisfying the boundary conditions.

The assumed solution is substituted in the left side of the equation, resulting in the approximate equation

$$\sum_{m=1}^{N} a_m \left[\sum \sum \sum \sum A_{ijkl} \frac{\partial^4 \omega_m}{\partial x_i \, \partial x_j \, \partial x_k \, \partial x_l} + \sum \sum \sum B_{ijk} \frac{\partial^3 \omega_m}{\partial x_i \, \partial x_j \, \partial x_k} \right.$$

$$\left. + \sum \sum C_{ij} \frac{\partial^2 \omega_m}{\partial x_i \, \partial x_j} + \sum D_i \frac{\partial \omega_m}{\partial x_i} + E \omega_m \right] + \lambda \sum_{m=1}^{N} a_m \omega_m \approx 0.$$

For brevity we denote the expression inside the brackets by $L\omega_m$, and write the equation in the form

$$\sum a_m L\omega_m + \lambda \sum a_m \omega_m \approx 0.$$

Now we multiply both sides of our approximate equation by ω_n and integrate over the domain Ω in which the solution is sought. We get

$$\iiint_{\Omega} \sum a_m \omega_n L\omega_m \, d\Omega + \lambda \iiint_{\Omega} \sum a_m \omega_m \omega_n \, d\Omega \approx 0,$$

which may be rewritten in the form

$$\sum_{m=1}^{N} a_m \iiint_{\Omega} \omega_n L\omega_m \, d\Omega + \lambda \sum_{m=1}^{N} a_m \iiint_{\Omega} \omega_m \omega_n \, d\Omega \approx 0.$$

If we set ourselves the aim of satisfying these equations exactly, we will have a system of algebraic equations of the first degree for the unknown coefficients a_m. The number of equations in the system will be equal to the number of unknowns, so that this system will have a nonvanishing solution only if its determinant is zero. If this determinant is expanded, we get an equation of the Nth degree for the unknown number λ.

After finding the value of λ and substituting it in the system, we solve this system to obtain approximate expressions of the function U.

Galerkin's method is not only suitable for equations of the fourth order, but may be applied to equations of different orders and different types.

2. The last of the methods that we will examine is called the method of finite differences or the method of nets.

The derivative of the function u with respect to the variable x is defined as the limit of the quotient

$$\frac{u(x + \Delta x) - u(x)}{\Delta x}.$$

This quotient in its turn may be represented in the form

$$\frac{1}{\Delta x} \int_x^{x+\Delta x} \frac{\partial u}{\partial x_1} \, dx_1 \, ,$$

and from the well-known theorem of the mean value (cf. Chapter II, §8):

$$\frac{u(x + \Delta x) - u(x)}{\Delta x} = \frac{\partial u}{\partial x} \Big|_{x=\xi} \, ,$$

where ξ is a point in the interval

$$x < \xi < x + \Delta x.$$

All the second derivatives of u, both the mixed derivatives and the derivatives with respect to one variable, may also be approximately represented in the form of difference quotients. Thus the difference quotient

$$\frac{u(x + \Delta x) - 2u(x) + u(x - \Delta x)}{(\Delta x)^2}$$

is represented in the form

$$\frac{1}{\Delta x} \left[\frac{u(x + \Delta x) - u(x)}{\Delta x} - \frac{u(x) - u(x - \Delta x)}{\Delta x} \right]$$

$$= \frac{1}{\Delta x} \left\{ \left[\frac{u(x_1 + \Delta x) - u(x_1)}{\Delta x} \right] \Big|_{x_1 = x - \Delta x}^{x_1 = x} \right\}.$$

From the mean-value theorem the difference quotient of the function

$$\phi(x_1) = \frac{u(x_1 + \Delta x) - u(x_1)}{\Delta x}$$

may be replaced by the value of the derivative. Consequently

$$\frac{\phi(x_1) - \phi(x_1 - \Delta x)}{\Delta x} = \phi'(\xi),$$

where ξ is some intermediate value in the interval

$$x - \varDelta x < \xi < x.$$

Thus

$$\left(\frac{1}{\varDelta x}\right)^2 [u(x + \varDelta x) - 2u(x) + u(x - \varDelta x)]$$

$$= \frac{1}{\varDelta x} [\phi(x) - \phi(x - \varDelta x)] = \phi'(\xi).$$

On the other hand

$$\phi(\xi) = \frac{u(\xi + \varDelta x) - u(\xi)}{\varDelta x},$$

which means that

$$\phi'(\xi) = \frac{u'(\xi + \varDelta x) - u'(\xi)}{\varDelta x}.$$

Once more using the formula for finite increments, we see that

$$\phi'(\xi) = u''(\eta),$$

where

$$\xi < \eta < \xi + \varDelta x.$$

Consequently,

$$\left(\frac{1}{\varDelta x}\right)^2 [u(x + \varDelta x) - 2u(x) + u(x - \varDelta x)] = u''(\eta),$$

where $x - \varDelta x < \eta < x + \varDelta x$.

If the derivative $u''(x)$ is continuous and the value of $\varDelta x$ is sufficiently small, then $u''(\eta)$ will be only slightly different from $u''(x)$. Thus our second derivative is arbitrarily close to the difference quotient in question. In exactly the same way it may be shown, for example, that the mixed second derivative

$$\frac{\partial^2 u}{\partial x\, \partial y}$$

can be approximately represented by the formula

$$\frac{\partial^2 u}{\partial x\, \partial y} = \frac{1}{\varDelta x\, \varDelta y} [u(x + \varDelta x, y + \varDelta y) - u(x + \varDelta x, y)$$

$$- u(x, y + \varDelta y) + u(x, y)].$$

We return now to our partial differential equation.

For definiteness, let us assume that we are dealing with the Laplace equation in two independent variables

$$\frac{\partial^2 u}{\partial x^2} + \frac{\partial^2 u}{\partial y^2} = 0.$$

Further, let the unknown function u be given on the boundary S of the domain Ω. As an approximation we assume that

$$\frac{\partial^2 u}{\partial x^2} = \frac{u(x + \Delta x, y) - 2u(x, y) + u(x - \Delta x, y)}{(\Delta x)^2},$$

$$\frac{\partial^2 u}{\partial y^2} = \frac{u(x, y + \Delta y) - 2u(x, y) + u(x, y - \Delta y)}{(\Delta y)^2}$$

If we put $\Delta x = \Delta y = h$, then

$$\frac{\partial^2 u}{\partial x^2} + \frac{\partial^2 u}{\partial y^2} = \frac{1}{h^2} [u(x + h, y) + u(x, y + h) + u(x - h, y)$$
$$+ u(x, y - h) - 4u(x, y)].$$

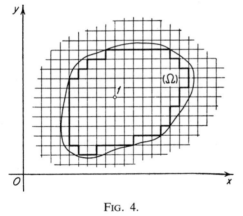

Now let us cover the domain Ω with a square net with vertices at the points $x = kh$, $y = bh$ (figure 4). We replace the domain by the polygon consisting of those squares of our net that fall inside Ω, so that the boundary of the domain is changed into a broken line. We take the values of the unknown function on this broken line to be those given on the boundary of S. The Laplace equation

FIG. 4.

is then approximated by the equation

$$u(x + h, y) + u(x, y + h) + u(x - h, y) + u(x, y - h) - 4u(x, y) = 0$$

for all interior points of the domain. This equation may be rewritten in the form

$$u(x, y) = \tfrac{1}{4} [u(x + h, y) + u(x, y + h) + u(x - h, y) + u(x, y - h)].$$

Then the value of u at any point of the net, for example the point 1 in figure 4, is equal to the arithmetic mean of its values at the four adjacent points.

We assume that inside the polygon there are N points of our net. At every such point we will have a corresponding equation. In this manner we get a system of N algebraic equations in N unknowns, the solution of which gives us the approximate values of the function u on the domain Ω.

It may be shown that for the Laplace equation the solution may be found to any desired degree of accuracy.

The method of finite differences reduces the problem to the solution of a system of N equations in N unknowns, where the unknowns are the values of the desired function at the knots of some net.

Further the method of finite differences can be shown to be applicable to other problems of mathematical physics: to other differential equations and to integral equations. However its application in many cases involves a number of difficulties.

It may turn out that the solution of the system of N algebraic equations in N unknowns, constructed by the method of nets, either does not exist in general or gives a result that is quite far from the true one. This happens when the solution of the system of equations leads to accumulation of errors; the smaller we take the length of the sides of the squares in the net the more equations we get, so that the accumulated error may become greater.

In the example given previously of the Laplace equation, this does not happen. The errors in solving this system do not accumulate but, on the contrary, steadily decrease if we solve the system, for example, by a method of successive approximations. For the equation of heat flow and for the wave equation it is essential to choose the nets properly. For these equations we may get both good and bad results.

If we are going to solve either of these equations by the method of nets, after choosing the net for the values of t, we must not choose too fine a net for the space variables. Otherwise we get a very unsatisfactory system of equations for the values of the unknown function; its solution gives a result that oscillates rapidly with large amplitudes and is thus very far from the true one.

The great variety of possible results may best be seen in a simple numerical example. Consider the equation

$$\frac{\partial u}{\partial t} = \frac{\partial^2 u}{\partial x^2}$$

for the equation of heat flow in the case in which the temperature does not depend on y or z. We take the mesh width of the net along the values of t equal to k and along the values of x equal to h

$$\frac{\partial u}{\partial t} \approx \frac{u(t+k, x) - u(t, x)}{k},$$

$$\frac{\partial^2 u}{\partial x^2} \approx \frac{u(t, x+h) - 2u(t, x) + u(t, x-h)}{h^2}.$$

Then our equation may be written approximately in the form

$$u(t + k, x) = \frac{k}{h^2} u(t, x + h) + \left(1 - 2\frac{k}{h^2}\right) u(t, x) + \frac{k}{h^2} u(t, x - h).$$

If, for a certain mesh-point value of t, we know the values of u at the points $x - h$, x, and $x + h$, it is easy to find the value of u at the point x and the next mesh point $t + k$. Assume that the constant k, i.e., the mesh width in the net with respect to t, is already chosen. Let us consider two cases for the choice of h. We put $h^2 = k$ in the first case and $h^2 = 2k$ in the second and solve the following problem by the method of nets.

At the initial instant, $u = 0$ for all negative values of x, and $u = 1$ for all nonnegative values of x. We will have, writing in one line the values of the unknown function u for the given instant, two tables:

Table 1

t \ x	−5h	−4h	−3h	−2h	−h	0	h	2h	3h	4h	5h
0	0	0	0	0	0	1	1	1	1	1	1
k	0	0	0	0	1	0	1	1	1	1	1
2k	0	0	0	1	−1	2	0	1	1	1	1
3k	0	0	1	−2	4	−3	3	0	1	1	1
4k	0	1	−3	7	−9	10	−6	4	0	1	1
5k	1	−4	11	−19	26	−25	20	−10	5	0	1

Table 2

t \ x	−5h	−4h	−3h	−2h	−h	0	h	2h	3h	4h	5h
0	0	0	0	0	0	1	1	1	1	1	1
k	0	0	0	0	$\frac{1}{2}$	$\frac{1}{2}$	1	1	1	1	1
2k	0	0	0	$\frac{1}{4}$	$\frac{1}{4}$	$\frac{3}{4}$	$\frac{3}{4}$	1	1	1	1
3k	0	0	$\frac{1}{8}$	$\frac{1}{8}$	$\frac{1}{2}$	$\frac{1}{2}$	$\frac{7}{8}$	$\frac{7}{8}$	1	1	1
4k	0	$\frac{1}{16}$	$\frac{1}{16}$	$\frac{5}{16}$	$\frac{5}{16}$	$\frac{11}{16}$	$\frac{11}{16}$	$\frac{15}{16}$	$\frac{15}{16}$	1	1
5k	$\frac{1}{32}$	$\frac{1}{32}$	$\frac{3}{16}$	$\frac{3}{16}$	$\frac{1}{2}$	$\frac{1}{2}$	$\frac{13}{16}$	$\frac{13}{16}$	$\frac{31}{32}$	$\frac{31}{32}$	1

In Table 2 we obtain values, for any given instant of time, which vary smoothly from point to point. This table gives a good approximation to the solution of the heat-flow equation. On the other hand, in Table 1, in which, as it would seem, the exactness should have been increased because of our finer division for the x-interval, the values of u oscillate very rapidly from positive values to negative ones and attain values that are much greater than the initially prescribed ones. It is clear that in this table the values are extraordinarily far from those that correspond to the true solution.

From these examples it is clear that if we wish to use the method of nets to get sufficiently accurate and reliable results, we must exercise great discretion in our choice of intervals in the net and must make preliminary investigations to justify the application of the method.

The solutions obtained by using the equations of mathematical physics for these or other problems of natural science give us a mathematical description of the expected course or the expected character of the physical events described by these equations.

Since the construction of a model is carried out by means of the equations of mathematical physics, we are forced to ignore, in our abstractions, many aspects of these events, to reject certain aspects as nonessential and to select others as basic, from which it follows that the results we obtain are not absolutely true. They are absolutely true only for that scheme or model that we have considered, but they must always be compared with experiment, if we are to be sure that our model of the event is close to the event itself and represents it with a sufficient degree of exactness.

The ultimate criterion of the truth of the results is thus practical experience only. In the final analysis, there is just one criterion, namely practical experience, although experience can only be properly understood in the light of a profound and well-developed theory.

If we consider the vibrating string of a musical instrument, we can understand how it produces its tones only if we are acquainted with the laws for superposition of characteristic oscillations. The relations that hold among the frequencies can be understood only if we investigate how these frequencies are determined by the material, by the tension in the string, and by the manner of fixing the ends. In this case the theory not only provides a method of calculating any desired numerical quantities but also indicates just which of these quantities are of fundamental importance, exactly how the physical process occurs, and what should be observed in it.

In this way a domain of science, namely mathematical physics, not only grew out of the requirements of practice but in turn exercised its own influence on that practice and pointed out paths for further progress.

Mathematical physics is very closely connected with other branches of mathematical analysis, but we cannot discuss these connections here, since they would lead us too far afield.

§6. Generalized Solutions

The range of problems in which a physical process is described by continuous, differentiable functions satisfying differential equations may be extended in an essential way by introducing into the discussion discontinuous solutions of these equations.

In a number of cases it is clear from the beginning that the problem under consideration cannot have solutions that are twice continuously differentiable; in other words, from the point of view of the classical statement of the problem given in the preceding section, such a problem has no solution. Nevertheless the corresponding physical process does occur, although we cannot find functions describing it in the preassigned class of twice-differentiable functions. Let us consider some simple examples.

1. If a string consists of two pieces of different density, then in the equation

$$\frac{\partial^2 u}{\partial t^2} = a^2 \frac{\partial^2 u}{\partial x^2} \tag{24}$$

the coefficient will be equal to a different constant on each of the corresponding pieces, and so equation (24) will not, in general, have classical (twice continuously differentiable) solutions.

2. Let the coefficient a be a constant, but in the initial position let the string have the form of a broken line given by the equation $u|_{i=0} = \phi(x)$. At the vertex of the broken line, the function $\phi(x)$ obviously cannot have a first derivative. It may be shown that there exists no classical solution of equation (24) satisfying the initial conditions

$$u|_{t=0} = \phi(x), \quad u_t|_{t=0} = 0$$

(here and in what follows u_t denotes $\partial u/\partial t$).

3. If a sharp blow is given to any small piece of the string, the resulting oscillations are described by the equation

$$\frac{\partial^2 u}{\partial t^2} = a^2 \frac{\partial^2 u}{\partial x^2} + f(x, t),$$

where $f(x, t)$ corresponds to the effect produced and is a discontinuous function, differing from zero only on the small piece of the string and during a short interval of time. Such an equation also, as can be easily established, cannot have classical solutions.

These examples show that requiring continuous derivatives for the desired solution strongly restricts the range of the problems we can solve. The search for a wider range of solvable problems proceeded first of all in the direction of allowing discontinuities of the first kind in the derivatives of highest order, for the functions serving as solutions to the problems, where these functions must satisfy the equations except at the points of discontinuity. It turns out that the solutions of an equation of the type $\Delta u = 0$ or $\partial u/\partial t - \Delta u = 0$ cannot have such (so-called weak) discontinuities inside the domain of definition. Solutions of the wave equation can have weak discontinuities in the space variables x, y, z, and in t only on surfaces of a special form, which are called characteristic surfaces. If a solution $u(x, y, z, t)$ of the wave equation is considered as a function defining, for $t = t_1$, a scalar field in the x, y, z space at the instant t_1, then the surfaces of discontinuity for the second derivatives of $u(x, y, z, t)$ will travel through the (x, y, z) space with a velocity equal to the square root of the coefficient of the Laplacian in the wave equation.

The second example for the string shows that it is also necessary to consider solutions in which there may be discontinuous first derivatives; and in the case of sound and light waves, we must even consider solutions that themselves have discontinuities.

The first question that comes up in investigating the introduction of discontinuous solutions consists in making clear exactly which discontinuous functions can be considered as physically admissible solutions of an equation or of the corresponding physical problem. We might, for example, assume that an arbitrary piecewise constant function is "a single solution" of the Laplace equation or the wave equation, since it satisfies the equation outside of the lines of discontinuity.

In order to clarify this question, the first thing that must be guaranteed is that in the wider class of functions, to which the admissible solutions must belong, we must have a uniqueness theorem. It is perfectly clear that if, for example, we allow arbitrary piecewise smooth functions, then this requirement will not be satisfied.

Historically, the first principle for selection of admissible functions was that they should be the limits (in some sense or other) of classical solutions of the same equation. Thus, in example 2, a solution of equation (24) corresponding to the function $\phi(x)$, which does not have a derivative at an angular point may be found as the uniform limit of classical solutions $u_n(x, t)$ of the same equation corresponding to the initial conditions $u_n|_{t=0} = \phi_n(x)$, $u_{n_t}|_{t=0} = 0$, where the $\phi_n(x)$ are twice continuously differentiable functions converging uniformly to $\phi(x)$ for $n \to \infty$.

In what follows, instead of this principle we will adopt the following: An admissible solution u must satisfy, instead of the equation $Lu = f$, an integral identity containing an arbitrary function Φ.

This identity is found as follows: We multiply both sides of the equation $Lu = f$ by an arbitrary function Φ, which has continuous derivatives with respect to all its arguments of orders up through the order of the equation and vanishes outside of the finite domain D in which the equation is defined. The equation thus found is integrated over D and then transformed by integration by parts so that it does not contain any derivatives of u. As a result we get the identity desired. For equation (24), for example, it has the form

$$\iint\limits_D u \left[\frac{\partial^2 \Phi}{\partial t^2} - \frac{\partial^2 (a^2 \Phi)}{\partial x^2} \right] dx\, dt = 0.$$

S. L. Sobolev has shown that for equations with constant coefficients these two principles for the selection of admissible (or as they are now usually called, generalized) solutions, are equivalent to each other. But for equations with variable coefficients, the first principle may turn out to be inapplicable, since these equations may in general have no classical solutions (cf. example 1). The second of these principles provides the possibility of selecting generalized solutions with very broad assumptions on the differentiability properties of the coefficients of the equations. It is true that this principle seems at first sight to be overly formal and to have a purely mathematical character, which does not directly indicate how the problems ought to be formulated in a manner similar to the classical problems.

We give here a modification that, it seems to us, is more appropriate physically, since it is directly connected with the well-known principle of Hamilton.

As is well known, analysis of the methods of deducing various equations of mathematical physics led in the first half of the 19th century to the discovery of a new law known as Hamilton's principle. Starting from this principle, it was possible to obtain in a uniform manner all the known equations of mathematical physics. We will illustrate this by the example of the problem considered in §3 for the oscillations of a string of finite length with fixed ends.

First of all we construct the so-called Lagrange function $L(t)$ for our string, namely the difference between the kinetic and potential energies. From what was said in §3 it follows that

$$L(t) = \int_0^l \left(\frac{1}{2} \rho u_t^2 - \frac{T}{2} u_x^2 \right) dx.$$

According to Hamilton's principle, the integral

$$S = \int_{t_1}^{t_2} L(t) \, dt$$

assumes its minimum value for the function $u(x, t)$, corresponding to the true motion of the string compared with all other functions $v(x, y)$ which are equal to zero for $x = 0$ and $x = l$ and coincide with $u(x, t_1)$ and $u(x, t_2)$ for $t = t_1$ and $t = t_2$. Here t_1 and t_2 are fixed arbitrarily, and the functions v must have finite integrals S. As a result of this principle the so-called first variation of S (cf. Chapter VIII) must be equal to zero, ie.,

$$\delta S = \int_{t_1}^{t_2} \int_0^l (\rho u_t \Phi_t - T u_x \Phi_x) \, dx \, dt = 0, \tag{25}$$

where $\Phi(x, t)$ is an arbitrary function differentiable with respect to x and t and equal to zero on the edges of the rectangle $0 \leqslant x \leqslant l$, $t_1 \leqslant t \leqslant t_2$.

Equation (25) is also the condition that must be met by the desired function $u(x, t)$. If we know that $u(x, t)$ has derivatives of the second order, then condition (25) may be put in a different form. Integrating (25) by parts and applying the fundamental lemma of the calculus of variations, we find that $u(x, t)$ must satisfy the equation

$$\frac{\partial}{\partial t} \left(\rho \frac{\partial u}{\partial t} \right) - \frac{\partial}{\partial x} \left(T \frac{\partial u}{\partial x} \right) = 0, \tag{26}$$

which is identical with (24), if ρ and T are constants and $T/\rho = a^2$.

It is not difficult to see that any solution $u(x, t)$ of equation (26) satisfies the identity (25) for all given Φ. The converse turns out to be false, since $u(x, t)$ may in general not have second derivatives. So we are extending the range of solvable problems, if we replace equation (26) by the identity (25).

To determine a specific oscillation of the string, we must add to the boundary conditions

$$u(0, t) = u(l, t) = 0, \tag{27}$$

the initial conditions

$$u(x, 0) = \phi_0(x),$$
$$u_t(x, 0) = \phi_1(x). \tag{28}$$

If a solution is sought in the class of continuously differentiable functions, then conditions (27) and (28) may be stated separately from (25) as requirements to be met. But if we allow the proposed solution to be "worse," then these conditions lose their meaning in the form given and they must be partly or wholly included in the integral identity (25).

For example, let $u(x, t)$ be continuous for $0 \leqslant x \leqslant l, 0 \leqslant t \leqslant T$, but let its first derivatives have discontinuities. The second equation in (28) then loses its meaning as a limiting condition. In this case the problem can be stated as follows: to find a continuous function u which fulfills condition (27) and the first of the conditions (28) for which the equation

$$\int_0^T \int_0^l (\rho u_t \Phi_t - T u_x \Phi_x) \, dx \, dt + \int_0^l \phi_1 \Phi(x, 0) \, dx = 0 \qquad (29)$$

is identically satisfied for all continuous $\Phi(x, t)$ equal to zero for $x = 0$, $x = l$ and $t = T$. Here the functions u and Φ must both have first derivatives whose squares are integrable in the sense of Lebesgue on the rectangle $0 \leqslant x \leqslant l$, $0 \leqslant t \leqslant T$. This last requirement for u means that the mean value with respect to time of the total energy of the string

$$\frac{1}{2T} \int_0^T \int_0^l (\rho u_t^2 + T u_x^2) \, dx \, dt$$

must be finite. Such a restriction on the function u, and thus also on its possible variations Φ, is a natural result of Hamilton's principle.

The identity (29) is precisely the condition that the first variation of the functional

$$\tilde{S} = \int_0^T \int_0^l \left(\frac{\rho}{2} u_t^2 - \frac{T}{2} u_x^2 \right) dx \, dt + \int_0^l \phi_1 u \big|_{t=0} \, dx$$

be equal to zero. Thus the problem of the vibration of a fixed string in the case considered may be stated as the problem of finding the minimum of the functional $\tilde{S}$ for all functions $v(x, t)$ which are continuous, satisfy condition (27), and are equal to $u(x, T)$ for $t = T$. Moreover, the desired function must satisfy the first of conditions (28).

This modification of Hamilton's principle allows us not only to widen the class of admissible solutions of equation (24) but also to state a well-defined boundary-value problem for them.

The fact that these generalized solutions or some of their derivatives are not defined at all points of the space does not lead to any contradiction with experiment, as was repeatedly pointed out by N. M. Gjunter, whose investigations were chiefly instrumental in establishing a new point of view for the concept of the solution of an equation of mathematical physics.

For example, if we wish to determine the flow of liquid in a channel, then in the classical presentation we must compute the velocity vector and the pressure at every point of the flow. But in practice we are never dealing with the pressure at a point but rather with the pressure on a certain area and never with the velocity vector at a given point but rather with the amount of the liquid passing through some area in a unit of time. The definition of generalized solution thus proposes essentially the computation of just those quantities that have direct physical meaning.

In order that a larger number of problems may be solvable, we must seek the solutions among functions belonging to the widest possible class of functions for which uniqueness theorems still hold. Frequently such a class is dictated by the physical nature of the problem. Thus, in quantum mechanics it is not the state function $\psi(x)$, defined as a solution of the Schrödinger equation, that has physical meaning but rather the integral $a_\nu = \int_E \psi(x)\,\psi_\nu(x)\,dx$, where the ψ_ν are certain functions for which $\int_E \psi_\nu^2\,dx < \infty$. Thus the solution ψ is to be sought not among the twice continuously differentiable functions but among the ones with integrable square. In the problems of quantum electrodynamics, it is still an open question which classes of functions are the ones in which we ought to seek solutions for the equations considered in that theory.

Progress in mathematical physics during the last thirty years has been closely connected with this new formulation of the problems and with the creation of the mathematical apparatus necessary for their solution. One of the central features of this apparatus is the so-called embedding theorem of S. L. Sobolev.

Particularly convenient methods of finding generalized solutions in one or another of these classes of functions are: the method of finite differences, the direct methods in the calculus of variations (Ritz method and Trefftz method), Galerkin's method, and functional-operator methods. These latter methods basically depend on a study of transformations generated by these problems. We have already spoken in §5 of the method of finite differences and of Galerkin's method. Here we will explain the basic ideas of the direct methods of the calculus of variations.

Let us consider the problem of defining the position of a uniformly stretched membrane with fixed boundary. From the principle of minimum potential energy in a state of stable equilibrium the function $u(x, y)$ must give the least value of the integral

$$J(u) = \iint_D (u_x^2 + u_y^2)\,dx\,dy$$

in comparison with all other continuously differentiable functions $v(x, y)$ satisfying the same condition on the boundary, $v|_S = \phi$, as the function u does. With some restrictions on ϕ and on the boundary S it can be shown that such a minimum exists and is attained by a harmonic function, so that the desired function u is a solution of the Dirichlet problem

$\Delta u = 0$, $u|_s = \phi$. The converse is also true: The solution of the Dirichlet problem gives a minimum to the integral J with respect to all v satisfying the boundary condition.

The proof of the existence of the function u, for which J attains its minimum, and its computation to any desired degree of accuracy may be carried out, for example, in the following manner (Ritz method). We choose an infinite family of twice continuously differentiable functions $\{v_n(x, y)\}$, $n = 0, 1, 2, \cdots$, equal to zero on the boundary for $n > 0$ and equal to ϕ for $n = 0$. We consider J for functions of the form

$$v = \sum_{k=1}^{n} C_k v_k + v_0,$$

where n is fixed and the C_k are arbitrary numbers. Then $J(v)$ will be a polynomial of second degree in the n independent variables C_1, C_2, $\cdots$, C_n. We determine the C_k from the condition that this polynomial should assume its minimum. This leads to a system of n linear algebraic equations in n unknowns, the determinant of which is different from zero. Thus the numbers C_k are uniquely defined. We denote the corresponding v by $v^n(x, y)$. It can be shown that if the system $\{v_n\}$ satisfies a certain condition of "completeness" the functions v^n will converge, as $n \to \infty$, to a function which will be the desired solution of the problem.

In conclusion, we note that in this chapter we have given a description of only the simplest linear problem of mechanics and have ignored many further questions, still far from completely worked out, which are connected with more general partial differential equations.

Suggested Reading

H. Bateman, *Partial differential equations of mathematical physics*, Dover, New York, 1944.

R. Courant and D. Hilbert, *Methods of mathematical physics*. II, *Partial differential equations*, Interscience, New York, 1962.

G. F. D. Duff, *Partial differential equations*, University of Toronto Press, 1956.

G. E. Forsythe and W. R. Wasow, *Finite-difference methods for partial differential equations*, Wiley, New York, 1960.

L. Hopf, *Introduction to the differential equations of physics*, Dover, New York, 1948.

I. G. Petrovskii, *Lectures on partial differential equations*, Interscience, New York, 1954.

H. Sagan, *Boundary and eigenvalue problems in mathematical physics*, Wiley, New York, 1961.

I. A. Sneddon, *Elements of partial differential equations*, McGraw-Hill, New York, 1957.

A. J. W. Sommerfeld, *Partial differential equations in physics*, Academic Press, New York, 1949.

A. G. Webster, *Partial differential equations of mathematical physics*, Dover, New York, 1955.

CHAPTER VII

CURVES
AND SURFACES

§1. Topics and Methods in the Theory of Curves and Surfaces

In a school course, geometry involves only the simplest curves: straight lines, broken lines, and circumferences and arcs of circles; and as for surfaces, merely planes, surfaces of polyhedra, spheres, cones, and cylinders. In more extended courses other curves are considered, chiefly the conic sections: ellipses, parabolas, and hyperbolas. But the study of an arbitrary curve or surface is completely alien to elementary geometry. At first sight it is even unclear how any general properties could be selected for investigation when we are speaking of arbitrary curves and surfaces. Yet such an investigation is completely natural and necessary.

In every kind of practical activity and experience of nature, we constantly encounter curves and surfaces of widely different forms. The path of a planet in space, of a ship at sea, or of a projectile in the air, the track of a chisel on metal, of a wheel on the road, of a pen on the tape of a recording device, the shape of a camshaft governing the valves of a motor, the contours of an artistic design, the form of a dangling rope, the shape of a spiral spring coiled for some specific purpose, such examples are endless. The surfaces of various objects, thin shells, cisterns, the framework of an airplane, casings, sheetlike materials, provide an endless diversity of surfaces. Methods for the processing of products, the optical properties of various objects, the streamlining of bodies, the rigidity or deformability of thin shells, these and many other features depend to a great extent on the geometric form of the surfaces of objects.

Of course, the gouge left by a chisel on metal is not a mathematical

57

curve. A cistern, even with thin walls, is not a mathematical surface. But to a first approximation, which is sufficient for the study of many questions, actual objects may be represented mathematically by curves and surfaces.

In introducing the concept of a mathematical curve, we disregard all the reasons why we cannot decrease the thickness without limit. By means of this abstract concept, we succeed in representing those (completely concrete) properties of an object that are preserved when its thickness and breadth are decreased in comparison with its length.

Similarly, if we disregard the limitations on our ability to decrease the thickness of a shell or to determine precisely the actual boundaries of a given object, we are led to the concept of a mathematical surface. We will not give a rigorous description of these well-known concepts but will only remark that the exact mathematical definitions are not simple and belong to topology.

Finally, an important source of interest in various curves and surfaces has been the development of mathematical analysis. It is sufficient to remember, for example, that a curve is the geometric representation of a function, which is the most important concept of analysis. Moreover, every one is familiar with graphs quite apart from any study of analysis.

In elementary geometry as created by the ancient Greeks, there was nothing about arbitrary curves or surfaces, but even in elementary analytic geometry we are accustomed to say "every curve is represented by an equation" or "every equation in the two variables x and y represents a curve in the coordinate plane." Similarly the coordinates of surfaces are given by the equations $z = f(x, y)$ or $F(x, y, z) = 0$, and in general the coordinate method, by establishing a close connection between elementary geometry and analysis, enables us to define many different curves and surfaces.

But analytic geometry, being restricted to the methods of algebra and elementary geometry, goes no further than the investigation of certain specific types of figures. The study of arbitrary curves and surfaces represents a new branch of mathematics, known as *differential geometry*.

It must be admitted at once that differential geometry imposes on its curves and surfaces certain conditions arising from the methods of analysis. However, this is not an essential limitation on the diversity of the allowable curves and surfaces, since in the great majority of cases they are capable of representing actual objects with the necessary degree of precision. The name "differential geometry" itself gives an indication of the methods of the theory; its basic tool is the differential calculus and it primarily investigates the "differential" properties of the curves

and surfaces, i.e., their properties "at a point."* Thus, the direction of
a curve at a point is determined by its tangent at that point and the
amount by which it twists is described by its curvature (the exact definition
of this term will be given below). Differential geometry investigates the
properties of small segments of curves and surfaces and only in its later
developments does it proceed to the study of their properties "in the
large," i.e., in their entire extent.

The development of differential geometry is inseparably connected
with the development of analysis. The basic operations of analysis,
namely differentiation and integration, have a direct geometric meaning.
As was mentioned in Chapter II, differentiating a function $f(x)$ corresponds
to drawing a tangent to the curve

$$y = f(x).$$

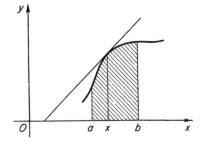

The slope of the tangent line (i.e.,
the trigonometric tangent of the
angle it makes with the axis Ox) is
precisely the derivative $f'(x)$ of the
function $f(x)$ at the corresponding
point (figure 1), and the area "under
the curve"

$$y = f(x)$$

Fig. 1.

is precisely the integral $\int_a^b f(x)\ dx$ of
this function, evaluated between the corresponding limits. Just as in analysis
we investigate arbitrary functions, so in differential geometry we examine
arbitrary curves and surfaces. In analysis, the first object of study is the
general course of a curve on a plane, its rise and fall, its greater or smaller
curvature, the direction of its convexity, its points of inflection, and so
forth. The close connection between analysis and the curves is indicated
by the name of the first textbook in analysis, by the French mathematician
l'Hôpital in 1695: "Infinitesimal analysis applied to the study of curves."

By the middle of the 18th century, the differential and integral calculus
had been sufficiently developed by the immediate successors of Newton
and Leibnitz that the way was open for more profound applications to
geometry. Indeed, it is only from this moment that one may properly

---

* The properties of curves and surfaces "at a point" are those properties that depend
only on an arbitrarily small neighborhood of the point. Properties of this sort are
defined in terms of the derivatives (at the given point) of the functions occurring in the
equations of the curve or surface. It is for this reason that differential geometry imposes
conditions guaranteeing that the differential calculus is applicable; it is required that
the curve or surface be defined by functions with a sufficient number of derivatives.

speak of a theory of curves and surfaces. For surfaces, and for curves in space, the analogous problems are immeasurably richer in content than for plane curves, so that with the passage of time these problems outgrew the framework of a simple application of analysis to geometry and led to the formation of an independent theory. During the second half of the 18th century, many mathematicians shared in building up the elements of this theory: Clairaut, Euler, Monge, and others, among whom Euler must be considered as the founder of the general theory of surfaces. The first comprehensive work on curves and surfaces was the book of Monge "Application of analysis to geometry," published in 1795.* From the investigations of these mathematicians, and, in particular, from the book of Monge, we can easily understand the upsurge of interest in differential geometry. This upsurge was due to the demands of mechanics, physics, and astronomy, i.e., in the final analysis to the needs of technology and industry, for which the available results of elementary geometry were completely insufficient.

The classical work of Gauss (1777-1855) in the theory of surfaces is also related to practical questions. His "General investigations concerning curved surfaces," published in 1827, is basic for the differential geometry of surfaces as an independent branch of mathematics. His general methods and problems, discussed later in §4, originated to a great degree in the practical needs of map making. The problem of cartography consists of finding as exact a representation as possible of parts of the surface of the earth on a plane. A completely exact representation here is impossible, the mutual relations of various lengths being necessarily distorted because of the curvature of the earth. Thus one has the problem of finding the most nearly exact methods possible. The drawing of maps goes back to remote antiquity, but the creation of a general theory is an achievement of recent times and would not have been possible without the general theory of surfaces and the general methods of mathematical analysis. We note that one of the difficult mathematical problems of cartography was investigated by P. L. Čebyšev (1821-1894), who obtained important results relating to nets of curved lines on surfaces. His investigations also arose from purely practical problems.

The general questions of deforming one surface so that it can be mapped on another still constitute one of the main branches of geometry. Important results in this direction were obtained in 1838 by F. Minding (1806-1885), professor at the University of Dorpat (now Tartu).

---

* Gaspard Monge (1746-1828) was not only an outstanding scientist but also an active French revolutionary (minister of naval affairs, and then director of the manufacture of cannon and powder). He followed the path, characteristic of the French bourgeois of the time, from Jacobin to adherent of the emperor Napoleon.

By the second half of the last century, the theory of curves and surfaces was already well established in its basic features, provided we are speaking of "classical differential geometry" in contrast with the newer directions discussed later in §5. The basic equations in the theory of curves, namely the so-called Frenet formulas, had already been obtained, and in 1853 K. M. Peterson (1828-1881), a student of Minding's at Tartu University, discovered and investigated in his dissertation the basic equations of the theory of surfaces, rediscovered 15 years later and published by the Italian mathematician Codazzi, with whose name these equations are usually associated. Peterson, after graduating from the university at Tartu, lived and worked in Moscow, as a teacher in a gymnasium. Though he never held any academic position corresponding to his outstanding scientific achievements, he was nevertheless one of the founders of the Moscow Mathematical Society and of the journal "Matematičeskiĭ Sbornik," published in Moscow from 1866 up to the present day. The Moscow school of differential geometry begins with Peterson.

The results to date of the "classical" differential geometry were summarized by the French geometer Darboux in his four-volume "Lectures on the general theory of surfaces," issued from 1887 to 1896. In the present century classical differential geometry continues to be studied, but the center of interest in curves and surfaces has largely shifted to new directions in which the class of figures under study has been even more widely extended.

§2. The Theory of Curves

Various methods of defining curves in differential geometry. From analysis and analytic geometry we are accustomed to the idea of defining curves by means of equations. In a rectangular coordinate system on the plane, a curve may be given either by the equation

$$y = f(x),$$

or by the more general equation

$$F(x, y) = 0.$$

However, this method of definition is suitable only for a plane curve, i.e., a line in the plane. We also require a method of writing equations of space curves not lying in any plane. An example of such a curve may be seen in the helix (figure 2).

For the purposes of differential geometry, and for many other questions

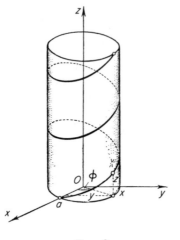

as well, it is most convenient to represent a curve as the trace of a continuous motion of a point. Of course, the given curve may have originated in some entirely different way, but we can always think of it as the path of a point moving along it.

Let us assume that we have a fixed Cartesian coordinate system in space. If a moving point X traces out a curve from time $t = a$ to $t = b$, then the coordinates of this moving point are given by the functions of the time $x(t)$, $y(t)$, and $z(t)$; the flight of an airplane or a projectile are examples. Conversely, if we are initially given the functions $x(t)$, $y(t)$, and $z(t)$, we

FIG. 2.

may let them define the coordinates of a moving point X, which traces out some curve. Consequently, curves in space may be given by three equations of the form

$$x = x(t), \quad y = y(t), \quad z = z(t).$$

In the same way a plane curve is defined by two equations

$$x = x(t), \quad y = y(t).$$

This is the most general manner of defining curves.

As an example we consider the helix. It is produced by the spiral motion of a point that revolves uniformly around a straight line, the axis of the helix, and at the same time moves uniformly in a direction parallel to this axis. Let us take the axis of the helix as the axis Oz and suppose that at time $t = 0$ the point lies on the axis Ox. We now wish to find how its coordinates depend on the time. If the motion parallel to the axis Oz has velocity c, then obviously the distance travelled in this direction at time t will be

$$z = ct.$$

Also, if ϕ is the angle of rotation around the axis Oz and a is the distance from the point to this axis, then, as can be seen in figure 2,

$$x = a \cos \phi, \quad y = a \sin \phi.$$

Since the rotation is uniform, the angle ϕ is proportional to time; that is, $\phi = \omega t$, where ω is the angular velocity of the rotation. In this manner we get

$$x = a \cos \omega t, \quad y = a \sin \omega t, \quad z = ct.$$

So these are the equations of the helix, which as t changes will be traced out by the moving point.

Of course the variable t or, as it is usually called, the parameter, need not be thought of as representing the time. Also, the given parameter t may be replaced by another; for example we may introduce a parameter u by the formula $t = u^3$, or, in general, by $t = f(u).$* In geometry the most natural choice of parameter is the length s of the arc of the curve measured from some fixed point A on it. Every possible value of the length s represents a corresponding arc AX. Thus the position of X is fully determined by the value of s and the coordinates of the point X are given by the functions of arc length s

$$x = x(s), \quad y = y(s), \quad z = z(s).$$

All these ways of defining curves, as well as other possible ones,† open up the possibility of numerical computation. Only when curves have been defined by equations can their properties be investigated by mathematical analysis.

In the differential geometry of plane curves, there are three basic concepts: length, tangent, and curvature. For space curves, there are in addition the osculating plane and the torsion. We now proceed to explain the meaning and significance of these concepts.

Length. Everyone has in mind a natural idea of what is meant by length, but this idea must be converted into an exact definition of the length of a mathematical curve, a definition with a specific numerical character, which will enable us to compute the length of a curve with any desired degree of accuracy and consequently to argue about lengths in a rigorous way. The same remarks apply to all mathematical concepts. The transition from informal ideas to exact measurements and definitions represents the transition from a prescientific understanding of objects to

---

* Here, strictly speaking, it is necessary that the function f be monotone.

† A curve in space may also be given as the intersection of two surfaces, defined by the equations: $F(x, y, z) = 0$, $G(x, y, z) = 0$, i.e., the curve is given by this pair of equations. In theoretical discussions a curve is most frequently given by a variable vector, i.e., the position of the point X of the curve is defined by the vector $r = \overrightarrow{OX}$, extending from the origin to this point. As the vector r changes, its end point X moves along the given curve (figure 3).

a scientific theory. The need for a precise definition of length arose in the final analysis from the requirements of technology and the natural sciences, whose development demanded investigation of the properties of lengths, areas, and other geometric entities.

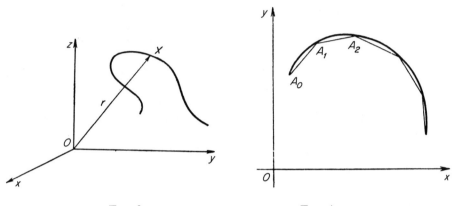

FIG. 3.   FIG. 4.

A simple and most useful definition of length is the following: The *length* of a curve is the limit of the length of broken lines inscribed in the curve under the condition that their vertices cluster closer and closer together on the curve.

This definition arises naturally from our everyday methods of measuring. On the curve we take a sequence of points A_0, A_1, A_2, $\cdots$ (figure 4) and measure the distances between them. The sum of these distances (which is the length of the broken line) expresses approximately the length of the curve. In order to define the length more exactly, it is natural to take the points A closer together, so that the broken line follows the twists of the curve more closely. Finally, the exact value of the length is defined as the limit of these approximations as the points A are chosen arbitrarily close together.* Thus the earlier definition of length is a generalization, based on taking finer and finer steps, of a completely practical manner of measuring length.

From this definition of length, it is easy to derive a formula for computing lengths when the curve is given analytically. We note, however, that mathematical formulas are useful for more than just computation.

---

* The existence of the indicated limit, i.e., the length of the curve, is not initially clear, even for curves lying in a bounded domain. If the curve is very twisted, its length may be very great, and it is possible mathematically to construct a plane curve which is so "twisted" that none of its arcs has a finite length since the lengths of broken lines inscribed in it increase beyond all bounds.

They are a brief statement of theorems that establish connections between different mathematical entities. The theoretical significance of such connections may far exceed the computational value of the formula. For example, the importance of the Pythagorean theorem, expressed by the formula

$$c^2 = a^2 + b^2,$$

is not confined to the computation of the square of the hypotenuse c but lies chiefly in the fact that it expresses a relation among the sides of a right triangle.

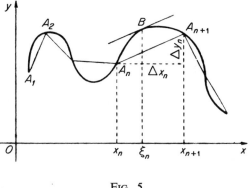

FIG. 5.

Let us now introduce a formula for the length of a plane curve, given in Cartesian coordinates by the equation $y = f(x)$, assuming that the function $f(x)$ has a first derivative.

We inscribe a broken line in the curve (figure 5). Let A_n, A_{n+1} be two of its adjacent vertices with coordinates x_n, y_n and x_{n+1}, y_{n+1}. The line segment A_nA_{n+1} is the hypotenuse of a right triangle the legs of which are equal to

$$\Delta x_n = |x_{n+1} - x_n|, \quad \Delta y_n = |y_{n+1} - y_n|.$$

Thus, by the Pythagorean theorem,

$$\overline{A_nA_{n+1}} = \sqrt{(\Delta x_n)^2 + (\Delta y_n)^2} = \sqrt{1 + \left(\frac{\Delta y_n}{\Delta x_n}\right)^2}\, \Delta x_n.$$

It is easy to see that if the straight line drawn through the points A_n and A_{n+1} is translated parallel to itself, then at the instant when the line leaves the curve it will assume the position of a tangent to this curve at some point B, i.e., on the arc of the curve A_nA_{n+1}, there is at least one point at which the tangent has the same direction as the chord A_nA_{n+1}. (This obvious conclusion can easily be given a rigorous proof.)

Thus we may replace the ratio $\Delta y_n/\Delta x_n$ by the slope of the tangent at B, i.e., by the derivative $y'(\xi_n)$, where ξ_n is the abscissa of the point B. Now the length of one link of the broken line is expressed by

$$\overline{A_nA_{n+1}} = \sqrt{1 + y'^2(\xi_n)}\, \Delta x_n.$$

The entire length of the broken line is the sum of the lengths of its pieces. Denoting the addition by the symbol Σ, we have

$$S_n = \sum \sqrt{1 + y'^2(\xi_n)}\, \Delta x_n \,.$$

To obtain the length of the curve, we must pass to the limit under the condition that the greatest of the values Δx_n tends to zero,

$$s = \lim_{\Delta x \to 0} \sum \sqrt{1 + y'^2(\xi_n)}\, \Delta x_n \,.$$

But this limit is exactly the integral defined in Chapter II, namely the integral of the function $\sqrt{1 + y'^2}$. Thus the length of a plane curve is expressed by the formula

$$s = \int_a^b \sqrt{1 + y'^2}\, dx, \tag{1}$$

where the limits of integration a and b are the values of x at the ends of the arc of the curve.

The corresponding, but somewhat different, formula for the length of a space curve is derived in basically the same way.

The actual computation of a length by means of these formulas is, of course, not always simple. Thus the calculation of the circumference of a circle from formula (1) is rather complicated. However, as we have said, the interest of formulas is not confined to computation; in particular, formula (1) is also important for investigating the general properties of length, its relations with other concepts, and so forth. We will have an opportunity to make use of formula (1) in Chapter VIII.

Tangent.   The tangent to a plane curve was already considered in Chapter II. Its meaning for a space curve is completely analogous. In order to define the tangent at a point A, we choose a point X on the curve, distinct from A, and consider the secant AX. Then we allow X to approach A along the curve. If the secant AX converges to some limiting position, then the straight line in this limiting position is called the tangent at the point A.*

If we distinguish between the initial point and the end point of the curve and thereby establish an order in which the points of the curve

---

* The limiting position of the secant may not exist, as can be seen from the example in figure 13, Chapter II. The curve represented by $y = x \sin 1/x$ oscillates near zero in such a way that the secant OA, as A approaches O, constantly oscillates between the straight lines OM and OL.

are traversed, then we may say which of the points A and X comes first and which comes second. (For example, if a train travels from Moscow to Vladivostok, then Omsk obviously precedes Irkutsk.) So we may define a direction along the secant from the first point to the second. The limit of such "directed secants" gives us a "directed tangent." In figure 6, the arrow shows the direction in which the point A is passed through. For the motion of a point along the curve, the velocity at each instant is directed along the tangent to the curve.

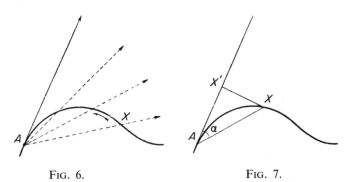

Fig. 6.   Fig. 7.

The tangent has an important geometric property: Near the point of tangency the curve departs less, in a well-defined sense, from this straight line than from any other. In other words, the distance from the points of the curve to the tangent is very small in comparison with their distance to the point of tangency. More precisely, the ratio XX'/AX (figure 7) tends to zero as X approaches A.* So a small segment of the curve may be replaced by a corresponding segment of the tangent with an error that is small in comparison with length of the segment. This procedure often allows us to simplify proofs, since in a passage to the limit it gives completely exact results.

It is interesting to observe that for a curve which is not a straight line, i.e., does not have a direction in the elementary sense, we have been able, by associating it with a straight line, to define its direction at each point. Thus the concept of direction has been extended; it has been given a meaning which it did not previously have. This new concept of direction reflects the actual nature of motion along a curve; at each instant the point is moving in some definite direction, which changes continuously.

---

* This result follows immediately from the definition of the tangent itself. Evidently, as is shown in figure 7, $XX'/AX = \sin \alpha$, where α is the angle between the tangent and the secant AX. Thus, as $\alpha \to 0$, XX'/AX also tends to zero.

Curvature. To be able to judge by eye whether a path, a thin rod, or a line in a drawing is more or less curved it is not necessary to be a mathematician. But for even the simplest problems of mechanics, a casual glance is not sufficient; we need an exact quantitative description of the curvature. This is obtained by giving precise expression to our intuitive impression of the curvature as the rapidity of change of direction of the curve.

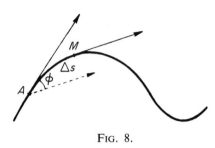

FIG. 8.

Let A be a point on the curve and M a point near A (figure 8). The angle between the tangents at these points expresses how much the curve has changed direction in the segment from A to M. Let us denote this angle by ϕ. The average rate of change of direction (more precisely, the average change per unit length of path along the segment AM of length Δs) will obviously be $\phi/\Delta s$. Then the curvature, namely the rate of change of direction of the curve at the point A itself, is naturally defined as the limit of the ratio $\phi/\Delta s$ as $M \to A$; in other words, as $\Delta s \to 0$. Thus the curvature is defined by the formula

$$k = \lim_{\Delta s \to 0} \frac{\phi}{\Delta s}.$$

As a particular example, let us consider the curvature of the circumference of a circle (figure 9). Obviously, the angle ϕ between the radii OA and OM is equal to the angle ϕ between the tangents at the points A and M, since the tangents are perpendicular to the radii. The arc AM, subtending the angle ϕ, has length $\Delta s = \phi r$, so that

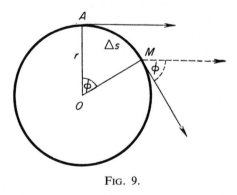

$$\frac{\phi}{\Delta s} = \frac{1}{r}.$$

FIG. 9.

This means that the ratio $\phi/\Delta s$ is constant, so that the curvature of the circumference of a circle, as the limiting value of this ratio, is equal at all points to the reciprocal of the radius.*

Let us derive the formula for the curvature of a plane curve given by the equation $y = f(x)$. As the initial point for arc length we take a fixed point N (figure 10). The angle ϕ between the tangents at the points A

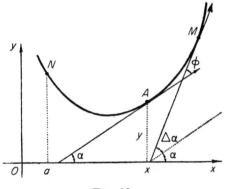

FIG. 10.

and M is obviously equal to the difference in the angle of inclination of the tangents at A to M.

$$\phi = |\varDelta\alpha|.$$

Since the angle α may decrease, we take the absolute value $|\varDelta\alpha|$. We are interested in the value

$$k = \lim_{\varDelta s \to 0} \frac{\phi}{\varDelta s} = \lim_{\varDelta s \to 0} \frac{|\varDelta\alpha|}{\varDelta s} = \lim_{\varDelta x \to 0} \frac{\dfrac{|\varDelta\alpha|}{\varDelta x}}{\dfrac{\varDelta s}{\varDelta x}} = \frac{|\alpha'|}{s'}.$$

The length of the arc of the curve NA is expressed by the integral

$$s = \int_a^x \sqrt{1 + y'^2}\, dx,$$

so that

$$s' = \sqrt{1 + y'^2}.$$

---

* We note that in general the concept of the curvature of a curve at a point may be defined by comparing the curve with the circumference of a certain circle, which plays the role of a model or standard for the curvature. For in fact, the curvature of the given curve proves to be equal to the reciprocal of the radius of the (unique) circle which fits the curve most closely in the neighborhood of the point.

It remains to find α'. We know that $\tan \alpha = y'$; thus $\alpha = \arctan y'$. Differentiating this last equation with respect to x, we get

$$\alpha' = \frac{1}{1 + y'^2} y''.$$

Thus, finally

$$k = \frac{|\alpha'|}{s'} = \frac{|y''|}{(1 + y'^2)^{3/2}}.$$

The corresponding formulas for other methods of representing plane and space curves are given in the usual courses in analysis or differential geometry.

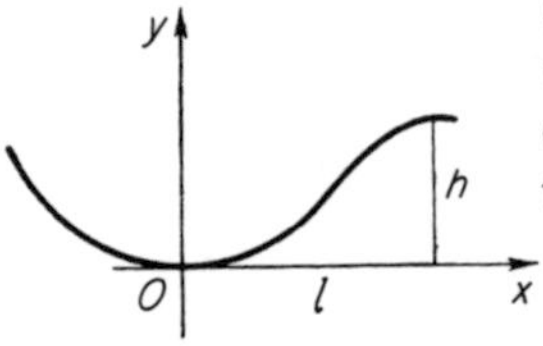

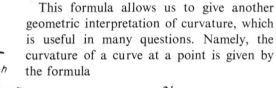

This formula allows us to give another geometric interpretation of curvature, which is useful in many questions. Namely, the curvature of a curve at a point is given by the formula

$$k = \lim_{l \to 0} \frac{2h}{l^2},$$

FIG. 11.

where h is the distance of a second point on the curve to the tangent at the given point and l is the length of the segment of the tangent between the point of tangency and the projection on the tangent of the other point on the curve (figure 11).

To prove this we choose a rectangular coordinate system such that the origin falls at the given point of the curve and the axis Ox is tangent to the curve at this point (figure 11). (For simplicity we assume that the curve is plane.) Then $y' = 0$ and $k = |y''|$. Expanding the function $y = f(x)$ by Taylor's formula, we get $y = \frac{1}{2} y'' x^2 + \epsilon x^2$ (where we have taken into account that $y' = 0$). Here $\epsilon \to 0$ as $x \to 0$. Hence it follows that $k = |y''| = \lim_{i \to 0} 2|y|/x^2$, and thus, since $|y| = h$, $x^2 = l^2$, we have

$$k = \lim_{l \to 0} \frac{2h}{l^2}.$$

This formula shows that the curvature describes the rate at which the curve leaves the tangent.

Let us now turn to some very important applications of curvature to problems of mechanics.

First we consider the following problem. Let a flexible string be stretched over a support (figure 12) in such a way that the string remains in one plane. We wish to find the pressure of the string on the support at every point, or to be more exact, to define the limit

$$p = \lim_{\Delta s \to 0} \frac{P}{\Delta s}, \tag{2}$$

where P is the magnitude of the force $\boldsymbol{P}$ acting on the support along a piece of length Δs containing the given point. We assume for simplicity that the magnitude T of the tension $\boldsymbol{T}$ is the same at all points of the string.

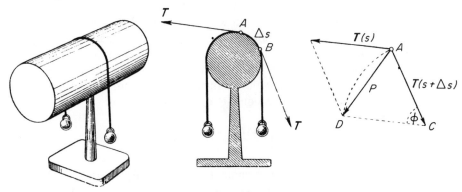

FIG. 12.

Now consider the point A and a segment of the string AB.* On this segment AB of length Δs, in addition to the reaction of the support, only two external forces are acting, namely the tensions at the ends, which are equal in magnitude and are directed along the tangents at the ends of the segment. Thus the force $\boldsymbol{P}$ exerted by the string on the support is equal to the geometric sum of the tensions at the ends. As can be seen from figure 12, the vector $\boldsymbol{P}$ is the base AD of the isosceles triangle CAD. The two equal sides of this triangle have length T and the angle at the vertex C is equal to the change of direction of the tangent in passing from A to B.

With decreasing Δs the angle ϕ decreases and the angle between $\boldsymbol{P}$ and the tangent at the point A approaches a right angle. Thus the pressure is perpendicular to the tangent.

To find the magnitude of the pressure, we make use of the fact that a small arc of the circumference has approximately the same length as

---

* It would be more natural to choose a segment with the point A in its interior; this would not change the result but would make the computation somewhat more complicated.

the chord subtending it. Thus we replace the length of the chord AD, i.e., the magnitude P, by the length $T\phi$ of the arc AD. Then by formula (2) we get

$$p = \lim_{\Delta s \to 0} \frac{P}{\Delta s} = \lim_{\Delta s \to 0} \frac{T\phi}{\Delta s} = T \lim_{\Delta s \to 0} \frac{\phi}{\Delta s} = Tk.$$

Hence the pressure at each point is equal to the product of the curvature and the tension on the string and is exerted perpendicularly to the tangent at this point.

Consider a second problem. Let a mathematical point (i.e., a very small body) move along a plane curve with a velocity of constant magnitude v. What is its acceleration at a given point A? By definition, the acceleration is equal to the limit of the ratio of the change in velocity (during the time Δt) to the increment Δt of the time. The velocity involves not only magnitude but also direction, i.e., we consider the change in the velocity vector. Therefore the mathematical problem of finding the magnitude of the acceleration consists of finding the limit

$$w = \lim_{\Delta t \to 0} \frac{|\, v(t + \Delta t) - v(t)\,|}{\Delta t},$$

where $v(t)$ is the velocity at the point A itself, and $|\, v(t + \Delta t) - v(t)|$ is the length of the vector difference of the velocities. The limit which concerns us may also be represented as

$$\lim_{\Delta s \to 0} \frac{|\, -v(t) + v(t + \Delta t)\,|}{\Delta s} \lim_{\Delta t \to 0} \frac{\Delta s}{\Delta t},$$

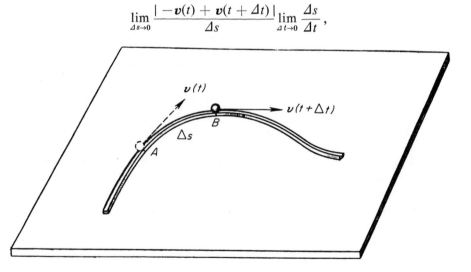

FIG. 13.

where Δs is the length of the arc AB traversed during time Δt. Turning to figure 13 and noting that the velocity at each point is directed along the tangent while remaining constant in magnitude, we see geometrically that finding the sum $-v(t) + v(t + \Delta t)$ is identical with finding the vector P in the preceding problem. So we may avail ourselves of the result there and, replacing tension by velocity, write

$$\lim_{\Delta s \to 0} \frac{|-v(t) + v(t + \Delta t)|}{\Delta s} = vk.$$

Moreover, $\lim_{\Delta t \to 0} \Delta s / \Delta t = v$. So we have the final result that the acceleration of a body in uniform motion along the curve is equal to the product of the curvature and the square of the velocity

$$w = kv^2 \tag{3}$$

and is directed along the normal to the curve, i.e., along a straight line perpendicular to the tangent.

Our recourse here to a geometric analogy, enabling us to use the solution of the problem of the pressure exerted by a string in order to solve a problem of the acceleration of a particle, shows once again how useful it is to make an abstraction from the particular concrete properties of a phenomenon to corresponding mathematical concepts and results; for we can then make use of these results in the most varied situations.

We also note that the curvature, which from a mechanical point of view reflects the change in the direction of motion, is seen to be closely connected with the forces causing this change. The equation which expresses this connection is easily derived if we multiply equation (3) by the mass m of the moving point. We have

$$F_n = mw = v^2 mk.$$

Here F_n is the magnitude of the normal component of the force acting on the point.

Osculating plane. Although a space curve does not lie in one plane, still with each point A of the curve it is possible, as a rule, to associate a plane P which in the neighborhood of this point lies closer to the curve than any other plane. This plane is called the *osculating plane* of the curve at the point.

Naturally the osculating plane, as the plane closest to the given curve, passes through the point A and contains the tangent T to the curve. But there are many planes containing the point A and the straight line T.

In order to choose from among them the one plane that least deviates from the curve, we investigate the deviation of the curve from the tangent. For this purpose let us see how the curve runs along the tangent T; in other words, let us project our curve onto the *normal plane Q*, which

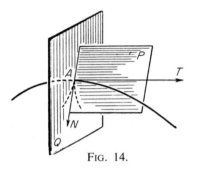

is perpendicular to T at the point A (figure 14). The projection on the plane Q of a segment of our curve containing A forms a new curve, indicated in figure 14 by a dotted line. Usually it has a cusp at the point A. If the curve so obtained has a tangent N at the point A, then the plane P determined by T and N will naturally be closest to the original curve in the neighborhood of the point A, i.e., it will be the

FIG. 14.

osculating plane at the point A. It may be shown that when the functions defining the original curve have second derivatives and the curvature of the curve at the point A is not zero, then the osculating plane necessarily exists, and its equation may be expressed very simply in terms of the first and second derivatives of the functions defining the curve.

We saw earlier that the properties of the tangent allow us to consider a small segment of a plane curve as though it were straight, thereby making an error which is small in comparison with the length of the segment; similarly the properties of the osculating plane allow us to consider a small segment of a space curve as though it were a plane curve, namely its projection on the osculating plane, and here the error will be small in comparison with the square of the length of the segment of the curve.

There are many straight lines in space that are perpendicular to the tangent; they form the normal plane at the given point of the curve. Among these straight lines there is one, the line N, which lies in the osculating plane. This line is called the *principal normal* to the curve. Usually we also fix a direction for it, namely the direction of the concavity of the projection of the curve on the osculating plane. The principal normal plays the same role for a space curve as the ordinary (unique) normal for a plane curve. In particular, if a thin string under tension T is stretched in the form of a space curve over a support, then the pressure of the string on the support has at each point the magnitude Tk and is directed along the principal normal. If a material point is moving along a space curve with a velocity of constant magnitude v, then its acceleration is equal to kv^2 and is directed along the principal normal.

Torsion. From point to point along a curve the position of the osculating plane will probably change. Just as the rate of change of direction of the tangent characterized the curvature, so the rate of change of direction of the osculating plane characterizes a new quantity, the *torsion* of the curve. Here, as in the case of curvature, the rate is taken with respect to arc length; that is, if ψ is the angle between the osculating planes at a fixed point A and at a nearby point X, and if Δs is the length of the arc AX, then the torsion τ at the point A is defined as the limit*

$$\tau = \lim_{\Delta s \to 0} \frac{\psi}{\Delta s}.$$

The sign of the torsion depends on the side of the curve toward which the osculating plane turns as it moves along the curve.

We may imagine the osculating curve as the blade of a fan with the two lines, the tangent and the principal normal, drawn on it. At each moment the tangent is turning in the direction of the normal at a rate determined by the curvature, while the osculating plane rotates around the tangent with a speed and direction determined by the torsion.

The simplest results of the theory of differential equations may be used to prove a fundamental theorem that states, roughly speaking, that two curves with the same curvature and the same torsion are identical with each other. Let us make this idea clearer. If we move along the curve to various distances A from our initial point, we will arrive at points where the curvature k and the torsion τ will have various values, depending on s. Thus $k(s)$ and $\tau(s)$ will be certain well-defined functions of the arc length s.

The theorem in question states that if two curves have identical curvature and torsion as functions of arc length, then the curves are identical (i.e., one of them may be rigidly moved so as to coincide with the other). In this manner curvature and torsion as functions of arc length define a curve completely except for its position in space; they describe all the properties of the curve by stating the relationship between its length, its curvature, and its torsion. In this way the three concepts constitute a sort of ultimate basis for questions concerning curves. With their help we can also express the simplest concepts in the theory of surfaces, to which we now turn.

---

* It may be shown that a helix has the same torsion at all its points and consequently that we may define the torsion of a curve by comparing the curve with the (unique) helix which best approximates the curve in the neighborhood of the given point. The torsion also characterizes the way in which a given space curve differs from a plane curve. With a certain analogy to curvature, it characterizes the rate at which the curve leaves its osculating plane.

Of course, the theory of curves has not been exhausted by our present remarks. There are many other concepts relating to curves: special types of curves, families of curves, the position of curves on surfaces, questions of the form of a curve as a whole, etc. These questions and the methods of answering them are connected with almost every branch of mathematics. The range of problems that may be solved by the theory of curves is extremely rich and varied.

§3. Basic Concepts in the Theory of Surfaces

The basic methods of defining a surface.   If we wish to study surfaces by means of analysis we must, of course, define them analytically. The simplest way is by an equation

$$z = f(x, y),$$

in which x, y, and z are Cartesian coordinates of a point lying on the surface. Here the function $f(x, y)$ need not necessarily be defined for all x, y; its domain may have various shapes. Thus, the surface illustrated in figure 15 is given by the function $f(x, y)$ defined inside an annulus. Examples of surfaces given by equations of the form $z = f(x, y)$ are also familiar from analytic geometry. We know, for example, that the equation $z = Ax + By + C$ represents a plane, and $z = x^2 + y^2$ a paraboloid of revolution (figure 16). For the application of differential calculus it is necessary that the function $f(x, y)$ have first, second, and sometimes even higher derivatives. A surface given by such an equation is called *regular*. Geometrically this means (though not quite precisely) that

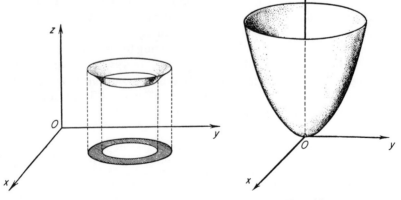

FIG. 15.   FIG. 16.

the surface curves continuously without breaks or other singularities. Surfaces that do not have this property, for example, those with cusps, breaks, or other singularities, require a new kind of investigation (cf. §5).

However, not every surface, even without singularities, can be entirely represented by an equation of the form $z = f(x, y)$. If every pair of values of x, y in the domain of $f(x, y)$ gives a completely determined z, then every straight line parallel to the axis Oz must intersect the surface at no more than one point (figure 17). Even such simple surfaces as

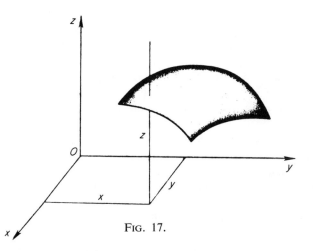

FIG. 17.

spheres or cylinders cannot be represented in the large by an equation of the form $z = f(x, y)$. In these cases the surface is defined in some other manner, for example by an equation of the form $F(x, y, z) = 0$. Thus a sphere of radius R with center at the origin has the equation

$$x^2 + y^2 + z^2 = R^2.$$

The equation $x^2 + y^2 = r^2$ gives a cylinder of radius r.

So when the investigation is concerned only with small segments of the surface, as is usually the case in classical differential geometry, the definition of a surface by an equation $z = f(x, y)$ is perfectly general, since every sufficiently small segment of a smooth surface can be represented in this form. We take this way as basic, and leave other methods of defining surfaces to be considered later in §§4 and 5.

Tangent plane. Just as at each point a smooth *curve* has a tangent line which is close to the curve in a neighborhood of the point, so also surfaces may have, at each of their points, a *tangent plane*.

The exact definition is as follows. A plane P, passing through a point M on a surface F, is said to be tangent to the surface F at this point if the angle α between the plane P and the secant MX, drawn from M to a point X of the surface, converges to zero as the point X approaches the point M (figure 18). All tangents to curves passing through the point M and lying on the surface obviously lie in the tangent plane.

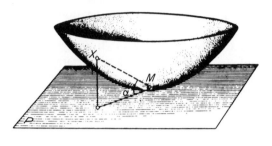

FIG. 18.

A surface F is called *smooth* if it has a tangent plane at each point and if, as we pass from point to point, the position of this plane varies continuously.

Near the point of tangency, the surface departs very little from its tangent plane: If the point X approaches the point M along the surface, then the distance of the point X from the tangent plane becomes smaller and smaller, even in comparison with its distance from the point M (the reader can easily verify this by considering how X approaches M in figure 18). In this way, the surface near the point M may be said to merge into the tangent plane. In the first approximation a small segment or, as it is called, an "element" of the surface may be replaced by a segment of the tangent plane. The perpendicular to the tangent plane which passes through the point of tangency acts as a perpendicular to the surface at this point and is called a *normal*.

This possibility of replacing an element of the surface by a segment of the tangent plane is useful in many situations. For example, the reflection of light on a curved surface takes place in the same way as the reflection on a plane, i.e., the direction of the reflected ray is defined by the usual law of reflection: The incident ray and the reflected ray lie in one plane together with the normal to the surface and they make equal angles with this normal (figure 19), just as if the reflection were occurring in the tangent plane. Similarly for the refraction of light in a curved surface, each ray is refracted by an element of the surface with the usual law of refraction, just as if the element were plane. These facts are the basis for all calculations of reflection and refraction of light in optical apparatus. Further, for example, solid bodies in contact with each other have a common tangent plane at their point of contact. The bodies are in contact over an element of their surface, and the pressure of one body on the other, in the absence of friction, is directed along the normal at the point of contact. This is also true when the bodies are tangent at more than one point, in which case the pressure is directed along the respective normals at each point of contact.

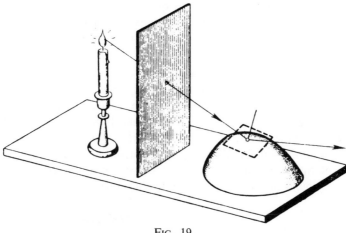

FIG. 19.

The replacement of elements of a surface by segments of the tangent planes can also serve as the basis of a definition of the area of various surfaces. The surface is decomposed into small pieces $F_1, F_2, \cdots, F_n$ and each piece is projected onto a plane tangent to the surface at some point of this piece (figure 20). We thus obtain a number of plane regions $P_1, P_2, \cdots, P_n$, the sum of whose areas gives an approximation to the

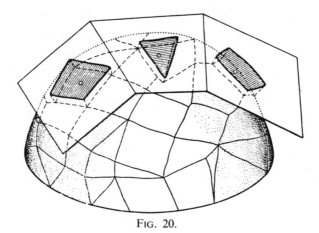

FIG. 20.

area of the surfaces. The area of the surface itself is defined as the limit of the sums of the areas of the segments $P_1, P_2, \cdots, P_n$ under the condition that the partitions of the surface become finer.* From this we can derive an exact expression for the area in the form of a double integral.

These remarks clearly demonstrate the significance of the concept of the tangent plane. However, in many questions the approximate representation of an element of a surface by means of a plane is inadequate and it is necessary to consider the curvature of the surface.

Curvature of curves on a surface. The curvature of a surface at a given point is characterized by the rate at which the surface leaves its tangent plane. But in different directions, the surface may leave its tangent plane at different rates. Thus the surface illustrated in figure 21 leaves the plane P in the direction OA at a faster rate than in the direction OB. So it is natural to define the curvature of a surface at a given point by means of the set of curvatures of all curves lying in the surface and passing through the given point in different directions.

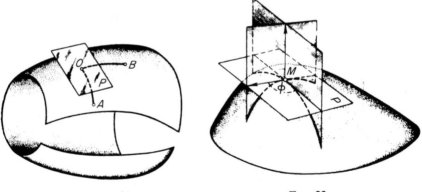

FIG. 21.   FIG. 22.

This is done as follows. We construct the tangent plane P through the point M and choose a specific direction for the normal (figure 22). Then we consider curves which are sections of the surface cut by planes passing through the normal at the point M; these curves are called *normal sections*. The curvature of a normal section is given a sign, which is plus if the section is concave in the direction of the normal and minus if it is concave in the opposite direction. Thus, in a surface which is saddle-shaped, as illustrated in figure 23 with the arrow indicating the

---

* This is exactly the expression for the area which was used in §1, Chapter VIII.

direction of the normal to the surface, the curvature of the section MA is positive and that of the section MB is negative.

A normal section is defined by the angle ϕ by which its plane is rotated from some initial ray in the tangent plane (figure 22). If we know the curvature of the normal section $k(\phi)$ in terms of the angle ϕ, we will have a rather complete picture of the behavior of the surface in the vicinity of the point M.

A surface may be curved in many different ways and thus it would appear that the dependence of the curvature k on the angle ϕ may be arbitrary. In fact this is not so. For the surfaces studied in differential geometry, there exists a simple law, due to Euler, that establishes the connection between the curvatures of the normal sections passing through a given point in various directions.

It is shown that at each point of a surface there exist two particular directions such that

1. They are mutually perpendicular;

2. The curvatures k_1 and k_2 of the normal sections in these directions are the smallest and largest values of the curvatures of all normal sections;*

3. The curvature $k(\phi)$ of the normal section rotated from the section with curvature k_1 by the angle ϕ is expressed by the formula

$$k(\phi) = k_1 \cos^2 \phi + k_2 \sin^2 \phi. \tag{4}$$

Such directions are called the *principal directions* and the curvatures k_1 and k_2 are called the *principal curvatures of the surface* at the given point.

This theorem of Euler shows that in spite of the diversity of surfaces, their form in the neighborhood of each point must be one of a very few completely defined types, with an accuracy to within magnitudes of the second order of smallness in comparison with the distance from the given point. In fact, if k_1 and k_2 have the same sign, then the sign of $k(\phi)$ is constant and the surface near the point has the form illustrated in figure 22. If k_1 and k_2 have opposite signs, for example $k_1 > 0$ and $k_2 < 0$, then the curvature of the normal section obviously changes sign. This is seen from the fact that for $\phi = 0$ the curvature $k = k_1 > 0$ and for $\phi = \pi/2$ we have $k = k_2 < 0$.

From formula (4) for $k(\phi)$, it is not difficult to prove that as ϕ changes

---

* In the particular case $k_1 = k_2$ the curvature of all sections is the same; as, for example, on a sphere.

from 0 to π the sign of $k(\phi)$ changes twice,* so that near the point the surface has a saddle-shaped form (figure 23).

When one of the numbers k_1 and k_2 is equal to zero, the curvature always has the same sign, except for the one value of ϕ, for which it vanishes. This occurs, for example, for every point on a cylinder (figure 24).

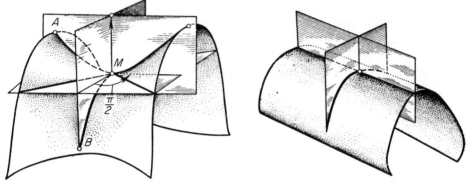

FIG. 23.   FIG. 24.

In the general case the surface near such point has a form close to that of a cylinder.

Finally, for $k_1 = k_2 = 0$ all normal sections have zero curvature. Near such a point the surface is especially "close" to its tangent plane. Such points are called *flat points*. One example of such a point is given in figure 25 (the point M). The properties of a surface near a flat point may be very complicated.

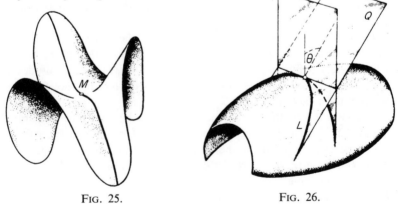

FIG. 25.   FIG. 26.

---

* It is a simple matter to show that $k(\phi) = k_1 \cos^2 \phi + k_2 \sin^2 \phi$ vanishes for $\phi = \arctan \sqrt{-k_1/k_2}$ and $\phi = \pi - \arctan \sqrt{-k_1/k_2}$, changing sign the first time from plus to minus and the second from minus to plus.

Let us now consider a section of the surface cut by an arbitrary plane Q (figure 26) not passing through the normal. The curvature k_L of such a curve L, as Meusnier showed,* is connected by a simple relation with the curvature k_N of the normal section in the same direction, i.e., the one that intersects the tangent plane in the same straight line. This connection is expressed by the formula

$$k_L = \frac{|k_N|}{\cos \theta},$$

where θ is the angle between the normal and the plane Q. The correctness of this formula may be visualized very conveniently on a sphere.

Finally, the curvature of *any* curve lying in the surface and having the plane Q as its osculating plane may be shown to be identical with the curvature of the intersection of Q with the surface.

Thus, if we know k_1 and k_2, the curvature of any curve in the surface is defined by the direction of its tangent and the angle between its osculating plane and the normal to the surface. Consequently, the character of the curvature of a surface at a given point is defined by the two numbers k_1 and k_2. Their absolute values are equal to the curvatures of two mutually perpendicular normal sections, and their signs show the direction of the concavity of the respective normal sections with respect to a chosen direction on the normal.

Let us now prove the theorems of Euler and Meusnier mentioned earlier.

1. For the proof of Euler's theorem we need the following lemma. If the function $f(x, y)$ has continuous second derivatives at a given point, then the coordinate axes may be rotated through an angle α such that in the new coordinate system the mixed derivative $f_{x'y'}$ will be equal to zero at this point.† We recall that after rotation of axes the new variables x', y' are connected with x and y by the formulas

$$x = x' \cos \alpha - y' \sin \alpha; \quad y = x' \sin \alpha + y' \cos \alpha$$

(cf. Chapter III, §7). For the proof of the lemma we note that

$$\frac{\partial x}{\partial x'} = \cos \alpha, \quad \frac{\partial y}{\partial x'} = \sin \alpha, \quad \frac{\partial x}{\partial y'} = -\sin \alpha, \quad \frac{\partial y}{\partial y'} = \cos \alpha.$$

---

* Meusnier (1754–1793) was a French mathematician, a student of Monge; he was a general in the revolutionary army and died of wounds received in battle.

† We will denote partial derivatives by subscripts; for example, in place of $\partial f/\partial x$ we write f_x, in place of $\partial^2 f/\partial y^2$ we write f_{yy}, etc.

Computing the derivative $f_{x'y'}$ by the chain rule, we arrive after some calculation at the result

$$f_{x'y'} = f_{xy} \cos 2\alpha + \tfrac{1}{2}(f_{yy} - f_{xx}) \sin 2\alpha,$$

from which it readily follows that for

$$\cot 2\alpha = \frac{1}{2} \frac{f_{xx} - f_{yy}}{f_{xy}}$$

we will have

$$f_{x'y'} = 0.$$

We now consider the surface F, given by the equation $z = f(x, y)$, in which the origin is at the point M under consideration and the axes Ox and Oy are so chosen in the tangent plane that $f_{xy}(0, 0) = 0$. In the surface P we take an arbitrary straight line making an angle ϕ with the

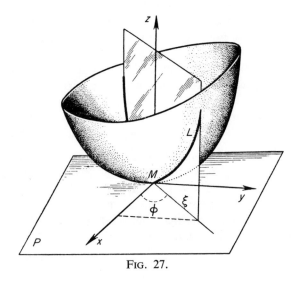

FIG. 27.

axis Ox and consider the normal section L in the direction of this straight line (figure 27). From the formula derived in §2, the curvature of L at the point M, taking its sign into account, is equal to

$$k_L = \lim_{\xi \to 0} \frac{2f(x, y)}{\xi^2}.$$

Here $f(x, y)$ is the distance (again taking its sign into account) of a point on L to the chosen straight line. Expanding $f(x, y)$ by Taylor's formula

(Chapter II, §9) and noting that $f_x(0, 0) = f_y(0, 0) = 0$ (since the axes Ox and Oy lie in the tangent plane) we get

$$f(x, y) = \tfrac{1}{2}(f_{xx}x^2 + f_{yy}y^2) + \epsilon(x^2 + y^2),$$

where $\epsilon \to 0$ as $x \to 0$, $y \to 0$. For a point on L, we have $x = \xi \cos\phi$, $y = \xi \sin\phi$, $\xi^2 = x^2 + y^2$ (figure 27), and thus

$$k_L = \lim_{\xi \to 0} \frac{f_{xx}\xi^2 \cos^2\phi + f_{yy}\xi^2 \sin^2\phi + 2\epsilon\xi^2}{\xi^2} = f_{xx}\cos^2\phi + f_{yy}\sin^2\phi.$$

Putting $\phi = 0$, $\phi = \pi/2$, we find that f_{xx} and f_{yy} are the curvatures k_1 and k_2 of the normal sections in the direction of the axes Ox and Oy. Thus the formula derived is actually Euler's formula: $k = k_1 \cos^2\phi + k_2 \sin^2\phi$. The fact that k_1 and k_2 are the maximal and minimal curvatures also follows from this formula.

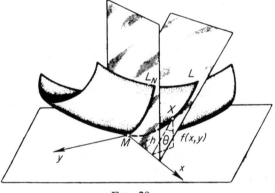

FIG. 28.

2. For the proof of Meusnier's theorem we consider a normal section L_N and a section L whose plane forms an angle θ with the plane of the section L_N, as in figure 28. The axes Ox and Oy lie in the tangent plane, and we also take the axis Ox to be tangent to the curves L_N and L at the origin. The distance $h(x, y)$ to the Ox axis of a point X on L with coordinates x, y, $f(x, y)$ is obviously equal to $h(x, y) = |f(x, y)|/\cos\theta$ (figure 28). Using Taylor's formula, we express the curvature k_L of the curve L in the following manner:

$$k_L = \lim_{x \to 0} \frac{2h(x, y)}{x^2} = \lim_{x \to 0} 2 \frac{|f(x, y)|}{x^2 \cos\theta}$$

$$= \lim_{x \to 0} \frac{|f_{xx}x^2 + 2f_{xy}xy + f_{yy}y^2 + 2\epsilon(x^2 + y^2)|}{x^2 \cos\theta}, \qquad (5)$$

where $\epsilon \to 0$ as x, $y \to 0$. Since the axis Ox is tangent to the curve L, obviously $\lim_{x \to 0} y/x = 0$. Thus, taking the limit in formula (5), we get

$$k_L = \frac{|f_{xx}|}{\cos \theta}.$$

But for the chosen coordinate system the curve L_N has the equation $z = f(x, 0)$, for which $|k_N| = |f_{xx}|$. Thus $k_L = |k_N|/\cos \theta$ and Meusnier's theorem is proved.

Mean curvature. In many questions of the theory of surfaces, the most important role is played not by the principal curvatures themselves but by certain quantities dependent on them, namely the *mean curvature* and the *Gaussian* or *total curvature* of the surface at a given point. Let us examine them in detail.

The mean curvature of a surface at a given point is the average of the principal curvatures

$$K_{\text{av}} = \tfrac{1}{2}(k_1 + k_2).$$

As an example of the usefulness of this concept, we consider the following mechanical problem. We assume that over the surface of some body F there is stretched a taut elastic rubber film. We ask about the pressure exerted by this film on each point of the surface of F.

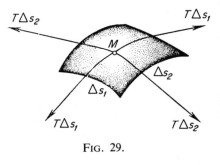

FIG. 29.

The pressure at a point M is measured by the force exerted by the film on a segment of the surface of unit area containing the point M; to be more exact, the pressure "at the point" M is defined as the limit of the ratio of this force to the area of the segment as the latter shrinks to the point M.

We surround the point M on the surface with a small curvilinear rectangle whose sides have lengths Δs_1 and Δs_2 and are perpendicular to the first and second principal directions at M (figure 29).* On each side of the rectangle there is exerted a force that is proportional (from the assumed uniformity of the tension) to the length of the side and the tension T acting on the film. Thus, on the sides perpendicular to

---

* Our reasoning here is not rigorous. However, by making estimates of the errors introduced, it is possible to give a rigorous proof of the result.

the first principal direction, there are exerted forces that are approximately equal to $T\Delta s_1$ and have the direction of the tangent to the surface. Similarly, forces equal to $T\Delta s_2$ act on the other pair of sides of the rectangle. In order to find the pressure at the point M, we must divide the resultant of these four forces by the area of the rectangle (approximately equal to $\Delta s_1 \Delta s_2$) and pass to the limit for Δs_1, $\Delta s_2 \to 0$. Let us begin by dividing the resultant of the first two forces by $\Delta s_1 \Delta s_2$.

If we examine the rectangle from its side (figure 30), we see that these forces are directed along tangents to the curve of the first normal section and that the distance between their points of application is exactly Δs_2. So we have the same problem here as in §2 for the pressure of a string on a support. Using the earlier result,

FIG. 30.

we find that the desired limit is equal to $k_1 T$, where k_1 is the curvature of the first normal section. With a similar expression for the other two forces, we obtain the formula:

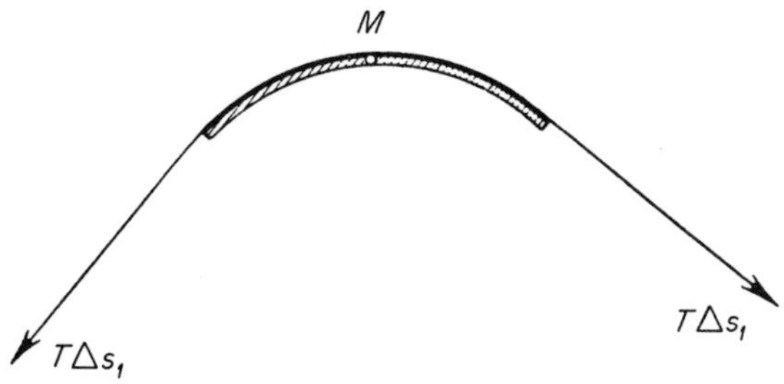

$$P_M = T(k_1 + k_2) = 2TK_{av}.$$

This result has many important consequences. Let us consider an example.

It is known that the surface film of a liquid is under a tension that is the same in all directions on the surface. For a mass of liquid bounded by a curved surface, this tension, by the previous result, exerts a pressure on the surface which is proportional to its mean curvature at the given point.

So in drops of very small diameter the pressures are very large, a fact that hinders the formation of such drops. In a cooling vapor the drops begin to form, as a rule, around specks of dust and around charged particles. In a completely pure, slightly cooled vapor, the formation of drops is delayed. But if, for example, a particle passes through the vapor at high speed, causing ionization of the molecules, then around the ions formed in its path there will momentarily appear small drops of vapor, constituting a visible track of the particle. This is the basis for construction of the Wilson chamber, widely used in nuclear physics for observing the motions of various charged particles.

Since the pressure exerted by a liquid is the same in all directions, a drop of liquid in the absence of other sources of pressure must assume a form for which at all points of the surface the mean curvature is the same. In the experiment of Plateau, we take two liquids of the same specific weight, so that a clot of one of them will float in equilibrium in the other. It may be assumed that the floating liquid is acted on only by surface tension,* and it turns out that the "floating" liquid always takes the form of a sphere. This result suggests that every closed surface with constant mean curvature is a sphere, a theorem that is in fact true, although the strict mathematical proof of it is very difficult.

It is possible to approach the question from still another side. In view of the fact that the surface tension tends to decrease the area of the surface, while the volume of the liquid cannot change, it is natural to expect that the floating mass of liquid will have the smallest surface for a given volume. It can be proved that a body with this property is a sphere.

The relation between the lateral pressure of the film and its mean curvature can also be used to determine the form of a soap film suspended in a contour. Since the lateral pressure over the surface of the film, being directed along the normal to the surface, is not opposed by any reaction of the support (the support in this case is simply not there), it must be equal to zero, so that for the desired surface we have the condition

$$K_{av} = 0. \tag{6}$$

From the analytic expression for mean curvature, we obtain a differential equation, and the problem consists of solving this equation under the condition that the desired surface passes through the given contour.† There have been many investigations of this difficult problem.

The same equation (6) arises from the problem of finding the surface of least area bounded by a given contour. From a physical point of view, the identity of these two problems is a natural one, since the film tends to decrease its area and reaches a position of stable equilibrium only when it attains the minimal area possible under the given conditions. Surfaces of zero mean curvature, by reason of their connection with this problem, are called *minimal*.

The mathematical investigation of minimal surfaces is of great interest, partly because of their wide variety of essentially different shapes, as

---

* The increase of pressure with depth may be ignored, since it is the same for both liquids because of their having the same specific weight. So on their common boundary the additional internal and external pressures caused by the depth are neutralized by each other.

† For a surface given by the equation $z = z(x, y)$, equation (6) assumes the form

$$(1 + z_y'^2)z_{xx}'' - 2z_x'z_y'z_{xy}'' + (1 + z_x'^2)z_{yy}'' = 0.$$

discovered by experiments with soap film. Figure 31 illustrates two soap films suspended from different contours.

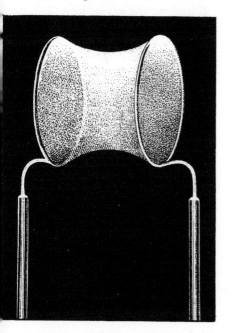
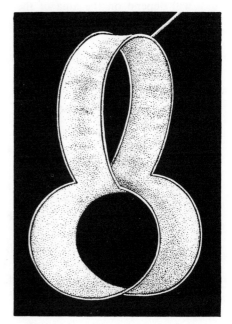

Fig. 31.

Gaussian curvature.   The *Gaussian curvature* of a surface at a given point is the product of the principal curvatures

$$K = k_1 k_2 .$$

The sign of the Gaussian curvature defines the character of the surface near the point under consideration. For $K > 0$ the surface has the form of a bowl (k_1 and k_2 have the same sign) and for $K < 0$, when k_1 and k_2 have different signs, the surface is like a saddle. The remaining cases, discussed earlier, correspond to zero Gaussian curvature. The absolute value of the Gaussian curvature gives the degree of curvature of the surface in general, as a sort of abstraction from the various curvatures in different directions. This becomes particularly clear if we consider a different definition of Gaussian curvature, which does not depend on investigating curves on the surface.

Let us consider a small segment G of the surface F, containing the point M in its interior, and at each point of this segment let us erect a normal to the surface.

If we translate the initial points of all these normals to one point, then they fill out a solid angle (figure 32). The size of this solid angle will depend on the area of the segment G and on the extent to which the surface is curved on this segment. Thus the degree of curvature of

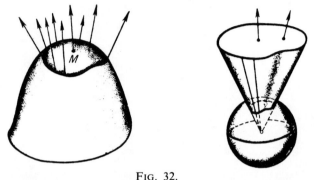

FIG. 32.

the segment G may be characterized by the ratio of the size of the solid angle to the area of G; so it is natural to define the curvature of the surface at a given point as the limit of this ratio when the segment G shrinks to the point M.* It turns out that this limit is equal to the absolute value of the Gaussian curvature at the point M.

The most remarkable property of the Gaussian curvature, which explains its great significance in the theory of surfaces, is the following. Let us suppose that the surface has been stamped out from a flexible but inextensible material, say a very thin sheet of tin, so that we can bend it into various shapes without stretching or tearing it. During this process the principal curvatures will change but, as Gauss showed, their product $k_1 k_2$ will remain unchanged at every point. This fundamental result shows that two surfaces with different Gaussian curvatures are inherently distinct from each other, the distinction consisting of the fact that if we deform them in every possible way, without stretching or tearing, we can never superpose them on each other. For example, a segment of the surface of a sphere can never be distorted so as to lie on a plane or on the surface of a sphere of different radius.

We have now considered certain basic concepts in the theory of surfaces. As for the methods used in this theory, they consist, as was stated previously, primarily in the application of analysis and above all of

---

* To measure the solid angle itself, we construct a sphere of unit radius with center at its vertex. The area of the region in which the sphere intersects the solid angle is then taken as the size of the solid angle (figure 32).

differential equations. Simple examples of the use of analysis are to be found in the proofs for the theorems of Euler and Meusnier. For more complicated questions, we require a special method of relating problems in the theory of surfaces to problems in analysis. This method is based on the introduction of so-called curvilinear coordinates and was first widely used in the work of Gauss on problems of the type discussed in the following section.

§4. Intrinsic Geometry and Deformation of Surfaces

Intrinsic geometry. As indicated previously, a deformation of a surface is defined as a change of shape that preserves the lengths of all curves lying in the surface. For example, rolling up a sheet of paper into a cylindrical tube represents, from the geometric point of view, a deformation of part of the plane, since in fact the paper undergoes practically no stretching, and the length of any curve drawn on it is not changed by its being rolled up. Certain other geometric quantities connected with the surface are also preserved; for example, the area of figures on it. All properties of a surface that are not changed by deformations make up what is called the *intrinsic geometry* of the surface.

But just which are these properties? It is clear that in a deformation only those properties can be preserved which in the final analysis depend entirely on lengths of curves, i.e., which may be determined by measurements carried out on the surface itself. A deformation is a change of shape preserving the length of curves, and any property which cannot change under *any* deformation must be definable in one way or another in terms of length. Thus intrinsic geometry is simply called *geometry on a surface*. The very meaning of the words "intrinsic geometry" is that it studies intrinsic properties of the surface itself, independent of the manner in which the surface is embedded in the surrounding space.* Thus, for example, if we join two points on a sheet of paper by a straight line and then bend the paper (figure 33), the segment becomes a curve but its property of being the shortest of all lines joining the given points on the surface is preserved; so this property belongs to intrinsic geometry. On the other hand, the curvature of this line will depend on how the paper was bent and thus is not a part of intrinsic geometry.

In general, since the proofs of plane geometry make no reference to the properties of the surrounding space, all its theorems belong to the

---

* We note that the ideas of intrinsic geometry have led to a wide generalization of the mathematical concept of space and have thereby played a very important role in contemporary physics; for details see Chapter XVII.

intrinsic geometry of any surface obtainable by deformation of a plane. One may say that plane geometry is the intrinsic geometry of the plane.

Another example of intrinsic geometry is familiar to everyone, namely geometry on the surface of a sphere, with which we usually have to deal

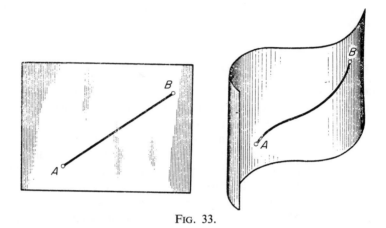

FIG. 33.

in making measurements on the surface of the earth. This example is a particularly good one to illustrate the essential nature of intrinsic geometry; because of the large radius of the earth, any immediately visible area of its surface appears to us as part of a plane, so that the deviations from plane geometry observable in the measurements of large distances impresses us as resulting not from the curvature of the earth's surface in space but from the inherent laws of "terrestrial geometry," expressing the geometric properties of the surface of the earth itself.

It remains to note that the idea of studying intrinsic geometry occurred to Gauss in connection with the problems of geodesy and cartography. Both these applied sciences are concerned in an essential way with the intrinsic geometry of the earth's surface. Cartography deals, in particular, with distortions in the ratios of distances when part of the surface of the earth is mapped on a plane and thus with distinguishing between plane geometry and the intrinsic geometry of the surface of the earth.

The intrinsic geometry of any surface may be pictured in the same way. Let us imagine that on a given surface there exist creatures so small that within the limits of their range of vision the surface appears to be plane (we know that a sufficiently small segment of any smooth surface differs very little from a tangent plane); then these creatures will not notice that the surface is curved in space, but in measuring large distances they will nevertheless convince themselves that in their geometry certain nonplanar laws prevail, corresponding to the intrinsic geometry of the surface on which they live. That these laws are actually different for different surfaces may easily be seen from the following simple discussion. Let us choose a point O on the surface and consider a curve L such that the distance of each of its points from the point O, measured on the surface (i.e., along the shortest curve connecting this point to the point O) is equal to a fixed number r (figure 34). The curve L, from the

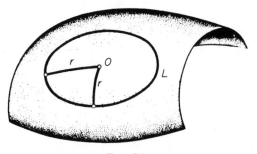

Fig. 34.

point of view of the intrinsic geometry of the surface, is simply the circumference of a circle of radius r. A formula expressing the length $s(r)$ in terms of r is part of the intrinsic geometry of the given surface. But such a formula may vary widely in character, depending on the nature of the surface: Thus on a plane, $s(r) = 2\pi r$; on a sphere of radius R, as can easily be shown, $s(r) = 2\pi R \sin r/R$; on the surface illustrated in figure 35, beginning with a certain value of r, the length of the cir-

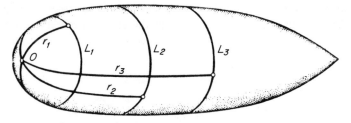

Fig. 35.

cumference with center O and radius r is at first independent of r but then begins to decrease. Consequently, all these surfaces have different intrinsic geometries.

The basic concepts of intrinsic geometry. To illustrate the wide range of concepts and theorems in intrinsic geometry, we may turn to plane geometry which, as we have seen, is the intrinsic geometry of the plane. Its subject matter consists of plane figures and their properties, which are usually expressed in the form of relations among basic geometric quantities such as length, angle, and area. For a rigorous proof that angle and area belong to the intrinsic geometry of the plane, it is necessary to show that they can be expressed in terms of length. But this is certainly so; in fact, an angle may be computed if we know the length of the sides of a triangle containing it, and the area of a triangle can also be computed in terms of its sides, while to compute the area of a polygon we need only divide it into triangles.

In considering plane geometry as the intrinsic geometry of the plane, there is no need to restrict ourselves to ideas learned in school. On the contrary, we may develop it as far as we like and study many new problems, provided only they can be stated, in the final analysis, in terms of length. Thus, in plane geometry we may successively introduce the length of a curve, the area of a surface bounded by curves, and so forth; they are all a part of the intrinsic geometry of the plane.

The same concepts are introduced in the intrinsic geometry of an arbitrary surface. The length of a curve is the initial concept; the definition of angles and areas is somewhat more complicated. If the intrinsic geometry of a given surface differs from plane geometry, we cannot use the customary formulas to define an angle or an area in terms of length. However, as we have seen, a surface near a given point differs little from its tangent plane. Speaking more precisely, the following is true: If a small segment of a surface containing a given point M is projected on the tangent plane at this point, then the distance between points, measured on the surface, differs from the distance between their projections by an infinitesimal of higher than the second order in comparison with distances from the point M. Thus in defining geometric quantities

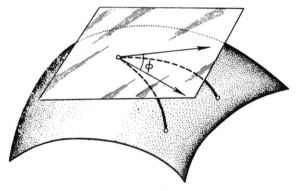

Fig. 36.

at a given point of a surface by taking a limit in which infinitesimals occur of order no higher than the second, we may replace a segment of the surface by its projection on the tangent plane. Thus the quantities determined by measurement in the tangent plane turn out to belong to the intrinsic geometry of the surface. This possibility of considering a small segment of the surface as a plane is the basis of the definitions of all the concepts of intrinsic geometry.

As an example let us consider the definitions of angle and area. Following the general principle, we define the angle between curves on a surface as the angle between their projections on the tangent plane (figure 36). Obviously the angle defined in this manner is identical with the angle between the tangents to the curves. The definition of area given in §3 is based on the same principle. Finally, in order that the tendency of a curve to twist in space may be defined "within" the surface itself, we introduce the concept of "geodesic curvature" the name being reminiscent of measurements on the surface of the earth. The *geodesic curvature* of a curve at a given point is defined as the curvature of its projection on the tangent plane (figure 37).

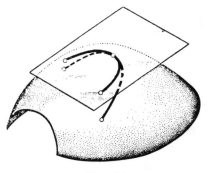

FIG. 37.

In this manner we see that the basic concepts of plane geometry may be introduced into the intrinsic geometry of an arbitrary surface.

In any arbitrary surface it is also easy to define figures analogous to the basic figures on the plane. For example, we have been dealing previously with circumferences of circles, which are defined precisely as in the case of the plane. Similarly, we may define the analogue of a line segment, namely a geodesic segment, as the shortest curve on the surface joining two given points. Further, it is natural to define a triangle as a figure bounded by three geodesic segments and similarly for a polygon, and so forth. Since the properties of all these figures and magnitudes depend on the surface, there exist in this sense infinitely many different intrinsic geometries. But intrinsic geometry, as a special branch of the theory of surfaces, pays particular attention to certain general laws holding for the intrinsic geometry of any surface and makes clear how these laws are expressed in terms of the quantities which characterize a given surface.

Thus, as we have noted earlier, one of the most important characteristics of a surface, its Gaussian curvature, is not changed by deformation, i.e., depends only on the intrinsic geometry of the surface. But it turns out that in general the Gaussian curvature already characterizes, to a remarkable degree, the extent to which the intrinsic geometry of the surface near a given point differs from plane geometry. As an example let us consider on a surface a circle L of very small radius r, with center at a given point O. On a plane the length $s(r)$ of its circumference is expressed by the formula $s(r) = 2\pi r$. On a surface differing from a plane, the dependence of the circumference on the radius is different; here the deviation of $s(r)$ from $2\pi r$, depends essentially, for small r, on the Gaussian curvature K at the center of the circle, namely;

$$s(r) = 2\pi r - \frac{\pi}{3} K r^3 + \epsilon r^3,$$

where $\epsilon \to 0$ as $r \to 0$. In other words, for small r the circumference may be computed by the usual formula if we disregard terms of the third degree of smallness, and in this case the error (with accuracy to terms of higher than the third order) is proportional to the Gaussian curvature. In particular, if $K > 0$, then the circumference of a circle of small radius is smaller than the circumference of a circle with the same radius in a plane, and if $K < 0$, it is larger. These latter facts are easy to visualize: Near a point with positive curvature the surface has the shape of a bowl so that circumferences are reduced, whereas near a point with negative curvature the circumference, being situated on a "saddle," has a wavelike shape and is thus considerably lengthened (figure 38).

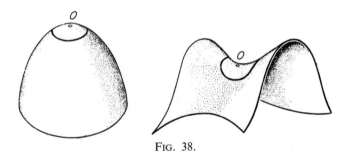

FIG. 38.

From the theorem just mentioned, it follows that a surface with varying Gaussian curvature is extremely inhomogeneous from a geometric point of view; the properties of its intrinsic geometry change from point to point. The general character of the problems of intrinsic geometry causes it to resemble plane geometry, but this inhomogeneity, on the other hand, makes it profoundly different from plane geometry. On the plane, for example, the sum of the angles of a triangle is equal to two right angles; but on an arbitrary surface the sum of the angles of a triangle, (with geodesics for sides) is undetermined even if we are told that it lies on a known surface and has sides of given length. However, if we know the Gaussian curvature K at every point of the triangle, then the sum of its angles, α, β, γ, can be computed by the formula

$$\alpha + \beta + \gamma = \pi + \iint K \, d\sigma,$$

where the integral is taken over the surface of the triangle. This formula contains as a special case the well-known theorems on the sum of the angles of a triangle in the plane and on the unit sphere. In the first case $K = 0$ and $\alpha + \beta + \gamma = \pi$, while in the second $K = 1$ and $\alpha + \beta + \gamma = \pi + S$, where S is the area of the spherical triangle.

It may be proved that every sufficiently small segment of a surface with zero Gaussian curvature may be deformed, or, as it is customary to say, developed into a plane, since it has the same intrinsic geometry as the plane. Such surfaces are called *developable*. And if the Gaussian curvature is near zero, then although the surface cannot be developed into a plane, still its intrinsic geometry differs little from plane geometry, which indicates once again that the Gaussian curvature acts as a measure of the extent to which the intrinsic geometry of a surface deviates from plane geometry.

Geodesic lines. In the intrinsic geometry of a surface the role of straight lines is played by geodesic lines, or, as they are usually called, "geodesics."

A straight line in a plane may be defined as a line made up of intervals overlapping one another. A geodesic is defined in exactly the same way, with geodesic segments taking the place of intervals. In other words, a *geodesic* is a curve on a surface such that every sufficiently small piece of it is a shortest path. Not every geodesic is a shortest path in the large, as may be noted on the surface of a sphere, where every arc of a great circle is a geodesic, although this arc will be the shortest path between its end points only if it is not greater than a semicircle. A geodesic, as we see, may even be a closed curve.

To illustrate certain important properties of geodesics, let us consider the following mechanical model.* On the surface F let there be stretched

---

* As noted previously, our reasoning here is not a strict proof of the properties of geodesic curves. It is given only to illustrate the most important of these properties.

a rubber string with fixed ends (figure 39).* The string will be in equilibrium when it has the shortest possible length, since any change in its position will then involve an increase of length, which could be produced only by external forces. In other words, the string will be in equilibrium if it is lying along a geodesic. But for equilibrium, it is necessary that the elastic forces on each segment of the string be counterbalanced by the resistance of the surface, directed along the normal to it. (We assume that the surface is smooth and that there is no friction between it and the string.)

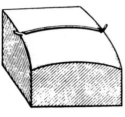

FIG. 39.

But it was proved in §2 that the pressure on the support caused by the tension of the string is directed along the principal normal to the curve along which the string lies. Thus we are led to the following result: The principal normal to a geodesic at each point coincides in direction with the normal to the surface. The converse of this theorem is also true: Every curve on a regular surface which has this property is a geodesic.

This property of a geodesic allows us to deduce the following important fact: If a material point is moving on a surface in such a way that there are no forces acting on it except for the reaction of the surface, then it follows a geodesic. For, as we know from §2, the normal acceleration of a point is directed along the principal normal to the trajectory and since the reaction of the surface is the only force acting on the point, the principal normal to the trajectory is identical with the normal to the surface, so that from the preceding theorem the trajectory is a geodesic. This last property of geodesics increases their resemblance to straight lines. Just as the motion of a free point, because of inertia, is along a straight line, so the motion of a point forced to stay on a surface, but not affected by external forces, will be along a geodesic.†

From the same property of geodesics comes the following theorem. If two surfaces are tangent along a curve that is a geodesic on one of them, then this curve will also be a geodesic on the other. For at each point of the curve, the surfaces have a common tangent plane and consequently a common normal, and since the curve is a geodesic on one of the surfaces, this normal coincides with the principal normal to the curve, so that on the second surface also the curve will be a geodesic.

---

* A stretched string will not remain on a surface unless the surface is convex; so in order not to make exceptions, it is better to imagine that the surface is in two layers, with the string running between them.

† Here by "external" forces we mean all forces except the reaction of the surface.

From these results follow two further intuitive properties of geodesic curves. In the first place, if an elastic rectangular plate (for example a steel ruler) lies with its median line completely on a surface, then it is tangent to this surface along a geodesic. (Evidently the line of contact is a geodesic on the ruler, so that it must be a geodesic also on the surface.) Second, if a surface rolls along a plane in such a way that the point of contact traces a straight line on the plane, then the trace of this straight line on the surface is a geodesic.* Both these properties are readily demonstrated on a cylinder, where it is easy to convince oneself by experiment that the median line of a straight plane strip lying on the cylinder (figure 40) coincides with either a generator or the circumference of a

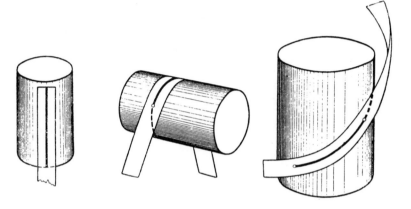

FIG. 40.

circle or a helix, and it is not difficult to prove that a geodesic curve on a cylinder can be only one of these three. The same curves will be traced out on a cylinder if we roll it on a plane on which we have drawn a straight line in chalk.

The analogy between geodesics and straight lines in a plane may be supplemented by still another important property, taken directly from the definition of a geodesic. Namely, straight lines in the plane may be defined as curves of zero curvature and geodesics on a surface as curves of zero geodesic curvature. (We recall that the geodesic curvature is the curvature of the projection of the curve on the tangent plane, cf. figure 37.) It is quite natural that our present definition of a geodesic should coincide with the earlier one; for if at every point of the curve the curvature of

---

* This proposition does not differ essentially from the preceding one, since the rolling of a surface on a plane is equivalent in a well-defined sense to the unwinding of a plane strip along the surface.

its projection on the tangent plane is equal to zero, then the curve departs from its tangent essentially in the direction of the normal to the surface, so that the principal normal to the curve is directed along the normal to the surface and the curve is a geodesic in the original sense. Conversely, if a curve is a geodesic, then its principal normal, and so also its deviation from the tangent line, are directed along the normal to the surface, so that in projecting on the tangent plane we get a curve in which the deviation from the tangent is essentially smaller than for the original curve, and the curvature of the projection so formed turns out to be equal to zero.

The course of a geodesic may vary widely for different surfaces. As an example, in figure 41 we trace some geodesics on a hyperboloid of revolution.

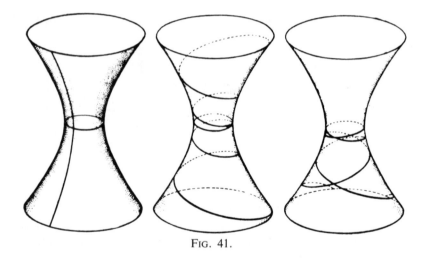

Fig. 41.

Deformation of surfaces. Since intrinsic geometry studies the properties of surfaces that are invariant under deformation, it naturally investigates these deformations themselves. The theory of deformation of surfaces is one of the most interesting and difficult branches of geometry and includes many problems which, although simple to state, have not yet been finally solved.

Certain questions about the deformation of surfaces were already considered by Euler and Minding, but general results for arbitrary surfaces were not derived until later.

In the general theory of deformation, we first of all raise the question whether deformation is possible for all surfaces and, if so, to what extent.

For analytic surfaces, i.e., surfaces defined by functions of the coordinates that can be expanded in a Taylor series, this question was solved at the end of the last century by the French mathematician Darboux. In particular, he showed the following: If on such a surface we consider any geodesic and assign in space an arbitrary (analytic) curve with the same length, and with curvature nowhere equal to zero, then a sufficiently narrow strip of the surface, containing the given geodesic, can be deformed so that the geodesic coincides with the given curve.* This theorem shows that a strip of the surface may be deformed rather arbitrarily. However, it has been proved that if a geodesic is to be transformed into a preassigned curve, then the surface may be deformed in no more than two ways. For example, if the curve is plane, then the two positions of the surface will be mirror images of each other in the plane. If the geodesic is a straight line, then this last proposition is not true, as can be shown by deforming a cylindrical surface.

We have defined a deformation as a transformation of the surface that preserves the lengths of all curves on the surface. Here we have considered only the final result of the transformation; the question of what happens to the curve during the process did not enter. However, in considering a surface as made from a flexible but unstretchable material, it is natural to consider a continuous transformation, at each instant of which the lengths remain unchanged (physically this corresponds to the unstretchability of the material). Such transformations are called *continuous* deformations.

At first glance it may seem that every deformation can be realized in a continuous manner, but this is not so. For example, it has been shown that a surface in the form of a circular trough (figure 42), does not admit

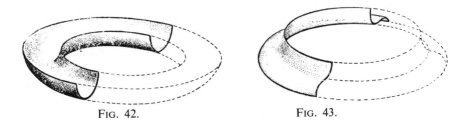

FIG. 42. FIG. 43.

continuous deformations (this explains, among other things, the familiar fact that a pail with a curved rim is considerably stronger than one with a plain rim) although deformations of such a surface are possible: for

---

* The case of transforming a geodesic into a curve with zero curvature is excluded, since it is easy to show that for surfaces of positive Gaussian curvature this is impossible.

example, one may cut the trough along the circle on which it rests on a horizontal plane and replace one half of it by its mirror image in this plane (compare figure 43 with figure 42; to aid visualization we have drawn only the left half of the surface). It is intuitively clear that the impossibility of a continuous deformation is due to the circular shape of the trough; for a straight trough such a deformation can be performed continuously.

If we restrict ourselves to a sufficiently small segment of the surface, then there are no obvious hindrances to its continuous deformation, and we might expect that every deformation of a small segment of the surface can be realized by a continuous transformation, followed perhaps by a mirror reflection. This is in fact true, but only under the condition that on the given small segment of the surface the Gaussian curvature never vanishes (excepting the case that it vanishes everywhere). But if the Gaussian curvature vanishes at isolated points, then, as N. V. Efimov showed in 1940, even arbitrarily small segments of a regular surface may not admit any continuous deformation without loss of regularity. For example, the surface defined by the equation $z = x^9 + \lambda x^6 y^3 + y^9$, where λ is a transcendental number, has the property that no segment containing the origin, no matter how small it may be, admits sufficiently regular continuous deformations. Efimov's theorem is a new and somewhat unexpected result in classical differential geometry.

In addition to these general questions about deformation, a great deal of attention is being paid to special types of deformation of surfaces.

The connection of the intrinsic geometry of a surface with the form of the surface in space. We already know that certain properties of a surface, and of the figures on it, are defined by the intrinsic geometry of the surface even though these properties are very closely related to other properties that depend on how the surface is embedded in the surrounding space, properties that are, as they say, "extrinsic" to the surface. For example, the principal curvatures are extrinsic properties of a surface, but their product (the Gaussian curvature) is intrinsic. Another example, in order that the principal normal of a curve lying on a surface should coincide with the normal to the surface, it is necessary and sufficient that this curve have a property defined by its intrinsic geometry, namely that it be a geodesic.

Consequently, the intrinsic geometry of a surface will determine its space form only to a certain extent.

The dependence of the space form of a surface on its intrinsic geometry may be expressed analytically in the form of equations containing certain quantities that characterize the intrinsic geometry and certain other quantities that characterize the way in which the curved surface is embedded in space. One of these equations is the formula expressing the Gaussian curvature in intrinsic terms and is due to Gauss. Two other such equations are those of Peterson and Codazzi, mentioned in §1.

The equations of Gauss, Peterson, and Codazzi completely express the connection between the intrinsic geometry of a surface and the character of its curvature in space, since all possible interrelations between intrinsic and extrinsic properties of an arbitrary surface are included, at least in implicit form, in these equations.

Since the form of a surface in space is not completely defined by its intrinsic geometry, we naturally ask, What extrinsic properties must still be assigned in order to determine the surface completely? It turns out that if two surfaces have the same intrinsic geometry and if, at corresponding points and in corresponding directions, the curvatures of the normal sections of these surfaces have the same sign, then the surfaces are congruent; that is, they can be translated so as to coincide with each other. We note that Peterson discovered this theorem 15 years earlier than Bonnet, with whose name it is usually associated.

Analytic apparatus in the theory of surfaces. The systematic application of analysis to the theory of surfaces led to the building up of an analytic apparatus especially suitable for this purpose. The decisive step in this direction was taken by Gauss, who introduced the method of representing surfaces by so-called curvilinear coordinates. This method is a natural generalization of the idea of Cartesian coordinates on the plane and is closely connected with the intrinsic geometry of the surface, for which the presentation of the surface by an equation of the form $z = f(x, y)$ is not convenient. The inconvenience consists of the fact that the x, y coordinates of a point on the surface change when the surface is deformed. To eliminate this difficulty, the coordinates are chosen on the surface itself; they define each point by two numbers u and v, which are associated with the given point and remain associated with it even after deformation of the surface. The space coordinates x, y, z of the point will in each case be functions of u and v. The numbers u and v defining the point on a surface are called its *curvilinear coordinates*. The choice of name is to be understood as follows: If we fix the value of one of these coordinates, say v, and vary the other, then we get a coordinate curve on the surface. The coordinate curves form a curvilinear net on the surface, similar to the coordinate net on a plane. We note that the familiar method of describing the position of a point on the surface of the earth by means of longitude and latitude consists simply of introducing curvilinear coordinates on the surface of a sphere; the coor-

dinate net in this case consists of circles, namely the meridians and
parallels* (figure 44). To describe the spatial position of a surface by
means of curvilinear coordinates, we need to define the position of each
point in terms of u and v, for example by giving, as a function of u and v,
the vector $r = r(u, v)$, issuing from some fixed origin to the points on
the surface and called the radius vector of the surface. (This is equivalent
to giving the x, y, and z components of the vector r as functions of u
and v.)† To define a curve lying on a given surface, we need to give the
coordinates u, v as functions of one parameter t; then the radius vector
to a point moving along this curve is expressed as a composite function

$$r[u(t), v(t)].$$

For vector functions the concepts of derivative and differential may be
generalized word for word; from the definition of the derivative as the
limit of $\Delta r / \Delta t$ when $\Delta t \to 0$ (r is a function of the parameter t) it follows

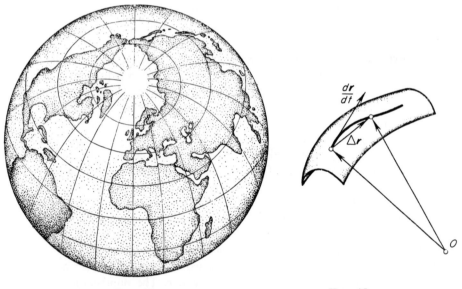

FIG. 44.   FIG. 45.

---

* It is characteristic that geographic coordinates and their practical applications
were known long in advance of Descartes' introduction of the usual coordinates in
the plane.

† Of course Gauss did not use vector notation, but defined the three coordinates
x, y, z of the points of the surface separately as functions of u and v. Vectors, which
were introduced as a result of the work of Hamilton and Grassmann, were at first used
widely in physics and only later (in fact, in the 20th century) became the traditional
apparatus for analytic and differential geometry.

at once that the derivative of the radius vector of a curve is a vector directed along the tangent to the curve (figure 45). For vector functions the basic properties of ordinary derivatives are still valid; for example, the chain rule

$$\frac{dr[u(t), v(t)]}{dt} = \frac{\partial r}{\partial u}\frac{du}{dt} + \frac{\partial r}{\partial v}\frac{dv}{dt} = r_u u_t' + r_v v_t', \tag{7}$$

where r_u and r_v are the partial derivatives of the vector function $r(u, v)$.

The length of a curve, as can be shown, is expressed by the integral

$$s = \int \sqrt{x'^2(t) + y'^2(t) + z'^2(t)}\, dt.$$

Thus, the differential of the length of a curve is equal to

$$ds = \sqrt{x'^2(t) + y'^2(t) + z'^2(t)}\, dt.$$

But since $x'(t)$, $y'(t)$, and $z'(t)$ are components of the vector $dr/dt = r_t'$, we may write $ds = |r_t'|\, dt$, where $|r_t'|$ denotes the length of the vector r_t'. For curves lying on a surface, we get from (7)

$$ds = |r_u u_t' + r_v v_t'|\, dt.$$

Computing the square of the length of the vector on the right we obtain, by the rules of vector algebra,*

$$ds^2 = [r_u^2 u_t'^2 + 2r_u r_v u_t' v_t' + r_v^2 v_t'^2]\, dt^2 .$$

Passing to differentials and introducing the notation

$$r_u^2 = E(u, v), \quad r_u r_v = F(u, v), \quad r_v^2 = G(u, v),$$

we have

$$ds^2 = E\, du^2 + 2F\, du\, dv + G\, dv^2.$$

We see that the square of the differential of arc length on a surface is a quadratic form in the differentials du and dv with coefficients depending on the point of the surface. This form is called the *first fundamental quadratic form* of the surface. Given the coefficients E, F, and G of this

---

* The square of the length of a vector is the scalar product of the vector with itself, and for scalar multiplication (cf. Chapter III, §9) the usual rules hold for the removal of brackets.

form at each point on a surface we may compute the length of any curve
on the surface by the formula

$$s = \int_{t_1}^{t_2} \sqrt{Eu_t'^2 + 2Fu_t'v_t' + Gv_t'^2}\, dt,$$

so that its intrinsic geometry is thereby completely determined.

We show, as an example, how to express angle and area in terms of
E, F, and G. Let two curves issue from a given point, one of them given
by the equations $u = u_1(t)$, $v = v_1(t)$ and the other by the equations
$u = u_2(t)$, $v = v_2(t)$. Then the tangents to these curves are given by the
vectors

$$\mathbf{r}_1 = \mathbf{r}_u \frac{du_1}{dt} + \mathbf{r}_v \frac{dv_1}{dt},$$

$$\mathbf{r}_2 = \mathbf{r}_u \frac{du_2}{dt} + \mathbf{r}_v \frac{dv_2}{dt}.$$

The cosine of the angle between these vectors is equal to the scalar
product $\mathbf{r}_1\mathbf{r}_2$ divided by the product of the lengths $r_1 r_2$

$$\cos \alpha = \frac{\mathbf{r}_1\mathbf{r}_2}{r_1 r_2}$$

$$= \frac{r_u^2 \dfrac{du_1}{dt}\dfrac{du_2}{dt} + \mathbf{r}_u\mathbf{r}_v \left(\dfrac{du_1}{dt}\dfrac{dv_2}{dt} + \dfrac{du_2}{dt}\dfrac{dv_1}{dt}\right) + r_v^2 \dfrac{dv_1}{dt}\cdot\dfrac{dv_2}{dt}}{r_1 r_2}.$$

Recalling that $r_u^2 = E$, $\mathbf{r}_u\mathbf{r}_v = F$, $r_v^2 = G$, we get

$$\cos \alpha =$$

$$\frac{E\dfrac{du_1}{dt}\dfrac{du_2}{dt} + F\left(\dfrac{du_1}{dt}\dfrac{dv_2}{dt} + \dfrac{du_2}{dt}\dfrac{dv_1}{dt}\right) + G\dfrac{dv_1}{dt}\dfrac{dv_2}{dt}}{\sqrt{E\left(\dfrac{du_1}{dt}\right)^2 + 2F\dfrac{du_1}{dt}\dfrac{dv_1}{dt} + G\left(\dfrac{dv_1}{dt}\right)^2}\sqrt{E\left(\dfrac{du_2}{dt}\right)^2 + 2F\dfrac{du_2}{dt}\dfrac{dv_2}{dt} + G\left(\dfrac{dv_2}{dt}\right)^2}}.$$

To obtain a formula for area, we consider a curvilinear rectangle
bounded by the coordinate curves $u = u_0$, $v = v_0$, $u = u_0 + \Delta u$,
$v = v_0 + \Delta v$, and we take as an approximation to it the parallelogram
lying in the tangent plane and bounded by the vectors $\mathbf{r}_u\,\Delta u$, $\mathbf{r}_v\,\Delta v$, tangent
to the coordinate curves (figure 46). The area of this parallelogram is

$\Delta s = |\, r_u\,|\,|\, r_v\,|\, \Delta u\, \Delta v \sin \phi$, where ϕ is the angle between r_u and r_v. Since $\sin \phi = \sqrt{1 - \cos^2 \phi}$, it follows that $\Delta s = |\, r_u\,|\,|\, r_v\,|\, \Delta u\, \Delta v \sqrt{1 - \cos^2 \phi}$ $= \sqrt{r_u^2 r_v^2 - |\, r_u\,|^2\,|\, r_v\,|^2 \cos^2 \phi}\, \Delta u\, \Delta v$. Recalling that $r_u^2 = E$, $r_v^2 = G$, $|\, r_u\,| \cdot |\, r_v\,| \cos \phi = r_u r_v = F$, we get $\Delta s = \sqrt{EG - F^2}\, \Delta u\, \Delta v$. Summing up the areas of the parallelograms and taking the limit as $\Delta u, \Delta v \to 0$ we obtain the formula for area $S = \iint_D \sqrt{EG - F^2}\, du\, dv$, where the integration is taken over the domain D of the variables u and v which describe the given segment of the surface.

In this way, curvilinear coordinates are very convenient for studying the intrinsic geometry of a surface.

It also turns out that the manner in which a curved surface is embedded in the surrounding space can be characterized by a certain quadratic form in the differentials du, dv. Thus if n is a unit vector normal to the surface at the point M, and Δr is the increment in the radius vector to

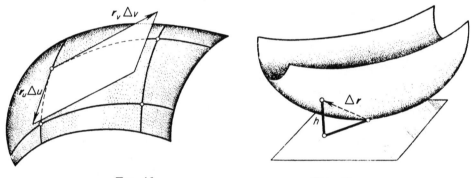

FIG. 46.   FIG. 47.

the surface as we move from this point, then the deviation h of the surface from the tangent plane (figure 47) is equal to $n\, \Delta r$. Expanding the increment Δr by Taylor's formula, we get

$$h = n\, dr + \tfrac{1}{2}\, n\, d^2 r + \epsilon(du^2 + dv^2),$$

where $\epsilon \to 0$ as $\sqrt{du^2 + dv^2} \to 0$. Since the vector dr lies in the tangent plane, we have $n\, dr = 0$. The last term, $\epsilon(du^2 + dv^2)$ is small in comparison with the squares of the differentials du and dv. There remains the principal term $\tfrac{1}{2} n\, d^2 r$. Thus twice the principal part of h, namely $n\, d^2 r$, is a quadratic form with respect to du and dv

$$n\, d^2 r = n r_{uu}\, du^2 + 2 n r_{uv}\, du\, dv + n r_{vv}\, dv^2.$$

This form describes the character of the deviation of the surface from the tangent plane. It is called the *second fundamental quadratic form* of the surface. Its coefficients, which depend on u and v, are usually written:

$$\mathbf{nr}_{uu} = L, \quad \mathbf{nr}_{uv} = M, \quad \mathbf{nr}_{vv} = N.$$

Knowing the second fundamental quadratic form, we can compute the curvature of any curve on a surface. Thus, applying the formula $k = \lim_{l \to 0} 2h/l^2$, we obtain the result that the curvature of the normal section in the direction corresponding to the ratio du/dv is equal to

$$k_n = \frac{n\, d^2 r}{ds^2} = \frac{L\, du^2 + 2M\, du\, dv + N\, dv^2}{E\, du^2 + 2F\, du\, dv + G\, dv^2}.$$

If the curve is not a normal section, then by Meusnier's theorem it is sufficient to divide the curvature of the normal section in the same direction by the cosine of the angle between the principal normal to the curve and the normal to the surface.

The introduction of the second fundamental quadratic form provides an analytic approach to the study of how the surface is curved in space. In particular, one may derive the theorems of Euler and Meusnier, the expressions for the Gaussian and mean curvature, and so forth, in a purely analytic way.

Peterson's theorem, mentioned earlier, shows that the two quadratic forms, taken together, define a surface up to its position in space, so that the analytic study of any properties of a surface consists of the study of these forms. In conclusion, we note that the coefficients of the two quadratic forms are not independent; the connection mentioned earlier between the intrinsic geometry of a curved surface and the way in which it is embedded in space is expressed analytically by three relations (the equations of Gauss-Codazzi) between the coefficients of the first and the second fundamental quadratic forms.

§5. New Developments in the Theory of Curves and Surfaces

Families of curves and surfaces. Even though the basic theory of curves and surfaces was to a large degree complete by the middle of the last century, it has continued to develop in several new directions, which greatly extend the range of figures and properties investigated in contemporary differential geometry. There is one of these developments whose origins go back to the beginning of differential geometry, namely the theory of "families" or of continuous collections of curves and surfaces, but this theory may be considered new in the sense that its more profound aspects were not investigated until after the basic theory of curves and surfaces was already completely developed.

In general a continuous collection of figures is called an *n-parameter family* if each figure of the collection is determined by the values of *n* parameters and all the quantities characterizing the figure (in respect to its position, form, and so forth) depend on these parameters in a manner which is at least continuous. From the point of view of this general definition, a curve may be considered as a one-parameter family of points and a surface as a two-parameter family of points. The collection of all circles in the plane is an example of a three-parameter family of curves, since a circle in the plane is determined by three parameters: the two coordinates of its center and its radius.

The simplest question in the theory of families of curves or surfaces consists of finding the so-called envelope of the family. A surface is called the *envelope* of a given family of surfaces if at each of its points it is tangent to one of the surfaces of the family and is in this way tangent to every one of them. For example, the envelope of a family of spheres of

FIG. 48.

equal radius with centers on a given straight line will be a cylinder (figure 48), and the envelope of such spheres with centers on all points of a given plane will consist of two parallel planes. The envelope of a

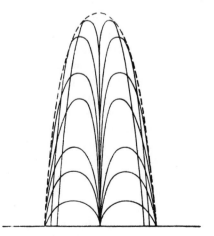

FIG. 49.

family of curves is defined similarly. Figure 49 diagrams jets of water issuing from a fountain at various angles; in any one plane they form a family of curves, which may be considered approximately as parabolas; their envelope stands out clearly as the general contour of the cascade of water. Of course, not every family of curves or surfaces has an envelope; for example, a family of parallel straight lines does not have one. There exists a simple general method of finding the envelope of any family; for a family of curves in the plane this method was given by Leibnitz.

Every curve is obviously the envelope of its tangents, and in exactly the same way every surface is the envelope of its tangent planes. Incidentally, this fact provides a new method of defining a curve or a surface by giving the family of its tangent lines or planes. For some problems this method turns out to be the most convenient.

Generally speaking, the tangent planes of a surface are different at different points, so that the family of tangents to the surface is obviously a two-parameter one. But in some cases, for example, a cylinder, it is one parameter. It can be shown that the following remarkable theorem holds. A one-parameter family of tangent planes occurs only for those surfaces that are developable into a plane, i.e., those in which any sufficiently small segment may be deformed into a plane segment; these are the developable surfaces noted in §4. Every analytic surface of this kind consists of segments of straight lines and is either cylindrical (parallel straight lines) or conical (straight lines passing through one point), or consists of the tangents to some space curve.

The theory of envelopes is particularly useful in engineering problems, for example in the theory of transmissions. We consider two gears *A*

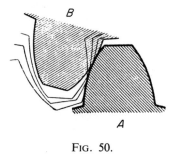

FIG. 50.

and *B*. To study their motion relative to each other, we may assume that gear *A* is stationary and gear *B* moves around it (figure 50). Then the contour of a cog on gear *B*, as it assumes various positions, traces out a family of curves in the plane of gear *A*, and the contour of gear *A* must at all times be tangent to them, i.e., must be the envelope of the family. Of course, this is not a complete statement of the situation, since in an actual transmission this engagement must be transferred from one pair of cogs to the next, but this condition is nevertheless the basic one which must be satisfied by every type of gear.

As we have said, the question of envelopes is a relatively simple one, solved long ago, in the theory of families of curves and surfaces. This theory is just as rich in interesting problems as, let us say, the theory of surfaces itself. Especially well developed is the theory of "congruences," i.e., two-parameter families of various curves (and in particular of straight lines: the so-called "straight-line" congruences). In this theory one applies essentially the same methods as in the theory of surfaces.

The theory of straight-line congruences originated in the paper of Monge, "On excavations and fills," the title of which already shows that

Monge undertook the investigation for practical purposes; the main idea was to find the most convenient way of transporting earth from an excavation to a fill.

The systematic development of the theory of congruences, beginning in the middle of the last century, is due in large measure to its connection with geometric optics; the set of rays of light in a homogeneous medium at any time constitutes a straight-line congruence.

Nonregular surfaces and geometry "in the large." The theory of curves and surfaces (and of families of them), as it had been constructed by the end of the last century, is usually called classical differential geometry; it has the following characteristic features.

First, it considers only "sufficiently smooth" (i.e., regular) curves and surfaces, namely those which are defined by functions with a sufficient number of derivatives. Thus, for example, surfaces with cusps or edges, such as polyhedral surfaces or the surface of a cone, are either excluded from the argument or are considered only on the parts where they remain smooth.

Second, classical differential geometry pays especial attention to properties of sufficiently small segments of curves and surfaces (geometry "in the small") and nowhere considers properties of an entire closed surface (geometry "in the large").

Typical examples, illustrating the distinction between geometry "in the small" and "in the large" are provided by the deformation of surfaces. For example, already in 1838 Minding showed that a sufficiently small segment of the surface of a sphere can be deformed, and this is a theorem "in the small." At the same time, he expressed the conjecture that the entire sphere cannot be deformed. This theorem was proved by other mathematicians as late as 1899. Incidentally, it is easy to confirm by experiment that a sphere of flexible but inextensible material cannot be deformed. For example, a ping-pong ball holds its shape perfectly well although the material it is made from is quite flexible. Another example, mentioned in §4, is the tin pail; it is rigid in the large, thanks to the presence of a curved flange, but separate pieces of it can easily be bent out of shape. As we see, there is an essential difference between properties of surfaces "in the small" and "in the large."

Other characteristic examples are provided by the theory of geodesics, discussed in §4. A geodesic "in the small," i.e., on a small segment of the surface, is a shortest path, but "in the large" it may not be so at all; for example, it may even be a closed curve, as was pointed out earlier for great circles of a sphere.

The reader will readily note that the theorems on geodesics formulated in §4 are basically theorems "in the small." Questions on the behavior of geodesic curves throughout their whole course will belong to geometry "in the large." It is known, for example, that on a regular surface two sufficiently adjacent points can be joined by a unique geodesic, remaining entirely in a certain small neighborhood of two points. But if we consider geodesics that during their course may depart as far as we like from the two points, then by a theorem of Morse any pair of points on a closed surface may be joined by an infinite number of geodesics. Thus, two points A and B on the lateral surface of a curved cylinder may be joined by very different geodesics: it is sufficient to consider helices which run from A to B but wind around the cylinder a different number of times. The theorem of Poincaré on closed geodesics, stated in §5 of Chapter XVIII, and proved by Ljusternik and Šnirelman, also belongs to geometry "in the large."

The proofs for these theorems, as for many theorems of geometry "in the large," were inaccessible with the usual tools of classical differential geometry and required the invention of new methods.

When these problems of geometry "in the large" were inevitably attracting the attention of mathematicians, the restriction to regular surfaces could no longer be maintained, if only because we are continually encountering surfaces that are not regular but have discontinuous curvature; for example, convex lenses with a sharp edge, and so forth. Moreover, there are many analytic surfaces that cannot be extended in any natural way without acquiring "singularities" in the form of edges or cusps and thus becoming nonregular.

Thus, a segment of the surface of a cone cannot be extended in a natural way without leading to the vertex, a cusp where the smoothness of the surface is destroyed.

This last result is only a particular case of the following remarkable theorem. Every developable surface other than a cylinder will lead, if naturally extended, to an edge (or a cusp in the case of a cone) beyond which it cannot be continued without losing its regularity.

Thus there is a profound connection between the behavior of a surface "in the large" and its singularities. This is the reason why the solution of problems "in the large" and the study of surfaces with "singularities" (edges, cusps, discontinuous curvature and the like) must be worked out together.

Similar new directions were taken in analysis. For example, the qualitative theory of differential equations mentioned in §7 of Chapter V, studies the properties of solutions of a differential equation in its entire domain of definition, i.e., "in the large," paying particular attention to "singularities," i.e., to violations of regularity, and to singular points of the equation. Moreover, contemporary analysis includes the study of nonregular functions which did not occur in classical analysis (cf. Chapter XV) and thereby provides geometry with a new means of studying more general surfaces. Finally, in the calculus of variations, where we are usually looking for curves or surfaces with some extremal property, it sometimes happens that the limit curve, for which the extreme is attained, is not regular. For such problems it is necessary that the class of curves or surfaces under consideration should be closed (that is, should include all its limit curves or surfaces), a fact which necessarily led to the study of at least the simplest nonregular curves and surfaces. In a word, the new directions taken by geometry did not originate in isolation but in close connection with the whole development of mathematics.

The turning of attention to problems "in the large" and nonregular surfaces began about 50 years ago and was shared by many mathematicians. The first essential step was taken by Hermann Minkowski (1864-1909), who laid the foundation for an extensive branch of geometry, the theory of convex bodies. Incidentally, one of the questions which started Minkowski on his investigations was the problem of regular lattices, which is closely connected with the theory of numbers and geometric crystallography.

A body is called *convex* if through each point of its surface we may pass a plane that does not intersect the body, i.e., at any point of its surface the body may rest on a plane (figure 51). A convex body is defined

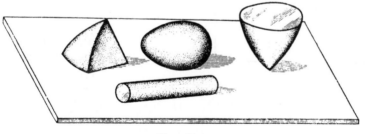

Fig. 51.

by its surface alone, so that for the most part it makes no difference whether we speak of the theory of convex bodies or of closed convex surfaces. The general theorems on convex bodies are proved, as a rule, without any additional assumptions about the smoothness or "regularity" of their surfaces. Thus these theorems are usually concerned with the whole convex body or surface, so that the restrictions of classical differential geometry are automatically removed. However, the two theories (of convex bodies and of nonregular surfaces) were at first very little connected with each other, the combination of the two taking place considerably later.

Beginning in 1940, A. D. Aleksandrov developed the theory of general curves and surfaces, including both the regular surfaces of classical differential geometry and also such nonsmooth surfaces as polyhedra, arbitrary convex sets, and others. In spite of the great generality of this theory, it is chiefly based on intuitive geometric concepts and methods, although it also makes essential use of contemporary analysis. One of the basic methods of the theory consists of approximating general surfaces by means of polyhedra (polyhedral surfaces). This device in its simplest form is known to every schoolboy, for example, in computing the area of the lateral surface of a cylinder as the limit of the areas of prisms. In a number of cases the method produces strong results that either cannot be derived in another way or else, if they are to be proved by an analytic method, require the introduction of complicated ideas. Its essential feature consists of the fact that the result is first obtained for polyhedra and is then extended to general surfaces by a limit process.

One of the beginnings of the theory of general convex surfaces was the theorem on the conditions under which a given evolute (cf. figure 52) may be pasted together to form a convex polyhedron. This theorem, completely elementary in its formulation, has a nonelementary proof and leads to far-reaching corollaries for general convex surfaces. The reader is, of course, familiar with the pasting together of a polyhedral surface from segments; for example, the assembling of a cube from the cross-shaped pattern in figure 52, or of a cylinder from a rectangle and two circles.

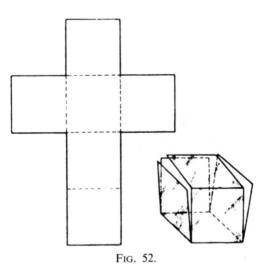

FIG. 52.

This simple example of assembling surfaces from segments of them is converted into a general method of "cutting apart and pasting together," which has produced profound results in various questions of the theory of surfaces and has found practical applications.

Deep-lying results in this theory were obtained by A. V. Pogorelov. In particular, he showed that every closed convex surface cannot be deformed as a whole with preservation of its convexity. This result, achieved in 1949, completes the efforts of many well-known mathematicians, who for the preceding 50 years had tried to prove it but had been successful only under various additional hypotheses. The results of Pogorelov, in conjunction with the "method of pasting together," not only provided a complete solution for the problem, but almost completely cleared up the whole question of the deformability or nondeformability of closed and nonclosed convex surfaces. They also established a close connection between the new theory and "classical" differential geometry.

In this way a theory of surfaces was constructed that included the classical theory as well as the theory of polyhedra, of arbitrary convex surfaces, and of very general nonconvex surfaces. Lack of space does not allow us to discuss in detail the results or the still unsolved problems of the theory, although this could readily be done, since they are for the most part quite easily visualized and, in spite of the difficulty of exact proofs, do not require any special knowledge.

In §4, in speaking of the deformation of surfaces, we had in mind deformations of a regular (continuously curved) surface that preserved its regularity. But in the theorem of Pogorelov, on the contrary, there is no requirement of regularity for either the initial or the deformed surface, although the requirement of convexity is imposed on both surfaces.

It is obvious that deformation of a sphere, for example, becomes possible if we allow breaks in the surface and violation of the convexity. It is sufficient to cut out a segment of the surface and then replace it after the deformation; that is, so to speak, to push a segment of the surface into the interior. Considerably more unexpected is the result obtained recently by the American mathematician Nash and the Dutch mathematician Kuiper. They showed that if we preserve only the smoothness of a surface and allow the appearance of any number of sharp jumps in the curvature of the surface (i.e., if we eliminate any requirement of continuity, boundedness, or even existence of the second derivatives of the functions defining the surface) then it turns out to be possible to deform the surface as a whole with a very great degree of arbitrariness. In particular a sphere may be deformed into an arbitrarily small ball, which has a smooth surface consisting of very shallow wavelike creases. Some idea of a deformation of this sort may be gained by the easily imagined possibility of rumpling up into almost any shape a spherical cover made of very soft cloth. On the other hand, a small celluloid ball behaves very differently. The elastic material of its surface resists not only extension but also sharp bending, so that such a ball is very rigid.

Differential geometry of various groups of transformations. At the beginning of this century, there arose from classical differential geometry a series of new developments based on one general idea, namely the study of properties of curves, surfaces, and families of curves and surfaces which remain invariant under various types of transformations. Classical differential geometry investigated properties invariant under translation; but of course there is nothing to prevent us from considering other geometric transformations. For example, a *projective transformation* is one in which straight lines remain straight, and projective geometry, which has been in existence for a long time, studies those properties of figures that remain invariant under projective transformations. Ordinary projective geometry remains similar, in the problems it investigates, to the usual elementary and analytic geometry, whereas "projective differential geometry" (the theory of curves, surfaces, and families developed at the beginning of the present century) is similar to classical differential geometry, except that it studies properties that are invariant under projective transformations. Fundamental in this last direction were the contributions of the American Wilczynski, the Italian Fubini, and the Czech mathematician, Čech.

In the same way arose "affine differential geometry," which studies the properties of curves, surfaces, and families invariant under affine transformations, i.e., under transformations that not only take straight lines into straight lines but also preserve parallelism. The work of the German mathematician Blaschke and his students developed this branch of geometry into a general theory. Let us also mention "conformal geometry," in which one studies the properties of figures invariant under transformations that do not change the angles between curves.

In general, the possible "geometries" are very diverse in character, since essentially any group of transformations may serve as the basis of a "geometry," which then studies just those properties of figures that are left unchanged by the transformations of the group. This principle for the definition of geometries will be discussed further in Chapter XVII.

Other new directions in differential geometry are being successfully developed by Soviet geometers, S. P. Finikov, G. F. Laptev, and others. But in our present outline it is not possible to give an account of all the various investigations that are taking place nowadays in the different branches of differential geometry.

Suggested Reading

H. Busemann, *Convex surfaces*, Interscience, New York, 1958.

H. S. M. Coxeter, *Introduction to geometry*, Wiley, New York, 1961.

H. G. Eggleston, *Convexity*, Cambridge University Press, New York, 1958.

D. Hilbert and S. Cohn-Vossen, *Geometry and the imagination*, Chelsea, New York, 1952.

I. M. Yaglom and V. G. Boltyanskiĭ, *Convex figures*, Holt, Rinehart and Winston, New York, 1961.

CHAPTER **VIII**

THE CALCULUS OF VARIATIONS

§1. Introduction

Examples of variational problems. We will be able to give a clearer description of the general range of problems studied in the calculus of variations,* if we first consider certain special problems.

1. The curve of fastest descent. The problem of the brachistochrone, or the curve of fastest descent, was historically the first problem in the development of the calculus of variations.

Among all curves connecting the points M_1 and M_2, it is required to find that one along which a mathematical point, moving under the force of gravity from M_1, with no initial velocity, arrives at the point M_2 in the least time.

To solve this problem we must consider all possible curves joining M_1 and M_2. If we choose a definite curve l, then to it will correspond some definite value T of the time taken for the descent of a material point along it. The time T will depend on the choice of l, and of all curves joining M_1 and M_2 we must choose the one which corresponds to the least value of T.

The problem of the brachistochrone may be expressed in the following way. We draw a vertical plane through the

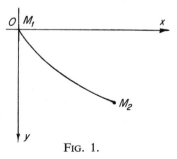

Fig. 1.

---

* The derivation of the name "calculus of variations" is explained later.

119

points M_1 and M_2. The curve of fastest descent must obviously lie in it, so that we may restrict ourselves to such curves. We take the point M_1 as the origin, the axis Ox horizontal, and the axis Oy vertical and directed downward (figure 1). The coordinates of the point M_1 will be $(0, 0)$; the coordinates of the point M_2 we will call (x_2, y_2). Let us consider an arbitrary curve described by the equation

$$y = f(x), \quad 0 \leqslant x \leqslant x_2, \tag{1}$$

where f is a continuously differentiable function. Since the curve passes through M_1 and M_2, the function f at the ends of the segment $[0, x_2]$ must satisfy the condition

$$f(0) = 0, \quad f(x_2) = y_2. \tag{2}$$

If we take an arbitrary point $M(x, y)$ on the curve, then the velocity v of a material point at this point of the curve will be connected with the y-coordinate of the point by the well-known physical relation

$$\tfrac{1}{2} v^2 = gy,$$

or

$$v = \sqrt{2gy}.$$

The time necessary for a material point to travel along an element ds of arc of the curve has the value

$$\frac{ds}{v} = \frac{\sqrt{1 + y'^2}}{\sqrt{2gy}}\, dx,$$

and thus the total time of the descent of the point along the curve from M_1 to M_2 is equal to

$$T = \frac{1}{\sqrt{2g}} \int_0^{x_2} \frac{\sqrt{1 + y'^2}}{\sqrt{y}}\, dx. \tag{3}$$

Finding the brachistochrone is equivalent to the solution of the following minimal problem: Among all possible functions (1) that satisfy conditions (2), find that one which corresponds to the least value of the integral (3).

2. The surface of revolution of the least area. Among the curves joining two points of a plane, it is required to find that one whose arc, by rotation around the axis Ox, generates the surface with the least area.

We denote the given points by $M_1(x_1, y_1)$ and $M_2(x_2, y_2)$ and consider an arbitrary curve given by the equation

$$y = f(x). \tag{4}$$

If the curve passes through M_1 and M_2, the function f will satisfy the condition

$$f(x_1) = y_1, \quad f(x_2) = y_2. \tag{5}$$

When rotated around the axis Ox this curve describes a surface with area numerically equal to the value of the integral

$$S = 2\pi \int_{x_1}^{x_2} y \sqrt{1 + y'^2}\, dx. \tag{6}$$

This value depends on the choice of the curve, or equivalently of the function $y = f(x)$. Among all functions (4) satisfying condition (5) we must find that function which gives the least value to the integral (6).

3. Uniform deformation of a membrane. By a membrane we usually mean an elastic surface that is plane in the state of rest, bends freely, and does work only against extension. We assume that the potential energy of a deformed membrane is proportional to the increase in the area of its surface.

In the state of rest let the membrane occupy a domain B of the Oxy plane (figure 2). We deform the boundary of the membrane in a direction perpendicular to Oxy and denote by $\phi(M)$ the displacement of the point M of the boundary. Then the interior of the membrane is also deformed, and we are required to find the position of equilibrium of the membrane for a given deformation of its boundary.

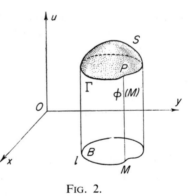

FIG. 2.

With a great degree of accuracy we may assume that all points of the membrane are displaced perpendicularly to the plane Oxy. We denote by $u(x, y)$ the displacement of the point (x, y). The area of the membrane in its displaced position will be*

$$\iint_B (1 + u_x^2 + u_y^2)^{1/2}\, dx\, dy.$$

---

* Here and everywhere in this chapter we use subscripts to denote the arguments with respect to which the partial derivatives are taken.

If the deformations of the elements of the membrane are so small that we can legitimately ignore higher powers of u_x and u_y, this expression for the area may be replaced by a simpler one:

$$\iint_B \left[1 + \frac{1}{2}(u_x^2 + u_y^2)\right] dx\, dy.$$

The change in the area of the membrane is equal to

$$\frac{1}{2}\iint_B (u_x^2 + u_y^2)\, dx\, dy;$$

so that the potential energy of the deformation will have the value

$$\frac{\mu}{2}\iint_B (u_x^2 + u_y^2)\, dx\, dy, \tag{7}$$

where μ is a constant depending on the elastic properties of the membrane.

Since the displacement of the points on the edge of the membrane is assumed to be given, the function $u(x, y)$ will satisfy the condition

$$u\,|_l = \phi(M) \tag{8}$$

on the boundary of the domain B.

In the position of equilibrium the potential energy of the deformation must have the smallest possible value, so that the function $u(x, y)$, describing the displacement of the points of the membrane, is to be found by solving the following mathematical problem: Among all functions $u(x, y)$ that are continuously differentiable on the domain B and satisfy condition (8) on the boundary, find the one which gives the least value to the integral (7).

Extreme values of functionals and the calculus of variations. These examples allow us to form some impression of the kind of problems considered, but to define exactly the position of the calculus of variations in mathematics, we must become acquainted with certain new concepts. We recall that one of the basic concepts of mathematical analysis is that of a function. In the simplest case the concept of functional dependence may be described as follows. Let M be any set of real numbers. If to every number x of the set M there corresponds a number y, we say that there is defined on the set M a function $y = f(x)$. The set M is often called the domain of definition of the function.

The concept of a functional is a direct and natural generalization of the concept of a function and includes it as a special case.

Let M be a set of objects of any kind. The nature of these objects is immaterial at this time. They may be numbers, points of a space, curves, functions, surfaces, states or even motions of a mechanical system. For brevity we will call them elements of the set M and denote them by the letter x.

If to every element x of the set M there corresponds a number y, we say that there is defined on the set M a functional $y = F(x)$.

If the set M is a set of numbers x, the functional $y = F(x)$ will be a function of one argument. When M is a set of pairs of numbers (x_1, x_2) or a set of points of a plane, the functional will be a function $y = F(x_1, x_2)$ of two arguments, and so forth.

For the functional $y = F(x)$, we state the following problem:

Among all elements x of M find that element for which the functional $y = F(x)$ has the smallest value.

The problem of the maximum of the functional is formulated in the same way.

We note that if we change the sign in the functional $F(x)$ and consider the functional $-F(x)$, the maximum (minimum) of $F(x)$ becomes the minimum (maximum) of $-F(x)$. So there is no need to study both maxima and minima; in what follows we will deal chiefly with minima of functionals.

In the problem of the curve of fastest descent, the functional whose minimum we seek will be the integral (3), the time of descent of a material point along a curve. This functional will be defined on all possible functions (1), satisfying condition (2).

In the problem of the position of equilibrium of a membrane, the functional is the potential energy (7) of the deformed membrane, and we must find its minimum on the set of functions $u(x, y)$ satisfying the boundary condition (8).

Every functional is defined by two factors: the set M of elements x on which it is given and the law by which every element x corresponds to a number, the value of the functional. The methods of seeking the least and greatest values of a functional will certainly depend on the properties of the set M.

The calculus of variations is a particular chapter in the theory of functionals. In it we consider functionals given on a set of functions, and our problem consists of the construction of a theory of extreme values for such functionals.

This branch of mathematics became particularly important after the discovery of its connection with many situations in physics and mechanics. The reason for this connection may be seen as follows. As will be made clear later, it is necessary, in order that a function provide an extreme value for a functional, that it satisfy a certain differential equation. On the other hand, as was mentioned in the chapters describing differential equations, the quantitative laws of mechanics and physics are often written in the form of differential equations. As it turned out, many equations of this type also occurred among the differential equations of the calculus of variations. So it became possible to consider the equations of mechanics and physics as extremal conditions for suitable functionals and to state the laws of physics in the form of requiring an extreme value, in particular a minimum, for certain quantities. New points of view could thus be introduced into mechanics and physics, since certain laws could be replaced by equivalent statements in terms of "minimal principles." This in turn opened up a new method of solving physical problems, either exactly or approximately, by seeking the minima of corresponding functionals.

§2. The Differential Equations of the Calculus of Variations

The Euler differential equation.   The reader will recall that a necessary condition for the existence of an extreme value of a differentiable function f at a point x is that the derivative f' be equal to zero at this point: $f'(x) = 0$; or what amounts to the same thing, that the differential of the function be equal to zero here: $df = f'(x) \, dx = 0$.

Our immediate goal will be to find an analogue of this condition in the calculus of variations, that is to say, to set up a necessary condition that a function must satisfy in order to provide an extreme value for a functional.

We will show that such a function must satisfy a certain differential equation. The form of the equation will depend on the kind of functional under consideration. We begin with the so-called simplest integral of the calculus of variations, by which we mean a functional with the following integral representation:

$$I(y) = \int_{x_1}^{x_2} F(x, y, y') \, dx. \tag{9}$$

The function F, occuring under the integral sign, depends on three arguments (x, y, y'). We will assume it is defined and is twice continuously differentiable with respect to the argument y' for all values of this argument, and with respect to the arguments x and y in some domain B of the Oxy plane. Below it is assumed that we always remain in the interior of this domain.

It is clear that y is a function of x

$$y = y(x), \qquad (10)$$

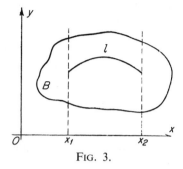

continuously differentiable on the segment $x_1 \leqslant x \leqslant x_2$, and that y' is its derivative.

Geometrically the function $y(x)$ may be represented on the Oxy plane by a curve l over the interval $[x_1, x_2]$ (figure 3).

The integral (9) is a generalization of the integrals (3) and (6), which we

Fig. 3.

encountered in the problem of the curve of fastest descent and the surface of revolution of least area. Its value depends on the choice of the function $y(x)$ or in other words of the curve l, and the problem of its minimum value is to be interpreted as follows:

Given some set M of functions (10) (curves l); among these we must find that function (curve l) for which the integral $I(y)$ has the least value.

We must first of all define exactly the set of functions M for which we will consider the value of the integral (9). In the calculus of variations the functions of this set are usually called admissible for comparison. We consider the problem with fixed boundary values. The set of admissible functions is defined here by the following two requirements:

1. $y(x)$ is continuously differentiable on the segment $[x_1, x_2]$;

2. At the ends of the segment $y(x)$ has values given in advance

$$y(x_1) = y_1, \quad y(x_2) = y_2. \qquad (11)$$

Otherwise the function $y(x)$ may be completely arbitrary. In the language of geometry, we are considering all possible smooth curves over the interval $[x_1, x_2]$, which pass through the two points $A(x_1, y_1)$ and $B(x_2, y_2)$ and can be represented by the equation (10). The function giving the minimum of the integral will be assumed to exist and we will call it $y(x)$.

The following simple and ingenious arguments, which can often be applied in the calculus of variations, lead to a particularly simple form of the necessary condition which $y(x)$ must satisfy. In essence they allow us to reduce the problem of the minimum of the integral (9) to the problem of the minimum of a function.

We consider the family of functions dependent on a numerical parameter α,

$$\bar{y}(x) = y(x) + \alpha\eta(x). \qquad (12)$$

In order that $\bar{y}(x)$ be an admissible function for arbitrary α, we must assume that $\eta(x)$ is continuously differentiable and vanishes at the ends of the interval $[x_1, x_2]$.

$$\eta(x_1) = \eta(x_2) = 0. \tag{13}$$

The integral (9) computed for $\bar{y}$ will be a function of the parameter α

$$I(\bar{y}) = \int_{x_1}^{x_2} F(x, y + \alpha\eta, y' + \alpha\eta') \, dx = \Phi(\alpha).*$$

Since $y(x)$ gives a minimum to the value of the integral, the function $\Phi(\alpha)$ must have a minimum for $\alpha = 0$, so that its derivative at this point must vanish

$$\Phi'(0) = \int_{x_1}^{x_2} [F_y(x, y, y') \, \eta + F_{y'}(x, y, y') \, \eta'] \, dx = 0. \tag{14}$$

This last equation must be satisfied for every continuously differentiable function $\eta(x)$ which vanishes at the ends of the segment $[x_1, x_2]$. In order to obtain the result which follows from this, it is convenient to transform the second term in condition (14) by integration by parts

$$\int_{x_1}^{x_2} F_{y'}\eta' \, dx = -\int_{x_1}^{x_2} \eta \frac{d}{dx} F_{y'} \, dx$$

so that condition (14) takes the new form

$$\Phi'(0) = \int_{x_1}^{x_2} \left(F_y - \frac{d}{dx} F_{y'}\right) \eta \, dx = 0. \tag{15}$$

It may be shown that the following simple lemma holds.

Let the following two conditions be fulfilled:

1. The function $f(x)$ is continuous on the interval $[a, b]$;

2. The function $\eta(x)$ is continuously differentiable on the interval $[a, b]$ and vanishes at the ends of this interval.

If for an arbitrary function $\eta(x)$ the integral $\int_a^b f(x) \, \eta(x) \, dx$ is equal to zero, then it follows that $f(x) \equiv 0$.

---

* The difference $\bar{y} - y = \alpha\eta$ is called the *variation* (change) *of the function y* and is denoted by δy, and the difference $I(\bar{y}) - I(y)$ is called the *total variation of the integral* (9). Hence we get the name calculus of variations.

For let us assume that at some point c the function f is different from zero and show that then a function $\eta(x)$ necessarily exists for which $\int_a^b f(x)\,\eta(x)\,dx \neq 0$, in contradiction to the condition of the lemma.

Since $f(c) \neq 0$ and f is continuous, there must exist a neighborhood $[\alpha, \beta]$ of c in which f will be everywhere different from zero and thus will have a constant sign throughout.

We can always construct a function $\eta(x)$ which is continuously differentiable on $[a, b]$, positive on $[\alpha, \beta]$, and equal to zero outside of $[\alpha, \beta]$ (figure 4).

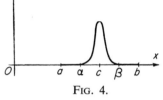

FIG. 4.

Such a function $\eta(x)$, for example, is defined by the equations

$$\eta(x) = \begin{cases} 0 & \text{on } [a, \alpha], \\ (x - \alpha)^2(\beta - x)^2 & \text{on } [\alpha, \beta], \\ 0 & \text{on } [\beta, b]. \end{cases}$$

But for such a function $\eta(x)$

$$\int_a^b f\eta \, dx = \int_a^\beta f\eta \, dx.$$

The latter of these integrals cannot be equal to zero since, in the interior of the interval of integration, the product $f\eta$ is different from zero and never changes its sign.

Since equation (15) must be satisfied for every $\eta(x)$ that is continuously differentiable and vanishes at the ends of the segment $[x_1, x_2]$, we may assert, on the basis of the lemma, that this can occur only in the case

$$F_y - \frac{d}{dx} F_{y'} = 0, \tag{16}$$

or, by computing the derivative with respect to x

$$F_y(x, y, y') - F_{xy'}(x, y, y') - F_{yy'}(x, y, y')y' - F_{y'y'}(x, y, y')y'' = 0. \tag{17}$$

This equation is a differential equation of the second order with respect to the function y. It is called *Euler's equation.*

We may state the following conclusion.

If a function $y(x)$ minimizes the integral $I(y)$, then it must satisfy Euler's differential equation (17). In the calculus of variations, this last statement has a meaning completely analogous to the necessary condition

$df = 0$ in the theory of extreme values of functions. It allows us immediately to exclude all admissible functions that do not satisfy this condition, since for them the integral cannot have a minimum, so that the set of admissible functions we need to study is very sharply reduced.

Solutions of equation (17) have the property that for them the derivative $[(d/d\alpha)I(y + \alpha\eta)]_{\alpha=0}$ vanishes for arbitrary $\eta(x)$, so that they are analogous in meaning to the stationary points of a function. Thus it is often said that for solutions of (17) the integral $I(y)$ has a stationary value.

In our problem with fixed boundary values, we do not need to find all solutions of the Euler equation but only those which take on the values y_1, y_2 at the points x_1, x_2.

We turn our attention to the fact that the Euler equation (17) is of the second order. Its general solution will contain two arbitrary constants

$$y = \phi(x, C_1, C_2).$$

These must be defined so that the integral curve passes through the points A and B, so we have the two equations for finding the constants C_1 and C_2

$$\phi(x_1, C_1, C_2) = y_1, \quad \phi(x_2, C_1, C_2) = y_2.$$

In many cases this system has only one solution and then there will exist only one integral curve passing through A and B.

The search for functions giving a minimum for this integral is thus reduced to the solution of the following boundary-value problem for differential equations: On the interval $[x_1, x_2]$ find those solutions of equation (17) that have the given values y_1, y_2 at the ends of the interval.

Frequently this last problem can be solved by using known methods in the theory of differential equations.

We emphasize again that every solution of such a boundary-value problem can provide only a suspected minimum and that it is necessary to verify whether or not it actually does give a minimum value to the integral. But in particular cases, especially in those occurring in the applications, Euler's equation completely solves the problem of finding the minimum of the integral. Suppose we know initially that a function giving a minimum for the integral exists, and assume, moreover, that the Euler equation (17) has only one solution satisfying the boundary conditions (11). Then only one of the admissible curves can be a suspected minimum, and we may be sure, under these circumstances, that the solution found for the equation (17) indeed gives a minimum for the integral.

Example. It was previously established that the problem of the curve of fastest descent may be reduced to finding the minimum of the integral

$$I(y) = \int_0^{x_2} \frac{\sqrt{1 + y'^2}}{\sqrt{y}}\, dx$$

among the set of functions satisfying the boundary conditions

$$y(0) = 0, \quad y(x_2) = y_2 .$$

In this problem

$$F = \frac{\sqrt{1 + y'^2}}{\sqrt{y}} .$$

Euler's equation has the form

$$-\frac{1}{2} y^{-3/2} \sqrt{1 + y'^2} - \frac{d}{dx} \left[y^{-1/2} \frac{y'}{\sqrt{1 + y'^2}} \right] = 0.$$

After some manipulation it takes the form

$$\frac{2y''}{1 + y'^2} = -\frac{1}{y}.$$

Multiplying both sides of the equation by y' and integrating, we get

$$\ln(1 + y'^2) = -\ln y + \ln k,$$

or

$$y'^2 = \frac{k}{y} - 1,$$

$$\sqrt{\frac{y}{k - y}}\, dy = \pm\, dx.$$

Now letting

$$y = \frac{k}{2}(1 - \cos u), \quad dy = \frac{k}{2} \sin u\, du,$$

we find after substituting and simplifying

$$\frac{k}{2}(1 - \cos u)\, du = \pm\, dx,$$

from which, by integrating, we get: $x = \pm\, k/2\, (u - \sin u) + C$. Since the curve must pass through the origin, it follows that we must put $C = 0$.

In this way we see that the brachistochrone is the cycloid

$$x = \frac{k}{2}(u - \sin u), \quad y = \frac{k}{2}(1 - \cos u).$$

The constant k must be found from the condition that this curve passes through the point $M_2(x_2, y_2)$.

Functionals depending on several functions.   The simplest functional in the calculus of variations (17) depended on only one function. In the applications such functionals will occur in those cases where the objects (or their behavior) are defined by only one functional dependence. For example, a curve in the plane is defined by the dependence of the ordinate of a point on its abscissa, the motion of a material point along an axis is defined by the dependence of its coordinate on time, etc.

But we must often deal with objects that cannot be defined so simply. In order to define a curve in space, we must know the functional dependence of two of its coordinates on the third. The motion of a point in space is defined by the dependence of its three coordinates on time, etc. Study of these more complicated objects leads to variational problems with several varying functions.

We will restrict ourselves to cases in which the functional depends on two functions $y(x)$ and $z(x)$, since the case of a larger number of functions does not differ in principle from this one.

We consider the following problem. Admissible pairs of functions $y(x)$ and $z(x)$ are defined by the conditions:

1. The functions

$$y = y(x), \quad z = z(x) \tag{18}$$

are continuously differentiable on the segment $[x_1, x_2]$;

2. At the ends of the segment these functions have given values

$$y(x_1) = y_1, \quad y(x_2) = y_2,$$
$$z(x_1) = z_1, \quad z(x_2) = z_2. \tag{19}$$

Among all possible pairs of functions $y(x)$ and $z(x)$, we must find the pair that gives the least value to the integral

$$I(y, z) = \int_{x_1}^{x_2} F(x, y, z, y', z')\, dx. \tag{20}$$

In the three-dimensional space x, y, z, each pair of admissible functions will correspond to a curve l, defined by equations (18) and passing through the points

$$M_1(x_1, y_1, z_1), \quad M_2(x_2, y_2, z_2).$$

We must find the minimum of the integral (20) on the set of all such curves.

We assume that the pair of functions giving the minimum of the integral (20) exists, and we will call these functions $y(x)$ and $z(x)$. Together with them we consider a second pair of functions

$$\bar{y} = y + \alpha\eta(x), \quad \bar{z} = z + \alpha\zeta(x),$$

where $\eta(x)$ and $\zeta(x)$ are any continuously differentiable functions vanishing at the ends x_1, x_2 of the segment; $\bar{y}$, $\bar{z}$ will also be admissible, and for $\alpha = 0$ they will coincide with the functions y, z. We substitute them in (20)

$$I(\bar{y}, \bar{z}) = \int_{x_1}^{x_2} F(x, y + \alpha\eta, z + \alpha\zeta, y' + \alpha\eta', z' + \alpha\zeta')\, dx = \Phi(\alpha).$$

The integral so derived will be a function of α. Since $\bar{y}$ and $\bar{z}$ coincide with y and z when $\alpha = 0$, the function $\Phi(\alpha)$ must have a minimum for $\alpha = 0$. But at a minimum point the derivative of Φ must vanish

$$\Phi'(0) = 0.$$

Computing the derivative gives

$$\int_{x_1}^{x_2} (F_y \cdot \eta + F_z \cdot \zeta + F_{y'} \cdot \eta' + F_{z'} \cdot \zeta')\, dx = 0,$$

or, if the terms in η' and ζ' are integrated by parts

$$\int_{x_1}^{x_2} \left[\left(F_y - \frac{d}{dx} F_{y'} \right) \eta(x) + \left(F_z - \frac{d}{dx} F_{z'} \right) \zeta(x) \right] dx = 0.$$

This last equation must be satisfied for any two continuously differentiable functions $\eta(x)$ and $\zeta(x)$ vanishing at the ends of the interval. Hence, from the basic lemma proved earlier, the following two conditions must be fulfilled:

$$F_y - \frac{d}{dx} F_{y'} = 0,$$

$$F_z - \frac{d}{dx} F_{z'} = 0. \tag{21}$$

Hence, if the functions y, z give a minimum for the integral (20), they must satisfy the system of Euler differential equations (21).

This result again allows us to replace a variational problem for the minimum of the integral (20) by a boundary-value problem in the theory of differential equations: On the interval $[x_1, x_2]$, we must find those solutions y, z of the system of differential equations (21) that satisfy the boundary conditions (19).

As in the preceding case, this opens up a possible path for the solution of the minimal problem.

As an example of an application of the Euler system (21), let us consider the variational principle of Ostrogradskiĭ-Hamilton in Newtonian mechanics. We restrict ourselves to the simplest form of this principle.

We consider a material body of mass m and assume that the dimensions and form of the body may be ignored, so that we may consider it as a material point.

We assume that the point moves from its position $M_1(x_1, y_1, z_1)$ at time t_1 to the position $M_2(x_2, y_2, z_2)$ at time t_2. We also assume that the motion occurs under the laws of Newtonian mechanics and is caused by application of a force $F(x, y, z, t)$ which depends on the position of the point and on the time t and possesses a potential function $U(x, y, z, t)$. This last condition means the following: the components F_x, F_y, F_z of the force F along the coordinate axes are the partial derivatives of a function U with respect to the corresponding coordinates

$$F_x = \frac{\partial U}{\partial x}, \quad F_y = \frac{\partial U}{\partial y}, \quad F_z = \frac{\partial U}{\partial z}.$$

We assume the motion to be free, that is, not subject to any kind of constraints.*

The equations of motion of Newton are

$$m\frac{d^2x}{dt^2} = \frac{\partial U}{\partial x}, \quad m\frac{d^2y}{dt^2} = \frac{\partial U}{\partial y}, \quad m\frac{d^2z}{dt^2} = \frac{\partial U}{\partial z}.$$

If the point obeys the laws of Newtonian mechanics, it moves in a completely determined manner. But together with these "Newtonian motions" of the point, let us consider other (non-Newtonian) motions, which for brevity we will call "admissible," and which will be defined by two requirements only, that at time t_1 the point is in the position M_1 and at time t_2 is in the position M_2.

How can we distinguish the "Newtonian motion" of the point from these other "admissible" motions? Such a possibility is given by the Ostrogradskiĭ-Hamilton principle.

We introduce the kinetic energy of the point

$$T = \tfrac{1}{2}m(x'^2 + y'^2 + z'^2)$$

---

* This is not essential for the Ostrogradskiĭ-Hamilton principle: We may impose any restraints we like on the mechanical system, even nonstationary ones, provided only that they are holonomic, i.e., that they may be described in the form of equations not containing derivatives of the coordinates with respect to time.

and form the so-called action integral

$$I = \int_{t_1}^{t_2} (T + U)\, dt.$$

The principle states: The "Newtonian motion" of the point is distinguished among all its "admissible" motions by the fact that it gives the action integral a stationary value.

The action integral I depends on three functions: $x(t)$, $y(t)$, $z(t)$.

Since for all the motions under comparison the initial and final positions of the point are identical, the boundary values of these functions are fixed. We are dealing here with a variational problem for three varying functions with fixed values at the ends of the interval $[t_1, t_2]$.

Previously we agreed to say that the integral (17) has a stationary value for any curve which is an integral curve of the Euler equation. In our problem we are integrating a function

$$F = T + U = \tfrac{1}{2}m(x'^2 + y'^2 + z'^2) + U(x, y, z, t)$$

which depends on three functions, so that for a stationary value of the integral we must satisfy the system of three differential equations

$$F_x - \frac{d}{dt} F_{x'} = 0,$$

$$F_y - \frac{d}{dt} F_{y'} = 0,$$

$$F_z - \frac{d}{dt} F_{z'} = 0.$$

Since $F_x = \partial U/\partial x$, $F_{x'} = mx'$, $\cdots$, the system of Euler equations is identical with the equations of motion of Newtonian mechanics, which provides a verification of the Ostrogradskiĭ-Hamilton principle.

The minimum problem for a multiple integral. The last problem in the calculus of variations to which we wish to draw the attention of the reader is the problem of minimizing a multiple integral. Since the facts connected with the solution of such problems are similar for integrals of any multiplicity, we will confine ourselves to the simplest case, that of double integrals.

Let B be a domain in the Oxy plane, bounded by the contour l. The set of admissible functions is defined by the conditions:

1. $u(x, y)$ is continuously differentiable on the domain B,

2. On l the function u takes given values

$$u\,|_l = f(M). \tag{22}$$

Among all functions we must find the one which gives a minimum value for the integral

$$I(u) = \iint_B F(x, y, u, u_x, u_y) \, dx \, dy. \tag{23}$$

The given boundary values (22) for the function u in the space (x, y, u) determine a given space curve Γ, lying above l (cf. figure 2, Chapter VII).

We consider all possible surfaces S passing through Γ and lying above B. Among these we want to find the one for which the integral (23) is minimal.

As before, we assume the existence of the minimizing function and denote it by u. At the same time we consider another function

$$\bar{u} = u + \alpha\eta(x, y),$$

where $\eta(x, y)$ is any continuously differentiable function vanishing on l. Then the function

$$I(\bar{u}) = \iint_B F(x, y, u + \alpha\eta, u_x + \alpha\eta_x, u_y + \alpha\eta_y) \, dx \, dy = \Phi(\alpha)$$

must have a minimum for $\alpha = 0$. In this case its first derivative must be equal to zero for $\alpha = 0$

$$\Phi'(0) = 0,$$

or

$$\iint_B (F_u\eta + F_{u_x}\eta_x + F_{u_y}\eta_y) \, dx \, dy = 0. \tag{24}$$

We transform the last two terms by Ostrogradskiĭ's formula

$$\iint_B (F_{u_x}\eta_x + F_{u_y}\eta_y) \, dx \, dy$$

$$= \iint_B \left[\frac{\partial}{\partial x}(F_{u_x}\eta) + \frac{\partial}{\partial y}(F_{u_y}\eta)\right] dx \, dy - \iint_B \left(\frac{\partial}{\partial x}F_{u_x} + \frac{\partial}{\partial y}F_{u_y}\right)\eta \, dx \, dy$$

$$= \int_l [F_{u_x}\cos(n, x) + F_{u_y}\cos(n, y)]\eta \, ds$$

$$- \iint_B \left(\frac{\partial}{\partial x}F_{u_x} + \frac{\partial}{\partial y}F_{u_y}\right)\eta \, dx \, dy.$$

The contour integral along l must vanish, since on the contour l the function η is equal to zero, so that condition (24) may be put in the form

$$\iint_B \left(F_u - \frac{\partial}{\partial x}F_{u_x} - \frac{\partial}{\partial y}F_{u_y}\right)\eta \, dx \, dy = 0.$$

This equation must be satisfied for every function η which is continuously differentiable and vanishes on the boundary l.

We may conclude, as before, that all points of the domain B the equation

$$F_u - \frac{\partial}{\partial x} F_{u_x} - \frac{\partial}{\partial y} F_{u_y} = 0 \tag{25}$$

must be satisfied.

So if the function u gives a minimum for the integral (23), it must satisfy the partial differential equation (25).

As in all the preceding problems, we have here established a connection between a variational problem of minimizing an integral and a boundary-value problem for a differential equation (in this case partial).

Example. The displacement $u(x, y)$ of points of a membrane with a deformed boundary is to be found from the condition of the minimum of the potential energy

$$\frac{\mu}{2} \iint\limits_{B} (u_x^2 + u_y^2) \, dx \, dy$$

for the given boundary values $u \mid_l, = \phi$.

Omitting, for simplicity, the constant factor μ, we may set

$$F = \frac{1}{2} (u_x^2 + u_y^2),$$

so that equation (25) has the form

$$-\frac{\partial}{\partial x} u_x - \frac{\partial}{\partial y} u_y = 0,$$

or

$$\Delta u = \frac{\partial^2 u}{\partial x^2} + \frac{\partial^2 u}{\partial y^2} = 0.$$

Thus the problem of determining the displacement of the points of a membrane has been reduced to that of finding a harmonic function u with given values on the boundary of the domain (cf. Chapter VI, §3).

§3. Methods of Approximate Solution of Problems in the Calculus of Variations

We conclude the present chapter with an indication of the ideas involved in some of the approximation methods in the calculus of variations.

For definiteness we discuss the simplest functional

$$I(y) = \int_{x_1}^{x_2} F(x, y, y')\, dx$$

for fixed boundary values of the admissible functions.

Let $y(x)$ be an exact solution of the problem of minimizing I, with $m = I(y)$ the corresponding minimal value of the integral. It would appear that if we determine an admissible function $\bar{y}$ for which the value of the integral $I(\bar{y})$ is very near to m, we may assume that $\bar{y}$ will also differ little from the exact solution y. Moreover, if we are able to construct a sequence of admissible functions $\bar{y}_1, \bar{y}_2, \cdots$ for which $I(\bar{y}_n) \to m$, we may expect that such a sequence will converge in some sense or other to the solution y, so that computation of $\bar{y}_n$ with sufficiently large index will allow us to find the solution to any desired degree of accuracy.

Depending on how we go about choosing the "minimizing sequence" $\bar{y}_n(n = 1, 2, \cdots)$, we will have one or another of the various approximation methods in the calculus of variations.

Historically, the first of these was the method of broken lines, or Euler's method. We decompose the interval $[x_1, x_2]$ into a number of segments. For example, if we choose these segments of equal length, the points of division will be

$$x_1,\, x_1 + h,\, x_1 + 2h,\, \cdots,\, x_1 + nh = x_2,\, h = \frac{x_2 - x_1}{n}.$$

We now construct the broken line p_{n-1} with vertices lying above the points of division. The ordinates of the vertices we denote by

$$b_0,\, b_1,\, b_2,\, \cdots,\, b_{n-1},\, b_n$$

and require that this broken line begin and end at the same points as the admissible curves, so that $b_0 = y_1$ and $b_n = y_2$. Then the broken line will be defined by the ordinates

$$b_1,\, b_2,\, \cdots,\, b_{n-1}.$$

The question now is to find out how to choose the broken line p_{n-1} (i.e., the ordinates b_i of its vertices) so as to approximate as closely as possible the exact solution of the problem.

To achieve this object it is natural to proceed as follows. We compute the integral I for the broken line. Its value will depend on the b_i

$$I(p_{n-1}) = \Phi(b_1,\, b_2,\, \cdots,\, b_{n-1})$$

and will therefore be a function of these ordinates. We now choose the b_i so that they give $I(p_{n-1})$ a minimum value. To define these b_i we will have the system of equations

$$\frac{\partial}{\partial b_i} I(p_{n-1}) = 0 \quad (i = 1, 2, \cdots, n - 1).$$

Since any admissible curve, and in particular the exact solution of the problem, may be approximated by broken lines with any desired accuracy, both in its position on the plane and in the directions of its tangents, it is clear that the sequence of broken lines p_{n-1} thus constructed will, in fact, be a minimizing sequence. By taking n sufficiently large, we may expect to approximate the solution with any desired degree of accuracy over the whole interval $[x_1, x_2]$. Of course, the fact of convergence must be investigated in each case.

The following method, which is very convenient for calculation, is widely used in physics and technology.

We choose any function $\phi_0(x)$ satisfying the boundary conditions $\phi_0(x_1) = y_1$ and $\phi_0(x_2) = y_2$, and a sequence of functions $\phi_1(x), \phi_2(x), \cdots,$ vanishing at the ends of the interval $[x_1, x_2]$.

We then form the linear combination

$$s_n(x) = \phi_0(x) + a_1\phi_1(x) + \cdots + a_n\phi_n(x).$$

For arbitrary values of the numerical coefficients $a_1, a_2, \cdots, a_n$, the function $s_n(x)$ will be admissible.

Replacing y by $s_n(x)$ in the integral I and making the necessary computations, we obtain a certain function of the coefficients a_i.

We now choose the a_i so that this function has the least possible value. The coefficients must be found from the system

$$\frac{\partial}{\partial a_i} I(s_n) = 0 \quad (i = 1, 2, \cdots, n).$$

Solving this system, we obtain, in general, the values of the coefficients $a_1, \cdots, a_n$ producing a minimum value for $I(s_n)$ and with them we construct an approximation to the solution

$$\bar{s}_n(x) = \phi_0(x) + \bar{a}_1\phi_1(x) + \cdots + \bar{a}_n\phi_n(x).$$

The sequence of approximations $\bar{s}_n$ ($n = 1, 2, \cdots$) constructed in this way will not be a minimizing sequence for arbitrary choice of the functions ϕ_i. The necessary condition for it to be so is that the sequence of functions ϕ_i satisfy a certain condition of "completeness" which we will not define here.

Suggested Reading

G. A. Bliss, *Calculus of variations*, Open Court, La Salle, Ill., 1925.

C. Lanczos, *The variational principles of mechanics*, University of Toronto Press, 1949.

G. Pólya and G. Szegö, *Isoperimetric inequalities in mathematical physics*, Princeton University Press, 1951.

R. Weinstock, *Calculus of variations, with applications to physics and engineering*, McGraw-Hill, New York, 1952.

CHAPTER IX

FUNCTIONS
OF A COMPLEX VARIABLE

§1. Complex Numbers and Functions of a Complex Variable

Complex numbers and their significance in algebra. Complex numbers were introduced into mathematics in connection with the solution of algebraic equations. The impossibility of solving the algebraic equation

$$x^2 + 1 = 0 \tag{1}$$

in the domain of real numbers led to the introduction of a conventional number, the imaginary unit i, defined by the equation

$$i^2 = -1. \tag{2}$$

Numbers of the form $a + bi$, where a and b are real numbers, were called *complex numbers*. These numbers were manipulated like real numbers, being added and multiplied as binomials. If we also make use of equation (2), the basic operations of arithmetic when carried out on complex numbers produce other complex numbers.* The division of complex numbers being defined as the inverse of multiplication, it turns out that this operation also is uniquely defined, provided only that the denominator is not equal to zero. In this manner, the introduction of complex numbers first brought to light the interesting, though for the time being purely formal, fact that in addition to the real numbers there exist other numbers, the complex ones, on which all the arithmetic operations can be performed.

---

* Complex numbers are known to the reader from secondary school. See also Chapter IV, §3.

The next step consists of the geometric representation of complex numbers. Every complex number $a + bi$ may be represented by a point in the Oxy plane with coordinates (a, b), or by a vector issuing from the origin to the point (a, b). This led to a new point of view concerning complex numbers. Complex numbers are pairs (a, b) of real numbers for which there are established definitions of the operations of addition and multiplication, obeying the same laws as for real numbers. Here we discover a remarkable situation: The sum of two complex numbers

$$(a + bi) + (c + di) = (a + c) + (b + d)i$$

is represented geometrically by the diagonal of the parallelogram constructed from the vectors representing the summands (figure 1). In this way, complex numbers are added by the same law as the vector quantities found in mechanics and physics: forces, velocities, and accelerations. This was a further reason for considering that complex numbers are not merely formal generalizations but may be used to represent actual physical quantities.

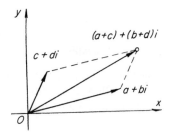

FIG. 1.

We will see later how this point of view is very successful in various problems of mathematical physics.

However, the introduction of complex numbers had its first successes in the discovery of the laws of algebra and analysis. The domain of real numbers, closed with respect to arithmetic operations, was seen to be not sufficiently extensive for algebra. Even such a simple equation as (1) does not have a root in the domain of real numbers, but for complex numbers we have the following remarkable fact, the so-called fundamental theorem of algebra: Every algebraic equation

$$z^n + a_1 z^{n-1} + \cdots + a_{n-1}z + a_n = 0$$

with complex coefficients has n complex roots.*

This theorem shows that the complex numbers form a system of numbers which, in a well-known sense, is complete with respect to the operations of algebra. It is not at all trivial that adjoining to the domain of real numbers a root of the single equation (1) leads to the numbers $a + bi$ in whose domain any algebraic equation is solvable. The fundamental theorem of algebra showed that the theory of polynomials, even

---

* Cf. Chapter IV, §3.

with real coefficients, may be given a finished form only when we consider the values of the polynomial in the whole complex plane. The further development of the theory of algebraic polynomials supported this point of view more and more. The properties of polynomials are discovered only by considering them as functions of a complex variable.

Power series and functions of a complex variable. The development of analysis brought to light a series of facts showing that the introduction of complex numbers was significant not only in the theory of polynomials but also for another very important class of functions, namely those which are expandable in a power series

$$f(x) = a_0 + a_1(x - a) + a_2(x - a)^2 + \cdots. \tag{3}$$

As was already mentioned in Chapter II, the development of the infinitesimal analysis required the establishment of a more precise point of view for the concept of a function and for the various possibilities of defining functions in mathematics. Without pausing here to discuss these interesting questions, we recall only that at the very beginning of the development of analysis it turned out that the most frequently encountered functions could be expanded in a power series in the neighborhood of every point in their domain of definition. For example, this property holds for all the so-called *elementary functions*.

The majority of the concrete problems of analysis led to functions that are expandable in power series. On the other hand, there was a desire to connect the definition of a "mathematical" function with a "mathematical" formula, and the power series represented a very inclusive kind of "mathematical" formula. This situation even led to serious attempts to restrict analysis to the study of functions that are expandable in power series and thus are called *analytic functions*. The development of science showed that such a restriction is inexpedient. The problems of mathematical physics began to extend beyond the class of analytic functions, which does not even include, for example, functions represented by curves with a sharp corner. However, the class of analytic functions, in view of its remarkable properties and numerous applications, proved to be the most important of all the classes of functions studied by mathematicians.

Since the computation of each term of a power series requires only arithmetic operations, the values of a function represented by a power series may be computed also for complex values of the argument, at least for those values for which the series is convergent. When we thus extend the definition of a function of a real variable to complex arguments, we speak of the "continuation" of the function into the complex domain.

Thus an analytic function, in the same way as a polynomial, may be considered not only for real values of the argument but also for complex. Further, we may also consider power series with complex coefficients. The properties of analytic functions, as also of polynomials, are fully revealed only when they are considered in the complex domain. To illustrate we turn now to an example.

Consider the two functions of a real variable

$$e^x \quad \text{and} \quad \frac{1}{1 + x^2} \, .$$

Both these functions are finite, continuous, and differentiable an arbitrary number of times on the whole axis Ox. They may be expanded in a Taylor series, for example, around the origin $x = 0$

$$e^x = 1 + \frac{x}{1!} + \frac{x^2}{2!} + \cdots, \tag{4}$$

$$\frac{1}{1 + x^2} = 1 - x^2 + x^4 - x^6 + \cdots. \tag{5}$$

The first of the series so obtained converges for all values of x, while the second series converges only for $-1 < x < +1$. Consideration of the function (5) for real values of the argument does not show why its Taylor series diverges for $|x| \geqslant 1$. Passing to the complex domain allows us to clear up the situation. We consider the series (5) for complex values of the argument

$$1 - z^2 + z^4 - z^6 + \cdots. \tag{6}$$

The sum of n terms of this series

$$s_n = 1 - z^2 + z^4 - z^6 + \cdots + (-1)^{n-1} z^{2n-2}$$

is computed in the same way as for real values of z:

$$s_n + z^2 s_n = 1 + (-1)^n z^{2n},$$

hence

$$s_n = \frac{1 + (-1)^n z^{2n}}{1 + z^2} \, .$$

This expression shows that for $|z| < 1$

$$\lim_{n \to \infty} s_n = \frac{1}{1 + z^2} \, ,$$

since $|z|^{2n} \rightarrow 0$. Thus for complex z satisfying the inequality $|z| < 1$ the series (6) converges and has the sum $1/(1 + z^2)$. For $|z| \geqslant 1$ the series (6) diverges, since in this case the difference $s_n - s_{n-1} = (-1)^{n-1}z^{2n-2}$ does not converge to zero.

The inequality $|z| < 1$ shows that the point z is located at a distance from the origin which is less than one. Thus the points at which the series (6) converges form a circle in the complex plane with center at the origin. On the circumference of this circle there lie two points i and $-i$ for which the function $1/(1 + z^2)$ becomes infinite; the presence of these points determines the restrictions on the domain of convergence of the series (6).

The domain of convergence of a power series. The domain of convergence of the power series

$$a_0 + a_1(z - a) + a_2(z - a)^2 + \cdots + a_n(z - a)^n + \cdots \qquad (7)$$

in the complex plane is always a circle with center at the point a.

Let us prove this proposition, which is called *Abel's theorem*.

First of all we note that a series whose terms are the complex numbers w_n

$$w_1 + w_2 + \cdots + w_n + \cdots, \qquad (8)$$

may be considered as two series, consisting of the real parts and the imaginary parts of the number $w_n = u_n + iv_n$

$$u_1 + u_2 + \cdots + u_n + \cdots, \qquad (9)$$

$$v_1 + v_2 + \cdots + v_n + \cdots. \qquad (10)$$

A partial sum s_n of the series (8) is expressed by the partial sums σ_n and τ_n of the series (9) and (10)

$$s_n = \sigma_n + i\tau_n,$$

so that convergence of the series (8) is equivalent to convergence of both the series (9) and (10), and the sum s of the series (8) is expressed by the sums σ and τ of the series (9) and (10)

$$s = \sigma + i\tau.$$

After these remarks the following lemma is obvious:

If the terms of the series (8) are less in absolute value than the terms of a convergent geometric progression

$$A + Aq + \cdots + Aq^n + \cdots$$

with positive A and q, where $q < 1$, then the series (8) converges.

For if $|w_n| < Aq^n$, then

$$|u_n| \leqslant |w_n| < Aq^n,$$

$$|v_n| \leqslant |w_n| < Aq^n,$$

so that (cf. Chapter II, §14) the series (9) and (10) converge and thus the series (8) also converges.

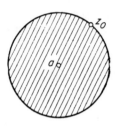

FIG. 2.

We now show that if the power series (7) converges at some point z_0, then it converges at all points lying inside the circle with center at a and having z_0 on its boundary (figure 2). From this proposition it follows readily that the domain of convergence of the series (7)

$$a_0 + a_1(z - a) + \cdots + a_n(z - a)^n + \cdots$$

is either the entire plane, or the single point $z = a$, or some circle of finite radius.

For let the series (7) converge at the point z_0; then the general term of the series (7) for $z = z_0$ converges to zero for $n \to \infty$, and this means that all the terms in the series (7) lie inside some circle; let A be the radius of such a circle, so that for any n

$$|a_n(z_0 - a)^n| < A. \tag{11}$$

We now take any point z closer than z_0 to a and show that at the point z the series converges.

Obviously

$$|z - a| < |z_0 - a|,$$

so that

$$q = \frac{|z - a|}{|z_0 - a|} < 1. \tag{12}$$

Let us estimate the general term of the series (7) at the point z

$$|a_n(z - a)^n| = \left| a_n(z_0 - a)^n \left(\frac{z - a}{z_0 - a}\right)^n \right| = |a_n(z_0 - a)^n| \left(\frac{|z - a|}{|z_0 - a|}\right)^n;$$

from inequalities (11) and (12) it follows that

$$|a_n(z - a)^n| < Aq^n;$$

i.e., the general term of the series (7) at the point z is less than the general term of a convergent geometric progression. From the basic lemma above, the series (7) converges at the point z.

The circle in which a power series converges, and outside of which it diverges, will be called the *circle of convergence*; the radius of this circle is called the *radius of convergence* of the power series. The boundary of the circle of convergence, as may be shown, always passes through the point of the complex plane nearest to a at which the regular behavior of the function ceases to hold.

The power series (4) converges on the whole complex plane; the power series (5), as was shown above, has a radius of convergence equal to one.

Exponential and trigonometric functions of a complex variable. A power series may serve to "continue" a function of a real variable into the complex domain. For example, for a complex value of z we define the function e^z by the power series

$$e^z = 1 + \frac{z}{1!} + \frac{z^2}{2!} + \cdots. \tag{13}$$

In like manner the trigonometric functions of a complex variable are introduced by

$$\sin z = \frac{z}{1!} - \frac{z^3}{3!} + \frac{z^5}{5!} - \cdots, \tag{14}$$

$$\cos z = 1 - \frac{z^2}{2!} + \frac{z^4}{4!} - \cdots. \tag{15}$$

These series converge on the whole plane.

It is interesting to note the connection which occurs between the exponential and trigonometric functions when we turn to the complex domain.

If in (13) we replace z by iz, we get

$$e^{iz} = 1 + i\frac{z}{1!} - \frac{z^2}{2!} - i\frac{z^3}{3!} + \frac{z^4}{4!} + \cdots.$$

Grouping everywhere the terms without the multiplier i and the terms with multiplier i, we have

$$e^{iz} = \cos z + i \sin z. \tag{16}$$

Similarly we can derive

$$e^{-iz} = \cos z - i \sin z. \tag{16'}$$

Formulas (16) and (16′) are called *Euler's formulas.* Solving (16) and (16′) for cos z and sin z, we get

$$\cos z = \frac{e^{iz} + e^{-iz}}{2},$$

$$\sin z = \frac{e^{iz} - e^{-iz}}{2i}. \tag{17}$$

It is very important that for complex values the simple rule of addition of exponents continue to hold

$$e^{z_1} \cdot e^{z_2} = e^{z_1 + z_2}. \tag{18}$$

Since for complex values of the argument we define the function e^z by the series (13), formula (18) must be proved on the basis of this definition. We give the proof:

$$e^{z_1} \cdot e^{z_2} = \left(1 + \frac{z_1}{1!} + \frac{z_1^2}{2!} + \cdots\right) \cdot \left(1 + \frac{z_2}{1!} + \frac{z_2^2}{2!} + \cdots\right).$$

We will carry out the multiplication of series termwise. The terms obtained in this multiplication of series may be written in the form of a square table

$$1 \cdot 1 + 1 \quad \cdot \frac{z_2}{1!} + 1 \quad \cdot \frac{z_2^2}{2!} + 1 \quad \cdot \frac{z_2^3}{3!} +$$

$$\cdots + \frac{z_1}{1!} \cdot 1 + \frac{z_1}{1!} \cdot \frac{z_2}{1!} + \frac{z_1}{1!} \cdot \frac{z_2^2}{2!} + \frac{z_1}{1!} \cdot \frac{z_2^3}{3!} +$$

$$\cdots + \frac{z_1^2}{2!} \cdot 1 + \frac{z_1^2}{2!} \cdot \frac{z_2}{1!} + \frac{z_1^2}{2!} \cdot \frac{z_2^2}{2!} + \frac{z_1^2}{2!} \cdot \frac{z_2^3}{3!} +$$

$$\cdots + \frac{z_1^3}{3!} \cdot 1 + \frac{z_1^3}{3!} \cdot \frac{z_2}{1!} + \frac{z_1^3}{3!} \cdot \frac{z_2^2}{2!} + \frac{z_1^3}{3!} \cdot \frac{z_2^3}{3!} + \cdots.$$

We now collect the terms which have the same sum of powers of z_1 and z_2. It is easy to see that such terms lie on the diagonals of our table. We get

$$e^{z_1} \cdot e^{z_2} = 1 + \left(\frac{z_2}{1!} + \frac{z_1}{1!}\right) + \left(\frac{z_2^2}{2!} + \frac{z_1}{1!}\frac{z_2}{1!} + \frac{z_1^2}{2!}\right) + \cdots. \tag{19}$$

The general term of this series will be

$$\frac{z_2^n}{n!} + \frac{z_2^{n-1}}{(n-1)!}\frac{z_1}{1!} + \frac{z_2^{n-2}}{(n-2)!}\frac{z_1^2}{2!} + \cdots + \frac{z_1^n}{n!}$$

$$= \frac{1}{n!}\left(z_2^n + \frac{n!}{1!(n-1)!}z_2^{n-1}z_1 + \frac{n!}{2!(n-2)!}z_2^{n-2}z_1^2 + \cdots + z_1^n\right).$$

Applying the binomial formula of Newton, we get the general term in the form

$$\frac{(z_1 + z_2)^n}{n!}.$$

So the general term of the series (19) is identical with the general term of the series for $e^{z_1+z_2}$, which proves the theorem on the rule for multiplication (18).

The multiplication theorem and Euler's formula allow us to derive an expression for the function e^z in terms of functions of real variables in finite form (without series). Thus, putting

$$z = x + iy,$$

we get

$$e^z = e^{x+iy} = e^x \cdot e^{iy},$$

and since

$$e^{iy} = \cos y + i \sin y,$$

we find that

$$e^z = e^x(\cos y + i \sin y). \tag{20}$$

The formula so derived is very convenient for investigating the properties of the function e^z. We note two of its properties: (1) the function e^z vanishes nowhere; for in fact, $e^x \neq 0$ and the functions $\cos y$ and $\sin y$ in formula (20) never vanish simultaneously; (2) the function e^z has period $2\pi i$, i.e.,

$$e^{z+2\pi i} = e^z.$$

This last statement follows from the multiplication theorem and the equality

$$e^{2\pi i} = \cos 2\pi + i \sin 2\pi = 1.$$

The formulas (17) allow us to investigate the functions $\cos z$ and $\sin z$ in the complex domain. We leave it as an exercise for the reader to prove that in the complex domain $\cos z$ and $\sin z$ have period 2π and that the theorems about the sine and cosine of a sum continue to hold for them.

The general concept of a function of a complex variable and the differentiability of functions.   Power series allow us to define analytic functions of a complex variable. However, it is of interest to study the basic operations of analysis for an arbitrary function of a complex variable and in particular the operation of differentiation. Here we uncover very deep-lying facts connected with the differentiation of functions of a complex variable. As we will see on the one hand, a function, having a first derivative at all points in a neighborhood of some point z_0, necessarily has derivatives of all orders at z_0, and further, it can be expanded in a power series centered at this point; i.e., it is analytic. Thus, if we consider differentiable functions of a complex variable, we return immediately to the class of analytic functions. On the other hand, a study of the derivative uncovers the geometric behavior of functions of a complex variable and the connections of the theory of these functions with problems in mathematical physics.

In view of what has been said, we will, in what follows, call a function *analytic at the point z_0* if it has a derivative at all points of some neighborhood of z_0.

We will say, following the general definition of a function, that a complex variable w is a function of the complex variable z if some law exists which allows us to find the value of w, given the value of z.

Every complex number $z = x + iy$ is represented by a point (x, y) on the Oxy plane, and the numbers $w = u + iv$ will also be represented by points on an Ouv plane, the plane of the function. Then from the geometric point of view a function of a complex variable $w = f(z)$ defines a law of correspondence between the points of the Oxy plane of the argument z and points of the Ouv plane of the value w of the function. In other words, a function of a complex variable determines a transformation of the plane of the argument to the plane of the function. To define a function of a complex variable means to give the correspondence between the pairs of numbers (x, y) and (u, v); defining a function of a complex variable is thus equivalent to defining two functions

$$u = \phi(x, y), \qquad v = \psi(x, y),$$

for which, obviously

$$w = u + iv = \phi(x, y) + i\psi(x, y).$$

For example, if

$$w = z^2 = (x + iy)^2 = x^2 - y^2 + 2ixy,$$

then

$$u = \phi(x, y) = x^2 - y^2, \qquad v = \psi(x, y) = 2xy.$$

The derivative of a function of a complex variable is defined formally in the same way as the derivative of a function of a real variable. The derivative is the limit of the difference quotient of the function

$$f'(z) = \lim_{\Delta z \to 0} \frac{f(z + \Delta z) - f(z)}{\Delta z}, \tag{21}$$

if this limit exists.

If we assume that the two real functions u and v, making up $w = f(z)$, have partial derivatives with respect to x and y, this is still not a sufficient condition that the derivative of the function $f(z)$ exists. The limit of the difference quotient, as a rule, depends on the direction in which the points $z' = z + \Delta z$ approximate the point z (figure 3). For the existence of the derivative $f'(z)$, it is necessary that the limit does not depend on the manner of approach of z' to z. Consider, for example, the case when z' approaches z parallel to the axis Ox or parallel to the axis Oy.

In the first case

$$\Delta z = \Delta x,$$

$$f(z + \Delta z) - f(z) = u(x + \Delta x, y) - u(x, y)$$
$$+ i[v(x + \Delta x, y) - v(x, y)],$$

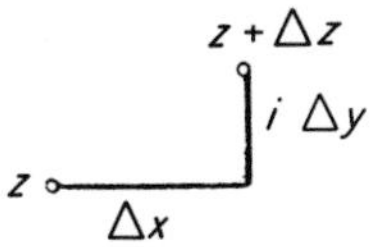

Fig. 3.

and the difference quotient

$$\frac{f(z + \Delta z) - f(z)}{\Delta z} = \frac{u(x + \Delta x, y) - u(x, y)}{\Delta x} + i \frac{v(x + \Delta x, y) - v(x, y)}{\Delta x}$$

for $\Delta x \to 0$ converges to

$$\frac{\partial u}{\partial x} + i \frac{\partial v}{\partial x}. \tag{22}$$

In the second case

$$\Delta z = i \Delta y,$$

and the difference quotient

$$\frac{f(z + \Delta z) - f(z)}{\Delta z} = -i \frac{u(x, y + \Delta y) - u(x, y)}{\Delta y} + \frac{v(x, y + \Delta y) - v(x, y)}{\Delta y}$$

leads in the limit to

$$\frac{\partial v}{\partial y} - i \frac{\partial u}{\partial y}. \tag{23}$$

If the function $w = f(x)$ has a derivative, these two expressions must be equal, and thus

$$\frac{\partial u}{\partial x} = \frac{\partial v}{\partial y},$$

$$\frac{\partial u}{\partial y} = -\frac{\partial v}{\partial x}. \tag{24}$$

Satisfying these equations is a necessary condition for the existence of the derivative of the function $w = u + iv$. It can be shown that condition (24) is not only necessary but also sufficient (if the functions u and v have a total differential). We will not give a proof of the sufficiency of conditions (24), which are called the *Cauchy-Riemann equations*.

It is easy to establish the fact that the usual rules for differentiating functions of a real variable carry over without alteration to functions of a complex variable. Certainly this is true for the derivative of the function z^n and for the derivative of a sum, a product, or a quotient. The method of proof remains exactly the same as for functions of a real variable, excepting only that in place of real quantities, complex ones are to be understood. This shows that every polynomial in z

$$w = a_0 + a_1 z + \cdots + a_n z^n$$

is an everywhere differentiable function. Any rational function, equal to the quotient of two polynomials

$$w = \frac{a_0 + a_1 z + \cdots + a_n z^n}{b_0 + b_1 z + \cdots + b_m z^m}$$

is differentiable at all points where the denominator is not zero.

In order to establish the differentiability of the function $w = e^z$, we may use the Cauchy-Riemann conditions. In this case, on the basis of formula (20)

$$u = e^x \cos y, \qquad v = e^x \sin y;$$

we substitute these functions in (24) and show that the Cauchy-Riemann equations are satisfied. The derivative may be computed, for example by formula (22). This gives

$$\frac{dw}{dz} = e^z.$$

On the basis of formula (17) it is easy to establish the differentiability of the trigonometric functions and the validity of the formulas known from analysis for the values of their derivatives.

The function Ln z. We will not give here an investigation of all the elementary functions of a complex variable. However, it is important for our purposes to become acquainted with some of the properties of the function Ln z. As in the case of the real domain, we set

$$w = \text{Ln } z,$$

if

$$z = e^w.$$

In order to analyze the function Ln z, we write the number z in trigonometric form

$$z = r(\cos \phi + i \sin \phi).$$

Applying the multiplication theorem to e^w, we get

$$z = e^w = e^{u+iv} = e^u e^{iv} = e^u(\cos v + i \sin v).$$

Equating the two expressions derived for z, we have

$$e^u = r, \tag{α}$$

$$\cos v + i \sin v = \cos \phi + i \sin \phi. \tag{β}$$

Since u and r are real numbers, from formula (α) we derive

$$u = \ln r,$$

where $\ln r$ is the usual value of the natural logarithm of a real number. Equation (β) can be satisfied only if

$$\cos v = \cos \phi, \quad \sin v = \sin \phi,$$

and in this case v and ϕ must differ by a number which is a multiple of 2π

$$v = \phi + 2\pi n,$$

where for any integer n equation (β) will be satisfied. On the basis of the expressions derived for u and v

$$\text{Ln } z = \ln r + i(\phi + 2\pi n). \tag{25}$$

Formula (25) defines the function Ln z for all values of the complex number z that are different from zero. It gives the definition of the logarithm not only for positive numbers but also for negative and complex numbers.

The expression derived for the function Ln z contains an arbitrary integer n. This means that Ln z is a multiple-valued function. For any value of n we get one of the possible values of the function Ln z. If we fix the value of n, we get one of the possible values of this function.

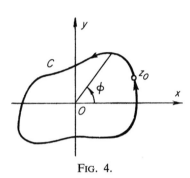

FIG. 4.

However, the different values of Ln z, as can be shown, are organically related to one another. In fact, let us fix, for example, the value $n = 0$ at the point z_0 and then let z move continuously around a closed curve C, which surrounds the origin and returns to the point z_0 (figure 4). During the motion of z, the angle ϕ will increase continuously and when z moves around the entire closed contour, ϕ will increase by 2π. In this manner, fixing the value of the logarithm at z_0

$$(\text{Ln } z)_0 = \ln r_0 + i\phi_0$$

and changing this value continuously while moving z along the closed curve surrounding the origin, we return to the point z_0 with another value of the function

$$(\text{Ln } z)_0 = \ln r_0 + i(\phi_0 + 2\pi).$$

This situation shows us that we may pass continuously from one value of Ln z to another. For this the point need only travel around the origin continuously a sufficient number of times. The point $z = 0$ is called a *branch point* of the function Ln z.

If we wish to restrict consideration to only one value of the function Ln z, we must prevent the point z from describing a closed curve surrounding the point $z = 0$. This may be done by drawing a continuous curve from the origin to infinity and preventing the point z from crossing this curve, which is called a *cut*. If z varies over the cut plane, then it never changes continuously from one value of Ln z to another and thus, starting from a specific value of logarithm at any point z_0, we get at each point only one value of the logarithm. The values of the function Ln z selected in this way constitute a single-valued branch of the function.

For example, if the cut lies along the negative part of the axis Ox, we get a single-valued branch of Ln z by restricting the argument to the limits

$$(2k - 1)\pi < \phi \leqslant (2k + 1)\pi,$$

where k is an arbitrary integer.

Considering a single-valued branch of the logarithm, we can study its differentiability. Putting

$$r = \sqrt{x^2 + y^2}, \qquad \phi = \arctan\frac{y}{x},$$

it is easy to show that Ln z satisfies the Cauchy-Riemann conditions and its derivative, calculated for example by formula (22), will be equal to

$$\frac{d \operatorname{Ln} z}{dz} = \frac{1}{z}.$$

We emphasize that the derivative of Ln z is also a single-valued function.

§2. The Connection Between Functions of a Complex Variable and the Problems of Mathematical Physics

Connection with problems of hydrodynamics. The Cauchy-Riemann conditions relate the problems of mathematical physics to the theory of functions of a complex variable. Let us illustrate this from the problems of hydrodynamics.

Among all possible motions of a fluid an important role is played by the *steady motions*. This name is given to motions of the fluid for which there is no change with time in the distribution of velocities in space. For example, an observer standing on a bridge and watching the flow of the river around a supporting pillar sees a steady flow. Sometimes a flow is steady for an observer in motion on some conveyance. In the case of a steamship travelling through rough water, the flow will appear nonsteady to an observer on the shore but steady to one on the ship. To a passenger seated in an airplane that is flying with constant velocity, the flow of the air as disturbed by the plane will still appear to be a steady one.

For steady motion the velocity vector V of the particle of the fluid passing through a given point of space does not change with time. If the motion is steady for a moving observer, then the velocity vector does not change with time at points having constant coordinates in a coordinate system which moves with the observer.

Among the motions of a fluid great importance has been attached to the class of *plane-parallel motions*. These are flows for which the velocity of the particles is everywhere parallel to some plane and the distribution of the velocities is identical on all planes parallel to the given plane.

If we imagine an infinitely extended mass of fluid, flowing around a cylindrical body in a direction perpendicular to a generator, the distribution of velocities will be the same on all planes perpendicular to the generator, so that the flow will be plane-parallel. In many cases the motion of a fluid is approximately plane-parallel. For example, if we consider the flow of air in a plane perpendicular to the wing of an airplane, the motion of the air may be considered as approximately plane-parallel, provided the plane in question is not very close either to the fuselage or to the tip of the wing.

We will show how the theory of functions of a complex variable may be applied to the study of steady plane-parallel flow.

Here we will assume that the liquid is incompressible, i.e., that its density does not change with change in pressure. This assumption holds, for example, for water, but it can be shown that even air may be considered incompressible in the study of its flow, if the velocity of the motion is not very large. The hypothesis of incompressibility of air will not produce a noticeable distortion if the velocities of motion do not exceed the range of 0.6 to 0.8 of the velocity of sound (330 m/sec).

The flow of a liquid is characterized by the distribution of the velocities of its particles. If the flow is plane-parallel, then it is sufficient to determine the velocities of the particles in one of the planes parallel to which the motion occurs.

We will denote by $V(x, y, t)$ the velocity vector of the particle passing through the point with coordinates x, y at the instant of time t. In the case of steady motion, V does not depend on time. The vector V will be given by its projections u and v on the coordinate axes. We consider the trajectories of particles of the fluid. In the case of steady motion, there is no change with time in the velocities of the successive particles issuing from a given point in space. If we know the field of the velocities, i.e., if we know the components of the velocity as functions of x, y, then the trajectories of the particles may be determined by using the fact that the velocity of a particle is everywhere tangent to the trajectory. This gives

$$\frac{dy}{dx} = \frac{v(x, y)}{u(x, y)}.$$

The equation so obtained is the differential equation for the trajectories. The trajectory of a particle in a steady motion is called a *streamline*. Through each point of the plane passes exactly one streamline.

An important role is played here by the so-called stream function. For a fixed streamline C_0 let us consider the imaginary channel bounded by the following four walls: One wall is the cylindrical surface (with generators perpendicular to the plane of the flow) passing through the streamline C_0; the second wall is the same cylindrical surface for a neighboring streamline C_1; the third is the plane of the flow; and the fourth is a parallel plane at unit distance (figure 5). If we consider two arbitrary cross sections of our channel, denoted by γ_1 and γ_2, then the quantity of fluid passing through the sections γ_1 and γ_2 in unit time will be the same, as follows from the fact that the quantity of fluid inside the part of the channel marked off by C_1, C_0 and γ_1, γ_2 cannot change, because of the constant density, since the side walls of the channel C_0 and C_1 are formed by streamlines, so that no fluid passes through them. Consequently the same amount of fluid must leave in unit time through γ_1 as enters through γ_2.

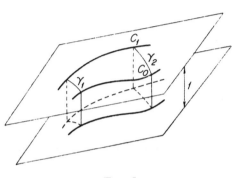

FIG. 5.

Now by the *stream function* we mean the function $\psi(x, y)$ that has a constant value on the streamline C_1 equal to the quantity of liquid passing in unit time through the cross section of the channel constructed on the curves C_0 and C_1.

The stream function is defined only up to an arbitrary constant, depending on the choice of the initial streamline C_0. If we know the stream function, then the equations for the streamlines are obviously

$$\psi(x, y) = \text{const.}$$

We now wish to express the components of the velocity of the flow at a given point $M(x, y)$ in terms of the derivatives of the stream function. To this end we consider the channel formed by the streamline C through the point $M(x, y)$ and a neighboring streamline C' through a nearby point $M'(x, y + \varDelta y)$, together with the two planes parallel to the plane of flow and a unit distance apart. Let us compute the quantity of the liquid q passing through the section MM' of the channel during time dt.

On the one hand, from the definition of the stream function

$$q = (\psi' - \psi)\, dt.$$

On the other hand, q is equal (figure 6) to the volume of the solid formed by drawing the vector $V\, dt$ from each point of the section MM'. If MM' is small, we may assume that V is constant over the whole of

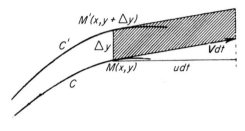

MM' and is equal to the value of V at the point M. The area of the base of the parallelepiped so constructed is $\Delta y \times 1$ (in figure 6 the unit thickness is not shown), and the altitude is the projection of the vector $V\, dt$ on the Ox axis, i.e., $u\, dt$ so that

$$q \approx u\, \Delta y\, dt$$

Fig. 6.

and thus

$$u\, \Delta y \approx \Delta \psi.$$

Dividing this equation by Δy, and passing to the limit, we get

$$u = \frac{\partial \psi}{\partial y}. \tag{26}$$

A similar argument gives for the second component

$$v = -\frac{\partial \psi}{\partial x}. \tag{26'}$$

To define the field of the velocity vectors, we introduce, in addition to the stream function, another function, which arises from considering the rotation of small particles of the liquid. If we imagine that a particular particle of the fluid were to become solidified, it would in general have a rotatory motion. However, if the motion of the fluid starts from rest and if there is no internal friction between particles, then it can be shown that rotation of the particles of the fluid cannot begin. Motions of a fluid in which there is no rotation of this sort are called irrotational; they play a fundamental role in the study of the motion of bodies in a fluid. In the theory of hydromechanics it is shown that for irrotational flow there exists a second function $\phi(x, y)$ such that the components of the velocity are expressed by the formulas

$$u = \frac{\partial \phi}{\partial x}, \qquad v = \frac{\partial \phi}{\partial y}; \tag{27}$$

the function ϕ is called the *velocity potential* of the flow. Later, we will consider motions with velocity potential.

Comparison of the formulas for the components of the velocity from the stream function and from the velocity potential gives the following remarkable result.

The velocity potential $\phi(x, y)$ and the stream function $\psi(x, y)$ for the flow of an incompressible fluid satisfy the Cauchy-Riemann equations

$$\frac{\partial \phi}{\partial x} = \frac{\partial \psi}{\partial y},$$

$$\frac{\partial \phi}{\partial y} = -\frac{\partial \psi}{\partial x}. \tag{28}$$

In other words, the function of a complex variable

$$w = \phi(x, y) + i\psi(x, y)$$

is a differentiable function of a complex variable. Conversely, if we choose an arbitrary differentiable function of a complex variable, its real and imaginary parts satisfy the Cauchy-Riemann conditions and may be considered as the velocity potential and the stream function of the flow of an incompressible fluid. The function w is called the *characteristic function of the flow*.

Let us now consider the significance of the derivative of w. Using, for example, formula (22), we have

$$\frac{dw}{dz} = \frac{\partial \phi}{\partial x} + i \frac{\partial \psi}{\partial x}.$$

From (27) and (26′) we find

$$\frac{dw}{dz} = u - iv$$

or, taking complex conjugates,

$$u + iv = \overline{\left(\frac{dw}{dz}\right)}, \tag{29}$$

where the bar over dw/dz denotes the complex conjugate.

Consequently, the velocity vector of the flow is equal to the conjugate of the value of the derivative of the characteristic function of the flow.

Examples of plane-parallel flow of a fluid. We consider several examples. Let

$$w = Az, \tag{30}$$

where A is a complex quantity. From (29) it follows that

$$u + iv = \bar{A}.$$

Thus the linear function (30) defines the flow of a fluid with constant vector velocity. If we set

$$A = u_0 - iv_0 ,$$

then, decomposing into the real and imaginary parts of w, we have

$$\phi(x, y) = u_0 x + v_0 y,$$
$$\psi(x, y) = u_0 y - v_0 x,$$

so that the streamlines will be straight lines parallel to the velocity vector (figure 7).

As a second example we consider the function

$$w = Az^2,$$

where the constant A is real. In order to graph the flow, we first determine the streamlines. In this case

$$\psi(x, y) = 2Axy,$$

and the equations of the streamlines are

$$xy = \text{const.}$$

These are hyperbolas with the coordinate axes as asymptotes (figure 8). The arrows show the direction of motion of the particles along the streamlines for $A > 0$. The axes Ox and Oy are also streamlines.

If the friction in the liquid is very small, we will not disturb the rest of the flow if we replace any streamline by a rigid wall, since the fluid

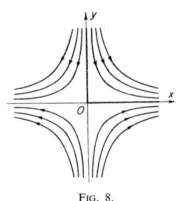

Fig. 7.   Fig. 8.

will glide along the wall. Using this principle to construct walls along the positive coordinate axes (in figure 8 they are represented by heavy lines), we have a diagram of how the fluid flows irrotationally, in this case around a corner.

An important example of a flow is given by the function

$$w = a\left(z + \frac{R^2}{z}\right),\tag{31}$$

where a and R are positive real quantities.

The stream function will be

$$\psi = a\left(y - \frac{R^2 y}{x^2 + y^2}\right),$$

and thus the equation for the streamlines is

$$y - \frac{R^2 y}{x^2 + y^2} = \text{const.}$$

In particular, taking the constant equal to zero, we have either $y = 0$ or $x^2 + y^2 = R^2$; thus, a circle of radius R is a streamline. If we replace the interior of this streamline by a solid body, we obtain the flow around a circular cylinder. A diagram of the streamlines of this flow is shown in figure 9. The velocity of the flow may be defined from formula (29) by

$$u + iv = a\left(1 - \frac{R^2}{\bar{z}^2}\right).$$

At a great distance from the cylinder we find

$$\lim_{z \to \infty} (u + iv) = a;$$

i.e., far from the cylinder the velocity tends to a constant value and thus the flow tends to be uniform. Consequently, formula (29) defines the flow which arises from the passage around a circular cylinder of a fluid which is in uniform motion at a distance from the cylinder.

The basic ideas of the theory of an air-plane wing; theorem of Žukovskiĭ.

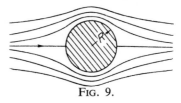

Fig. 9.

The application of the theory of functions of a complex variable to the study of plane-parallel flows of a fluid was the source of several remarkable discoveries in aerodynamics by Žukovskiĭ and Čaplygin. The study of streamlines of bodies led them to discover the law for the formation of lifting force on the wing on an airplane. In order to present the ideas which led to this discovery, we need to consider one more concrete example of fluid flow. Let us consider the characteristic function

$$w = \frac{\Gamma}{2\pi i} \text{Ln } z,$$

where Γ is a real constant. Although w is a multiple-valued function, its derivative

$$\frac{dw}{dz} = \frac{\Gamma}{2\pi i} \frac{1}{z} \tag{32}$$

is single valued, so that our function uniquely defines the velocity field of some fluid flow. If we set $z = re^{i\theta}$, the velocity potential and the stream function may be computed from (25) as

$$\phi = \frac{\Gamma}{2\pi} \theta, \qquad \psi = -\frac{\Gamma}{2\pi} \ln r.$$

The second of these formulas shows that the streamlines are the circles $r = \text{const}$ (figure 10).

The velocity of the flow is defined by formula (29) as

$$u + iv = -\frac{\Gamma}{2\pi i} \frac{1}{\bar{z}}.$$

In particular, it follows that the value of the velocity vector will be

$$V = |u + iv| = \frac{|\Gamma|}{2\pi} \frac{1}{r},$$

i.e., the velocity is constant on every streamline. A more detailed investigation shows that the flow goes counterclockwise for $\Gamma > 0$ and clockwise for $\Gamma < 0$.

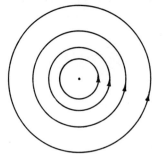

If we replace one of the streamlines by a rigid boundary, we obtain the circular motion of a fluid around a cylinder. Such a motion is called *circulatory*.

However, the potential of our motion is not a single-valued function. In one passage over a closed contour around the cylinder the potential is changed by an amount Γ. This change in potential is called the *circulation of the flow*.

Fig. 10.

If to the characteristic function of a flow past a cylinder (31), we add the characteristic function of a circulatory flow (with clockwise circuit), we get a new characteristic function

$$w = a\left(z + \frac{R^2}{z}\right) - \frac{\Gamma}{2\pi i}\, \mathrm{Ln}\, z. \qquad (33)$$

This characteristic function also represents the flow around a cylinder of radius R. In fact, the stream function will be constant on a circumference of radius R, since there the coefficients of the imaginary parts of both terms are constant. The velocity of the flow, defined by the function (33), will again converge to a as $z \to \infty$. This shows that the characteristic function (33) defines, for any value of Γ, the streamlines of a translational flow past a cylinder. Figure 11 illustrates the character of the flow for $\Gamma > 0$. This flow will not be symmetric, since the stagnation points a and b where the streams meet and leave the cylinder are displaced downward. The potential of the flow under consideration will be a multiple-valued function. As the result of one circuit around the cylinder it will change by an amount equal to Γ.

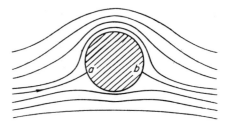

Fig. 11.

Because of symmetry, the flow around a cylinder will usually be of the form defined by the functions (32), but for nonsymmetric bodies the flow which arises usually has a multiple-valued potential. Later we will discuss the physical significance of this fact. The methods of the theory of functions of a complex variable allow us to define the possible flows around bodies of arbitrary shape. These methods will be discussed in the following section. With their help we can make use of the flow around a cylinder to construct the flow, with single-valued or multiple-valued potential, around any body.

In studying the streamlines of the wing of an airplane, we are dealing with a body with a sharp edge at the rear. The profile of the wing of an airplane always narrows toward the rear. If for such a profile we construct a flow with a single-valued potential, then the stagnation point where the stream leaves the wing proves not to be at the edge (figure 12a). But it

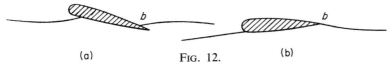

(a)   Fig. 12.   (b)

turns out that such a flow is physically impossible. (Infinite velocity, with consequent infinite rarefaction of the fluid would occur at the sharp edge.) The flow for which the point b falls on the edge of the wing (figure 12b) is the uniquely possible flow, and this flow, as a rule, will have a multiple-valued potential, i.e., will be a circulatory flow. The circulation Γ of such a flow again is defined as the change in the potential for a circuit of a closed contour around the wing.

The physical realizability of a flow around the profile of a wing with a stream leaving the rear edge is called *Čaplygin's postulate.*

The remarkable discovery of Žukovskiĭ consists of the fact that the existence of circulation in the flow causes a lifting force on the wing,

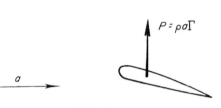

FIG. 13.

in a direction perpendicular to the velocity a of the oncoming flow and equal in magnitude to the quantity

$$\rho a \Gamma,$$

where ρ is the density of the medium and Γ is the circulation (figure 13).

This theorem of Žukovskiĭ about the lifting force on a wing is basic for all contemporary aerodynamics. We will not give the proof here, merely noting that the usual proofs are based on the theory of integrals of functions of a complex variable.

The basic results in aerodynamics as established by Žukovskiĭ and Čaplygin have been extensively developed by the work of Soviet scientists.

Applications to other problems of mathematical physics. The theory of functions of a complex variable has found wide application not only in wing theory but in many other problems of hydrodynamics.

However, the domain of application of the theory of functions is not restricted to hydrodynamics; it is much wider than that, including many other problems of mathematical physics. To illustrate, we return to the Cauchy-Riemann conditions

$$\frac{\partial u}{\partial x} = \frac{\partial v}{\partial y},$$

$$\frac{\partial u}{\partial y} = -\frac{\partial v}{\partial x}$$

and deduce from them an equation which is satisfied by the real part of an analytic function of a complex variable. If the first of these equations is differentiated with respect to x, and the second with respect to y, we obtain by addition

$$\frac{\partial^2 u}{\partial x^2} + \frac{\partial^2 u}{\partial y^2} = 0.$$

This equation (which we have already met in Chapter VI) is known as the *Laplace equation*. A large number of problems of physics and mechanics involve the Laplace equation. For example, if the heat in a body is in equilibrium, the temperature satisfies the Laplace equation. The study of magnetic or electrostatic fields is connected with this equation. In the investigation of the filtration of a liquid through a porous medium, we also arrive at the Laplace equation. In all these problems involving the solution of the Laplace equation the methods of the theory of functions have found wide application.

Not only the Laplace equation but also the more general equations of mathematical physics can be brought into connection with the theory of functions of a complex variable. One of the most remarkable examples is provided by planar problems in the theory of elasticity. The foundations of the application of functions of a complex variable to this domain were laid by the Soviet scientists G. B. Kolosov and N. I. Mushelišvili.

§3. The Connection of Functions of a Complex Variable with Geometry

Geometric properties of differentiable functions. As in the case of functions of a real variable, a great role is played in the theory of analytic functions of a complex variable by the geometric interpretation of these functions. Broadly speaking, the geometric properties of functions of a complex variable have not only provided a natural means of visualizing the analytic properties of the functions but have also given rise to a special set of problems. The range of problems connected with the geometric properties of functions has been called the *geometric theory of functions*. As we said earlier, from the geometric point of view a function of a complex variable $w = f(z)$ is a transformation from the z-plane to the w-plane. This transformation may also be defined by two functions of two real variables

$$u = u(x, y),$$

$$v = v(x, y).$$

If we wish to study the character of the transformation in a very small neighborhood of some point, we may expand these functions into

Taylor series and restrict ourselves to the leading terms of the expansion

$$u - u_0 = \left(\frac{\partial u}{\partial x}\right)_0 (x - x_0) + \left(\frac{\partial u}{\partial y}\right)_0 (y - y_0) + \cdots,$$

$$v - v_0 = \left(\frac{\partial v}{\partial x}\right)_0 (x - x_0) + \left(\frac{\partial v}{\partial y}\right)_0 (y - y_0) + \cdots,$$

where the derivatives are taken at the point (x_0, y_0). Thus, in the neighborhood of a point, any transformation may be considered approximately as an affine transformation*

$$u - u_0 = a(x - x_0) + b(y - y_0),$$
$$v - v_0 = c(x - x_0) + d(y - y_0),$$

where

$$a = \left(\frac{\partial u}{\partial x}\right)_0, \qquad b = \left(\frac{\partial u}{\partial y}\right)_0,$$

$$c = \left(\frac{\partial v}{\partial x}\right)_0, \qquad d = \left(\frac{\partial v}{\partial y}\right)_0.$$

Let us consider the properties of the transformation effected by the analytic function near the point $z = x + iy$. Let C be a curve issuing from the point z; on the w-plane the corresponding points trace out the curve Γ, issuing from the point w. If z' is a neighboring point and w' is the point corresponding to it, then for $z' \to z$ we will have $w' \to w$ and

$$\frac{w' - w}{z' - z} \to f'(z). \tag{34}$$

In particular, it follows that

$$\frac{|w' - w|}{|z' - z|} \to |f'(z)|. \tag{35}$$

This fact may be formulated in the following manner.

The limit of the ratio of the lengths of corresponding chords in the w-plane and in the z-plane at the point z is the same for all curves issuing from the given point z, or as it is also expressed, the ratio of linear elements on the w-plane and on the z-plane at a given point does not depend on the curve issuing from z.

The quantity $|f'(z)|$, which characterizes the magnification of linear elements at the point z, is called the *coefficient of dilation* at the point z.

---

* Cf. Chapter III, §11.

We now suppose that at some point z the derivative $f'(z) \neq 0$, so that $f'(z)$ has a uniquely determined argument.* Let us compute this argument, using (34)

$$\arg \frac{w' - w}{z' - z} = \arg (w' - w) - \arg (z' - z),$$

but $\arg (w' - w)$ is the angle β' between the chord ww' and the real axis, and $\arg (z' - z)$ is the angle α' between the chord zz' and the real axis.

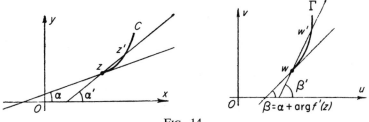

FIG. 14.

If we denote by α and β the corresponding angles for the tangents to the curves C and Γ at the points z and w (figure 14), then for $z' \to z$

$$\alpha' \to \alpha, \quad \beta' \to \beta,$$

so that in the limit we get

$$\arg f'(z) = \beta - \alpha. \tag{36}$$

This equation shows that $\arg f'(z)$ is equal to the angle ϕ through which the direction of the tangent to the curve C at the point z must be turned to assume the direction of the tangent to the curve Γ at the point w. From this property $\arg f'(z)$ is called the *rotation of the transformation* at the point z.

From equation (36) the reader can easily derive the following propositions.

As we pass from the z-plane to the w-plane, the tangents to all curves issuing from a given point are rotated through the same angle.

If C_1 and C_2 are two curves issuing from the point z, and Γ_1 and Γ_2 are the corresponding curves from the point w, then the angle between Γ_1 and Γ_2 at the point w is equal to the angle between C_1 and C_2 at the point z.

---

* Cf. Chapter IV, §3.

In this manner, for the transformation effected by an analytic function, at each point where $f'(z) \neq 0$, all linear elements are changed by the same ratio, and the angles between corresponding directions are not changed.

Transformations with these properties are called *conformal* transformations.

From the geometric properties just proved for transformations near a point at which $f'(z_0) \neq 0$, it is natural to expect that in a small neighborhood of z_0 the transformation will be one-to-one; i.e., not only will each point z correspond to only one point w, but also conversely each point w will correspond to only one point z. This proposition can be rigorously proved.

To show more clearly how conformal transformations are distinguished from various other types of transformations, it is useful to consider an arbitrary transformation in a small neighborhood of a point. If we consider the leading terms of the Taylor expansions of the functions u and v effecting the transformation, we get

$$u - u_0 = \left(\frac{\partial u}{\partial x}\right)_0 (x - x_0) + \left(\frac{\partial u}{\partial y}\right)_0 (y - y_0) + \cdots,$$

$$v - v_0 = \left(\frac{\partial v}{\partial x}\right)_0 (x - x_0) + \left(\frac{\partial v}{\partial y}\right)_0 (y - y_0) + \cdots.$$

If in a small neighborhood of the point (x_0, y_0) we ignore the terms of higher order, then our transformation will act like an affine transformation. This transformation has an inverse if its determinant does not vanish

$$\Delta = \left(\frac{\partial u}{\partial x}\right)_0 \left(\frac{\partial v}{\partial y}\right)_0 - \left(\frac{\partial u}{\partial y}\right)_0 \left(\frac{\partial v}{\partial x}\right)_0 \neq 0.$$

If $\Delta = 0$, then to describe the behavior of the transformation near the point (x_0, y_0) we must consider terms of higher order.*

In case $u + iv$ is an analytic function, we can express the derivatives with respect to y in terms of the derivatives with respect to x by using the Cauchy-Riemann conditions, from which we get

$$\Delta = \left(\frac{\partial u}{\partial x}\right)_0^2 + \left(\frac{\partial v}{\partial x}\right)_0^2 = \left|\left(\frac{\partial u}{\partial x}\right)_0 + i\left(\frac{\partial v}{\partial x}\right)_0\right|^2 = |f'(z_0)|^2,$$

---

* In this last case, i.e., for $\Delta = 0$, the transformation is not called affine. For affine transformations see also Chapter III, §11.

i.e., the transformation has an inverse when $f'(z_0) \neq 0$. If we set $f'(z_0) = r(\cos \phi + i \sin \phi)$, then

$$\left(\frac{\partial u}{\partial x}\right)_0 = \left(\frac{\partial v}{\partial y}\right)_0 = r \cos \phi,$$

$$\left(\frac{\partial u}{\partial y}\right)_0 = -\left(\frac{\partial v}{\partial x}\right)_0 = -r \sin \phi,$$

and the transformation near the point (x_0, y_0) will have the form

$$u - u_0 = r[(x - x_0) \cos \phi - (y - y_0) \sin \phi] + \cdots,$$
$$v - v_0 = r[(x - x_0) \sin \phi + (y - y_0) \cos \phi] + \cdots.$$

These formulas show that in the case of an analytic function $w = u + iv$, the transformation near the point (x_0, y_0) consists of rotation through the angle ϕ and dilation with coefficient r. In fact, the expressions inside the brackets are the well-known formulas from analytic geometry for rotation in the plane through an angle ϕ, and multiplication by r gives the dilation.

To form an idea of the possibilities when $f'(z) = 0$ it is useful to consider the function

$$w = z^n. \tag{37}$$

The derivative of this function $w' = nz^{n-1}$ vanishes for $z = 0$. The transformation (37) is most conveniently considered by using polar coordinates or the trigonometric form of a complex number. Let

$$z = r(\cos \phi + i \sin \phi),$$
$$w = \rho(\cos \theta + i \sin \theta).$$

Using the fact that in multiplying complex numbers the moduli are multiplied and the arguments added, we get

$$z^n = r^n(\cos n\phi + i \sin n\phi),$$

and thus

$$\rho = r^n,$$
$$\theta = n\phi.$$

From the last formula we see that the ray $\phi = $ const. of the z-plane transforms into the ray $\theta = n\phi = $ const. in the w-plane. Thus an angle α between two rays in the z-plane will transform into an angle of magnitude $\beta = n\alpha$. The transformation of the z-plane into the w-plane ceases to be one-to-one. In fact, a given point w with modulus ρ and argument θ

may be obtained as the image of each of the n points with moduli $r = \sqrt[n]{\rho}$ and arguments

$$\phi = \frac{\theta}{n}, \frac{\theta}{n} + \frac{2\pi}{n}, \cdots, \frac{\theta}{n} + \frac{2\pi}{n}(n-1).$$

When raised to the power n, the moduli of the corresponding points will all be equal to ρ and their arguments will be equal to

$$\theta, \theta + 2\pi, \cdots, \theta + 2\pi(n-1),$$

and since changing the value of the argument by a multiple of 2π does not change the geometric position of the point, all the images on the w-plane are identical.

Conformal transformations. If an analytic function $w = f(z)$ takes a domain D of the z-plane into a domain Δ of the w-plane in a one-to-one manner, then we say that it effects a conformal transformation of the domain D into the domain Δ.

The great role of conformal transformations in the theory of functions and its applications is due to the following almost trivial theorem.

If $\zeta = F(w)$ is an analytic function on the domain Δ, then the composite function $F[f(z)]$ is an analytic function on the domain D. This theorem results from the equation

$$\frac{\Delta \zeta}{\Delta z} = \frac{\Delta \zeta}{\Delta w} \cdot \frac{\Delta w}{\Delta z}.$$

In view of the fact that the functions $\zeta = F(w)$ and $w = f(z)$ are analytic, we conclude that both factors on the right side have a limit, and thus at each point of the domain D the quotient $\Delta\zeta/\Delta z$ has a unique limit $d\zeta/dz$. This shows that the function $\zeta = F[f(z)]$ is analytic.

The theorem just proved shows that the study of analytic functions on the domain Δ may be reduced to the study of analytic functions on the domain D. If the geometric structure of the domain D is simpler, this fact simplifies the study of the functions.

The most important class of domains in which it is necessary to study analytic functions is the class of *simply connected* domains. This is the name given to domains whose boundary consists of one piece (figure 15a) as opposed to domains whose

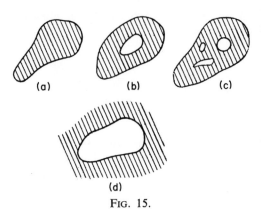

(a)   (b)   (c)

(d)

FIG. 15.

boundary falls into several pieces (for example, the domains illustrated in figures 15b and 15c).

We note that sometimes we are interested in investigating functions on a domain lying outside a curve rather than inside it. If the boundary of such a domain consists of only one piece, then the domain is also called simply connected (figure 15d).

At the foundations of the theory of conformal transformations lies the following remarkable theorem of Riemann.

For an arbitrary simply connected domain Δ, it is possible to construct an analytic function which effects a conformal transformation of the circle with unit radius and center at the origin into the given domain in such a way that the center of the circle is transformed into a given point w_0 of the domain Δ, and a curve in an arbitrary direction at the center of the circle transforms into a curve with an arbitrary direction at the point w_0. This theorem shows that the study of functions of a complex variable on arbitrary simply connected domains may be reduced to the study of functions defined, for example, on the unit circle.

We will now explain in general outline how these facts may be applied to problems in the theory of the wing of an airplane. Let us suppose that we wish to study the flow around a curved profile of arbitrary shape.

If we can construct a conformal transformation of the domain outside the profile to the domain outside the unit circle, then we can make use of the characteristic function for the flow around the circle to construct the characteristic function for the flow around the profile.

Let ζ be the plane of the circle, z the plane of the profile, and $\zeta = f(z)$ a function effecting the transformation of the domain outside the profile to the domain outside the circle, where

$$\lim_{z \to \infty} \zeta = \infty.$$

We denote by a the point of the circle corresponding to the edge of the profile A and construct the circulatory flow past the circle with one of the streamlines leaving the circle at a (figure 16). This function will be denoted by $W(\zeta)$:

$$W(\zeta) = \Phi + i\Psi.$$

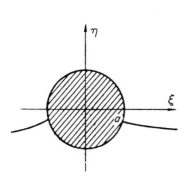

Fig. 16.

The streamlines of this flow are defined by the equation

$$\Psi = \text{const.}$$

We now consider the function

$$w(z) = W[f(z)],$$

and set

$$w = \phi + i\psi.$$

We show that $w(z)$ is the characteristic function of the flow past the profile with a streamline leaving the profile at the point A. First of all the flow defined by the function $w(z)$ is actually a flow past the profile. To prove this, we must show that the contour of the profile is a streamline curve, i.e., that on the contour of the profile

$$\psi(x, y) = \text{const.}$$

But this follows from the fact that

$$\psi(x, y) = \Psi(\xi, \eta),$$

and the points (x, y) lying on the profile correspond to the points (ξ, η) lying on the circle, where $\Psi(\xi, \eta) = \text{const.}$

It is also simple to show that A is a stagnation point for the flow, and it may be proved that by suitable choice of velocity for the flow past the circle, we may obtain a flow past the profile with any desired velocity.

The important role played by conformal transformations in the theory of functions and their applications gave rise to many problems of finding the conformal transformation of one domain into another of a given geometric form. In a series of simple but useful cases this problem may be solved by means of elementary functions. But in the general case the elementary functions are not enough. As we saw earlier, the general theorem in the theory of conformal transformations was stated by Riemann, although he did not give a rigorous proof. In fact, a complete proof required the efforts of many great mathematicians over a period of several decades.

In close connection with the different approaches to the proof of Riemann's theorem came approximation methods for the general construction of conformal transformations of domains. The actual construction of the conformal transformation of one domain onto another is sometimes a very difficult problem. For investigation of many of the general properties of functions, it is often not necessary to know the actual transformation of one domain onto another, but it is sufficient to exploit some of its geometric properties. This fact has led to a wide study of the geometric properties of conformal transformations. To illustrate the nature of theorems of this sort we will formulate one of them.

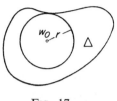

FIG. 17.

Let the circle of unit radius on the z-plane with center at the origin be transformed into some domain (figure 17). If we consider a completely arbitrary transformation of the circle into the domain Δ, we cannot make any statements about its behavior at the point $z = 0$. But for conformal transformations we have the following remarkable theorem.

The dilation at the origin does not exceed four times the radius of the circle with center at w_0, inscribed in the domain

$$|f'(0)| \leqslant 4r.$$

Various questions in the theory of conformal transformations were considered in a large number of studies by Soviet mathematicians. In these works exact formulas were derived for many interesting classes of conformal transformations, methods for approximate calculation of conformal transformations were developed, and many general geometric theorems on conformal transformations were established.

Quasi-conformal transformations. Conformal transformations are closely connected with the investigation of analytic functions, i.e., with the study of a pair of functions satisfying the Cauchy-Riemann conditions

$$\frac{\partial u}{\partial x} = \frac{\partial v}{\partial y},$$

$$\frac{\partial u}{\partial y} = -\frac{\partial v}{\partial x}.$$

But many problems in mathematical physics involve more general systems of differential equations, which may also be connected with transformations from one plane to another, and these transformations will have specific geometric properties in the neighborhood of points in the Oxy

plane. To illustrate, we consider the following example of differential equations

$$\frac{\partial u}{\partial x} = p(x, y) \frac{\partial v}{\partial y},$$

$$\frac{\partial v}{\partial x} = -p(x, y) \frac{\partial u}{\partial y}. \tag{38}$$

If $p(x, y) = 1$, this is the system of Cauchy-Riemann equations. In the general case of an arbitrary function $p(x, y)$, we can also consider every solution of the system (38) as a transformation of the Oxy plane to the Ouv plane. Let us examine the geometric properties of this transformation in the neighborhood of a point (x_0, y_0). Taking a small neighborhood of (x_0, y_0), we retain only the first terms in the expansion of the functions u and v in powers of $x - x_0$ and $y - y_0$, and thereby consider the following affine transformation

$$u - u_0 = \left(\frac{\partial u}{\partial x}\right)_0 (x - x_0) + \left(\frac{\partial u}{\partial y}\right)_0 (y - y_0),$$

$$v - v_0 = \left(\frac{\partial v}{\partial x}\right)_0 (x - x_0) + \left(\frac{\partial v}{\partial y}\right)_0 (y - y_0). \tag{39}$$

If the functions u and v satisfy the system of equations (38), then for this affine transformation we have the following property.

Ellipses with center at the point (x_0, y_0) with principal axes parallel to the coordinate axes, and with ratio of semiaxes

$$\frac{b}{a} = p(x_0, y_0)$$

are transformed in the Ouv plane to circles with center at the point (u_0, v_0).

Let us prove this proposition. The equation of the circle with center (u_0, v_0) in the Ouv plane will be

$$(u - u_0)^2 + (v - v_0)^2 = \rho^2.$$

Replacing $u - u_0$ and $v - v_0$ by their expressions in terms of x and y, we get the equation for the corresponding curve in the Oxy plane:

$$\left[\left(\frac{\partial u}{\partial x}\right)_0^2 + \left(\frac{\partial v}{\partial x}\right)_0^2\right] (x - x_0)^2$$

$$+ 2 \left[\left(\frac{\partial u}{\partial x}\right)_0 \left(\frac{\partial u}{\partial y}\right)_0 + \left(\frac{\partial v}{\partial x}\right)_0 \left(\frac{\partial v}{\partial y}\right)_0\right] (x - x_0)(y - y_0)$$

$$+ \left[\left(\frac{\partial u}{\partial y}\right)_0^2 + \left(\frac{\partial v}{\partial y}\right)_0^2\right] (y - y_0)^2 = \rho^2.$$

Using the equations in (38) to express the derivatives of v in terms of the derivatives of u, we get

$$\left[\left(\frac{\partial u}{\partial x}\right)_0^2 + p^2 \left(\frac{\partial u}{\partial y}\right)_0^2\right] (x - x_0)^2 + \frac{1}{p^2} \left[\left(\frac{\partial u}{\partial x}\right)_0^2 + p^2 \left(\frac{\partial u}{\partial y}\right)_0^2\right] (y - y_0)^2 = \rho^2.$$

If we set

$$a = \frac{\rho}{\sqrt{\left(\frac{\partial u}{\partial x}\right)_0^2 + p^2 \left(\frac{\partial u}{\partial y}\right)_0^2}},$$

$$b = \frac{p\rho}{\sqrt{\left(\frac{\partial u}{\partial x}\right)_0^2 + p^2 \left(\frac{\partial u}{\partial y}\right)_0^2}},$$

this equation takes the form

$$\frac{(x - x_0)^2}{a^2} + \frac{(y - y_0)^2}{b^2} = 1.$$

Thus the curve that is transformed into a circle is in fact an ellipse with the indicated properties.

If we do not consider the affine transformation given by the first terms of the expansion but rather the exact transformation itself, then the above property of the transformation will hold more and more exactly for smaller and smaller ellipses, so that we may say that the property holds for infinitely small ellipses.

In this manner, from equations (38) it follows that at every point the infinitesimal ellipse that is transformed into a circle has its semiaxes completely determined by the transformation, both with respect to their direction and to the ratio of their lengths. It can be shown that this geometric property completely characterizes the system of differential equations (38); i.e., if the functions u and v effect a transformation with the given geometric property, then they satisfy this system of equations. In this way, the problem of investigating the solutions of equations (38) is equivalent to investigating transformations with the given properties.

We note, in particular, that for the Cauchy-Riemann equations this property is formulated in the following manner.

An infinitesimal circle with center at the point (x_0, y_0) is transformed into an infinitesimal circle with center at the point (u_0, v_0).

A very wide class of equations of mathematical physics may be reduced to the study of transformations with the following geometric properties. For each point (x, y) of the argument plane, we are given the direction of the semiaxes of two ellipses and also the ratio of the lengths of these semiaxes. We wish to construct a transformation of the Oxy plane to the Ouv plane such that an infinitesimal ellipse of the first family transforms into an infinitesimal ellipse of the second with center at the point (u, v).

Transformations connected with such general systems of equations were introduced by the Soviet mathematician M. A. Lavrent'ev and have received the name *quasi-conformal*. The idea of studying transformations defined by systems of differential equations made it possible to extend the methods of the theory of analytic functions to a very wide class of problems. Lavrent'ev and his students developed the study of quasi-conformal transformations and found a large number of applications to various problems of mathematical physics, mechanics, and geometry. It is interesting to note that the study of quasi-conformal transformations has proved very fruitful in the theory of analytic functions itself. Of course, we cannot dwell here on all the various applications of the geometric method in the theory of functions of a complex variable.

§4. The Line Integral; Cauchy's Formula and Its Corollaries

Integrals of functions of a complex variable. In the study of the properties of analytic functions the concept of a complex variable plays a very important role. Corresponding to the definite integral of a function of a real variable, we here deal with the integral of a function of a complex variable along a curve. We consider in the plane a curve C beginning at the point z_0 and ending at the point z, and a function $f(z)$ defined on a domain containing the curve C. We divide the curve C into small segments (figure 18) at the points

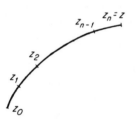

F<small>IG</small>. 18.

$$z_0, z_1, \cdots, z_n = z$$

and consider the sum

$$S = \sum_{k=1}^{n} f(z_k)\,(z_k - z_{k-1}).$$

If the function $f(z)$ is continuous and the curve C has finite length, we can prove, just as for real functions, that as the number of points of division is increased and the distance between neighboring points decreases to zero, the sum S approaches a completely determined limit.

This limit is called the *integral along the curve C* and is denoted by

$$\int_C f(z)\, dz.$$

We note that in this definition of the integral we have distinguished between the beginning and the end of the curve C; in other words, we have chosen a specific direction of motion on the curve C.

It is easy to prove a number of simple properties of the integral.

1. The integral of the sum of two functions is equal to the sum of the integrals of the individual functions:

$$\int_C [f(z) + g(z)]\, dz = \int_C f(z)\, dz + \int_C g(z)\, dz.$$

2. A constant multiple may be taken outside the integral sign:

$$\int_C Af(z)\, dz = A \int_C f(z)\, dz.$$

3. If the curve C is the sum of the curves C_1 and C_2, then

$$\int_C f(z)\, dz = \int_{C_1} f(z)\, dz + \int_{C_2} f(z)\, dz.$$

4. If $\bar{C}$ is the curve C with opposite orientation, then

$$\int_{\bar{C}} f(z)\, dz = - \int_C f(z)\, dz.$$

All these properties are obvious for the approximating sums and carry over to the integral in passing to the limit.

5. If the length of the curve C is equal to L and if everywhere on C the inequality

$$|f(z)| \leqslant M$$

is satisfied, then

$$\left| \int_C f(z)\, dz \right| \leqslant ML.$$

Let us prove this property. It is sufficient to prove the inequality for the sum S, since then it will carry over in the limit for the integral also.

For the sum

$$| S | = \left| \sum f(z_k)(z_k - z_{k-1}) \right| \leqslant \sum | f(z_k) | \, | z_k - z_{k-1} | \leqslant M \sum | z_k - z_{k-1} | \, .$$

But the sum in the second factor is equal to the sum of the lengths of the segments of the broken line inscribed in the curve C with vertices at the points z_k. The length of the broken line, as is well known, is not greater than the length of the curve, so that

$$| S | \leqslant ML.$$

We consider the integral of the simplest function $f(z) = 1$. Obviously in this case

$$S = (z_1 - z_0) + (z_2 - z_1) + \cdots + (z_n - z_{n-1}) = z_n - z_0 = z - z_0 \, .$$

This proves that

$$\int_C 1 \cdot dz = z - z_0 \, .$$

This result shows that for the function $f(z) = 1$ the value of the integral for all curves joining the points z_0 and z is the same. In other words, the value of the integral depends only on the beginning and end points of the path of integration. But it is easy to show that this property does not hold for arbitrary functions of a complex variable. For example, if $f(z) = x$, then a simple computation shows that

$$\int_{C_1} x \, dz = \frac{x^2}{2} + iyx, \quad \int_{C_2} x \, dz = \frac{x^2}{2}, \quad z = x + iy,$$

where C_1 and C_2 are the paths of integration shown in figure 19.

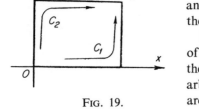

We leave it to the reader to verify these equations.

A remarkable fact in the theory of analytic functions is the following theorem of Cauchy.

If $f(z)$ is differentiable at every point of a simply connected domain D, then the integrals over all paths joining two arbitrary points of the domain z_0 and z are the same.

FIG. 19.

We will not give a proof of Cauchy's theorem here, but refer the interested reader to any course in the theory of functions of a complex variable. Let us mention here some important consequences of this theorem.

First of all, Cauchy's theorem allows us to introduce the indefinite integral of an analytic function. For let us fix the point z_0 and consider the integral along curves connecting z_0 and z:

$$F(z) = \int_{z_0}^{z} f(\zeta)\, d\zeta.$$

Here we may take the integral over any curve joining z_0 and z, since changing the curve does not change the value of the integral, which thus depends only on z. The function $F(z)$ is called an *indefinite integral* of $f(z)$.

An indefinite integral of $f(z)$ has a derivative equal to $f(z)$.

In many applications it is convenient to have a slightly different formulation of Cauchy's theorem, as follows.

If $f(z)$ is everywhere differentiable in a simply connected domain, then the integral over any closed contour lying in this domain is equal to zero:

$$\int_{\Gamma} f(z)\, dz = 0.$$

This is obvious since a closed contour has the same beginning and end, so that z_0 and z may be joined by a null path.

By a closed contour we will understand a contour traversed in the counterclockwise direction. If the contour is traversed in the clockwise direction we will denote it by $\bar{\Gamma}$.

The Cauchy integral.   On the basis of the last theorem we can prove the following fundamental formula of Cauchy that expresses the value of a differentiable function at interior points of a closed contour in terms of the values of the function on the contour itself

$$f(z) = \frac{1}{2\pi i} \int_{C} \frac{f(\zeta)\, d\zeta}{\zeta - z}.$$

We give a proof of this formula. Let z be fixed and ζ be an independent variable. The function

$$\phi(\zeta) = \frac{f(\zeta)}{\zeta - z}$$

will be continuous and differentiable at every point ζ inside the domain D, with the exception of the point $\zeta = z$, where the denominator vanishes, a circumstance that prevents the application of Cauchy's theorem to the function $\phi(\zeta)$ on the contour C.

We consider a circle K_ρ with center at the point z and radius ρ and show that

$$\int_C \phi(\zeta)\,d\zeta = \int_{K_\rho} \phi(\zeta)\,d\zeta. \tag{40}$$

To this end we construct the auxiliary closed contour Γ_ρ, consisting of

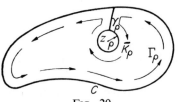

the contour C, the path γ_ρ connecting C with the circle, and the circle $\bar{K}_\rho$, taken with the opposite orientation (figure 20). The contour Γ_ρ is indicated by arrows. Since the point $\zeta = z$ is excluded, the function $\phi(\zeta)$ is differentiable everywhere inside Γ_ρ and thus

FIG. 20.

$$\int_{\Gamma_\rho} \phi(\zeta)\,d\zeta = 0. \tag{41}$$

But the contour Γ_ρ is divided into four parts: C, γ_ρ, $\bar{K}_\rho$ and $\bar{\gamma}_\rho$, so that from property 3 in the last subsection, we have

$$\int_{\Gamma_\rho} \phi(\zeta)\,d\zeta = \int_C \phi(\zeta)\,d\zeta + \int_{\gamma_\rho} \phi(\zeta)\,d\zeta + \int_{\bar{K}_\rho} \phi(\zeta)\,d\zeta + \int_{\bar{\gamma}_\rho} \phi(\zeta)\,d\zeta = 0.$$

Replacing the integrals along $\bar{K}_\rho$ and $\bar{\gamma}_\rho$ by integrals along K_ρ and γ_ρ, and using property 4, we get

$$\int_{\Gamma_\rho} \phi(\zeta)\,d\zeta = \int_C \phi(\zeta)\,d\zeta - \int_{K_\rho} \phi(\zeta)\,d\zeta = 0,$$

which proves formula (40).

To compute the right side of (40), we set

$$\int_{K_\rho} \phi(\zeta)\,d\zeta = \int_{K_\rho} \frac{f(\zeta)}{\zeta - z}\,d\zeta = \int_{K_\rho} \frac{f(\zeta) - f(z)}{\zeta - z}\,d\zeta + \int_{K_\rho} \frac{f(z)\,d\zeta}{\zeta - z}$$

$$= \int_{K_\rho} \frac{f(\zeta) - f(z)}{\zeta - z}\,d\zeta + f(z)\int_{K_\rho} \frac{d\zeta}{\zeta - z}. \tag{42}$$

We compute the second term first. On the circle K_ρ,

$$\zeta = z + \rho(\cos\theta + i\sin\theta).$$

Using the fact that z and ρ are constant, we get

$$d\zeta = \rho(-\sin\theta + i\cos\theta)\,d\theta = i\rho(\cos\theta + i\sin\theta)\,d\theta,$$

and thus

$$\zeta - z = \rho(\cos\theta + i\sin\theta),$$

so that

$$\int_{K_\rho} \frac{d\zeta}{\zeta - z} = \int_{K_\rho} i\,d\theta = 2\pi i,$$

since for a circuit of the circumference the total change in θ is equal to 2π. From (40) and (42) we have

$$\int_C \frac{f(\zeta)\,d\zeta}{\zeta - z} = 2\pi i\,f(z) + \int_{K_\rho} \frac{f(\zeta) - f(z)}{\zeta - z}\,d\zeta.$$

In this equation let us take limits as $\rho \to 0$. The left side and the first term of the right side will remain unchanged. We will show that the limit of the second term is equal to zero. Then for $\rho \to 0$ our equation gives us Cauchy's formula. In order to prove that the second term tends to zero as $\rho \to 0$ we note that

$$\lim_{\zeta \to z} \frac{f(\zeta) - f(z)}{\zeta - z} = f'(\zeta),$$

i.e., the expression under the integral sign has a finite limit, and thus is bounded

$$\left| \frac{f(\zeta) - f(z)}{\zeta - z} \right| < M.$$

Applying property 5 of the integral, we have

$$\left| \int_{K_\rho} \frac{f(\zeta) - f(z)}{\zeta - z}\,d\zeta \right| \leqslant M2\pi\rho \to 0.$$

This completes the proof of Cauchy's formula. Cauchy's formula is one of the basic tools of investigation in the theory of functions of a complex variable.

Expansion of differentiable functions in a power series. We apply Cauchy's theorem to establish two basic properties of differentiable functions of a complex variable.

Every function of a complex variable that has a first derivative in a domain D has derivatives of all orders.

In fact, inside a closed contour our function may be expressed by the Cauchy integral formula

$$f(z) = \frac{1}{2\pi i} \int_c \frac{f(\zeta)}{\zeta - z} \, d\zeta.$$

The function of z under the sign of integration is a differentiable function; thus, differentiating under the integral sign, we get

$$f'(z) = \frac{1}{2\pi i} \int_c \frac{f(\zeta)}{(\zeta - z)^2} \, d\zeta.$$

Under the integral sign there is again a differentiable function; thus we can again differentiate, obtaining

$$f''(z) = \frac{1 \cdot 2}{2\pi i} \int_c \frac{f(\zeta) \, d\zeta}{(\zeta - z)^3}.$$

Continuing the differentiation, we get the general formula

$$f^{(n)}(z) = \frac{n!}{2\pi i} \int_c \frac{f(\zeta) \, d\zeta}{(\zeta - z)^{n+1}}.$$

In this manner we may compute the derivative of any order. To make this proof completely rigorous, we need also to show that the differentiation under the integral sign is valid. We will not give this part of the proof.

The second property is the following:

If $f(z)$ is everywhere differentiable on a circle K with center at the point a, then $f(z)$ can be expanded in a Taylor series

$$f(z) = f(a) + \frac{f'(a)}{1!} (z - a) + \cdots + \frac{f^{(n)}(a)}{n!}(z - a)^{n+1} + \cdots,$$

which converges inside K.

In §1 we defined analytic functions of a complex variable as functions that can be expanded in power series. This last theorem says that every differentiable function of a complex variable is an analytic function. This is a special property of functions of a complex variable that has no analogue in the real domain. A function of a real variable that has a first derivative may fail to have a second derivative at every point.

We prove the theorem formulated in the previous paragraphs.

Let $f(z)$ have a derivative inside and on the boundary of the circle K with center at the point a. Then inside K the function $f(z)$ can be expressed by the Cauchy integral

$$f(z) = \frac{1}{2\pi i} \int_C \frac{f(\zeta)\, d\zeta}{\zeta - z}. \tag{43}$$

We write

$$\zeta - z = (\zeta - a) - (z - a),$$

then

$$\frac{1}{\zeta - z} = \frac{1}{(\zeta - a) - (z - a)} = \frac{1}{\zeta - a} \frac{1}{1 - \dfrac{z - a}{\zeta - a}}. \tag{44}$$

Using the fact that the point z lies inside the circle, and ζ is on the circumference we get

$$\left| \frac{z - a}{\zeta - a} \right| < 1,$$

so that from the basic formula for a geometric progression

$$\frac{1}{1 - \dfrac{z - a}{\zeta - a}} = 1 + \left(\frac{z - a}{\zeta - a}\right) + \cdots + \left(\frac{z - a}{\zeta - a}\right)^n + \cdots, \tag{45}$$

and the series on the right converges. Using (44) and (45), we can represent formula (43) in the form

$$f(z) = \frac{1}{2\pi i} \int_C \left[\frac{f(\zeta)}{\zeta - a} + (z - a) \frac{f(\zeta)}{(\zeta - a)^2} + \cdots \right.$$
$$\left. + (z - a)^n \frac{f(\zeta)}{(\zeta - a)^{n+1}} + \cdots \right] d\zeta.$$

We now apply term-by-term integration to the series inside the brackets. (The validity of this operation can be established rigorously.) Removing the factor $(z - a)^n$, which does not depend on ζ, from the integral sign in each term, we get

$$f(z) = \frac{1}{2\pi i} \int_C \frac{f(\zeta)\, d\zeta}{\zeta - a} + \frac{z - a}{2\pi i} \int_C \frac{f(\zeta)\, d\zeta}{(\zeta - a)^2} + \cdots$$
$$+ \frac{(z - a)^n}{2\pi i} \int_C \frac{f(\zeta)\, d\zeta}{(\zeta - a)^{n+1}} + \cdots.$$

Now using the integral formulas for the sequence of derivatives, we may write

$$\frac{1}{2\pi i} \int_C \frac{f(\zeta)\, d\zeta}{(\zeta - a)^{n+1}} = \frac{f^{(n)}(a)}{n!},$$

so that we get

$$f(z) = f(a) + \frac{f'(a)}{1!}(z - a) + \cdots + \frac{f^{(n)}(a)}{n!}(z - a)^n + \cdots.$$

We have shown that differentiable functions of a complex variable can be expanded in power series. Conversely, functions represented by power series are differentiable. Their derivatives may be found by term-by-term differentiation of the series. (The validity of this operation can be established rigorously.)

Entire functions. A power series gives an analytic representation of a function only in some circle. This circle has a radius equal to the distance to the nearest point at which the function ceases to be analytic, i.e., to the nearest singular point of the function.

Among analytic functions it is natural to single out the class of functions that are analytic for all finite values of their argument. Such functions are represented by power series, converging for all values of the argument z, and are called *entire functions* of z. If we consider expansions about the origin, then an entire function will be expressed by a series of the form

$$G(z) = c_0 + c_1 z + c_2 z^2 + \cdots + c_n z^n + \cdots.$$

If in this series all the coefficients, from a certain one on, are equal to zero, the function is simply a polynomial, or an entire rational function

$$P(z) = c_0 + c_1 z + \cdots + c_n z^n.$$

If in the expansion there are infinitely many terms that are different from zero, then the entire function is called *transcendental*.

Examples of such functions are:

$$e^z = 1 + \frac{z}{1!} + \frac{z^2}{2!} + \cdots,$$

$$\sin z = \frac{z}{1!} - \frac{z^3}{3!} + \frac{z^5}{5!} - \cdots,$$

$$\cos z = 1 - \frac{z^2}{2!} + \frac{z^4}{4!} - \cdots.$$

In the study of properties of polynomials, an important role is played by the distribution of the roots of the equation

$$P(z) = 0,$$

or, more generally speaking, we may raise the question of the distribution of the points for which the polynomial has a given value A

$$P(z) = A.$$

The fundamental theorem of algebra says that every polynomial takes a given value A in at least one point. This property cannot be extended to an arbitrary entire function. For example, the function $w = e^z$ does not take the value zero at any point of the z-plane. However, we do have the following theorem of Picard: Every entire function assumes every arbitrarily preassigned value an infinite number of times, with the possible exception of one value.

The distribution of the points of the plane at which an entire function takes on a given value A is one of the central questions in the theory of entire functions.

The number of roots of a polynomial is equal to its degree. The degree of a polynomial is closely related to the rapidity of growth of $|P(z)|$ as $|z| \to \infty$. In fact, we can write

$$|P(z)| = |z|^n \cdot \left| a_n + \frac{a_{n-1}}{z} + \cdots + \frac{a_0}{z^n} \right|,$$

and since for $|z| \to \infty$, the second factor tends to $|a_n|$, a polynomial of degree n, for large values of $|z|$, grows like $|a_n| \cdot |z|^n$. So it is clear that for larger values of n, the growth of $|P_n(z)|$ for $|z| \to \infty$ will be faster and also the polynomial will have more roots. It turns out that this principle is also valid for entire functions. However, for an entire function $f(z)$, generally speaking, there are infinitely many roots, and thus the question of the number of roots has no meaning. Nevertheless, we can consider the number of roots $n(r, a)$ of the equation

$$f(z) = a$$

in a circle of radius r, and investigate how this number changes with increasing r. The rate of growth of $n(r, a)$ proves to be connected with the rate of growth of the maximum $M(r)$ of the modulus of the entire function on the circle of radius r. As stated earlier, for an entire function there may exist one exceptional value of a for which the equation may not have even one root. For all other values of a, the rate of growth of the number $n(r, a)$ is comparable to the rate of growth of the quantity ln $M(r)$. We cannot give more exact formulations here for these laws.

The properties of the distribution of the roots of entire functions are connected with problems in the theory of numbers and have enabled mathematicians to establish many important properties of the Riemann zeta functions,* on the basis of which it is possible to prove many theorems about prime numbers.

Fractional or meromorphic functions. The class of entire functions may be considered as an extension of the class of algebraic polynomials. From the polynomials we may derive the wider class of rational functions

$$R(z) = \frac{P(z)}{Q(z)},$$

which are the quotients of two polynomials.

Similarly it is natural to form a new class of functions by means of entire functions. A function $f(z)$ which is the quotient of two entire functions $G_1(z)$ and $G_2(z)$

$$f(z) = \frac{G_1(z)}{G_2(z)}$$

is called a *fractional* or *meromorphic* function. The class of functions arising in this way plays a large role in mathematical analysis. Among the elementary functions contained in the class of meromorphic functions are, for example:

$$\tan z = \frac{\sin z}{\cos z}, \qquad \cot z = \frac{\cos z}{\sin z}.$$

A meromorphic function will not be analytic on the whole complex plane. At those points where the denominator $G_2(z)$ vanishes, the function $f(z)$ becomes infinite. The roots of $G_2(z)$ form a set of isolated points in the plane. In neighborhoods of these points, the function $f(z)$ naturally cannot be expanded in a Taylor series; in a neighborhood of such a point a, however, a meromorphic function may be represented by a power series that also contains a certain number of negative powers of $(z - a)$:

$$f(z) = \frac{C_{-m}}{(z-a)^m} + \cdots + \frac{C_{-1}}{z-a} + C_0 + C_1(z-a) + \cdots + C_n(z-a)^n + \cdots.$$
$$(46)$$

---

* Cf. Chapter X on the theory of numbers.

As z approaches the point a, the value of $f(z)$ tends to infinity. An isolated singular point at which an analytic function goes to infinity is called a *pole*. The loss of analyticity of the function at the point a comes from the terms with negative powers of $z - a$ in the expansion (46). The expression

$$\frac{C_{-m}}{(z - a)^m} + \cdots + \frac{C_{-1}}{(z - a)}$$

characterizes the behavior of a meromorphic function near a singular point and is called the *principal part* of the expansion (46). The behavior of a meromorphic function is determined by its principal part in a neighborhood of a pole. In many cases, if we know the principal part of the expansion of a meromorphic function in the neighborhood of all its poles, we may construct the function. Thus, for example, if $f(z)$ is rational and vanishes at infinity, then it is equal to the sum of the principal parts of its expansions about all of its poles, the number of which, for a rational function, is finite:

$$f(z) = \sum_{(k)} \left[\frac{C_{-m_k}^{(k)}}{(z - a_k)^{m_k}} + \cdots + \frac{C_{-1}^{(k)}}{z - a_k} \right].$$

In the general case a rational function may be represented as the sum of all of its principal parts and a polynomial

$$f(z) = \sum_{(k)} \left[\frac{C_{-m_k}^{(k)}}{(z - a_k)^{m_k}} + \cdots + \frac{C_{-1}^{(k)}}{z - a_k} \right] + C_0 + C_1 z + \cdots + C_m z^m.$$
$$(47)$$

Formula (47) gives an expression for a rational function in which the role played by its singular points is clear. Expression (47) for a rational function is very convenient for various applications of rational functions and also has great theoretical interest as showing how the singular points of the function define its structure everywhere. It turns out that, just as in the case of a rational function, every meromorphic function may be constructed from the principal parts of its poles. We introduce without proof the appropriate expression, for example, for the function $\cot z$. The poles of the function $\cot z$ are obtained as the roots of the equation

$$\sin z = 0$$

and are situated at the points: $\cdots, -k\pi, \cdots, -\pi, 0, \pi, \cdots, k\pi, \cdots$. It may be shown that the principal part of the expansion of the function $\cot z$ in a power series at the pole $z = k\pi$ will be

$$\frac{1}{z - k\pi},$$

and the function $\cot z$ is equal to the sum of the principal parts with respect to all poles

$$\cot z = \frac{1}{z} + \sum_{k=1}^{\infty} \left(\frac{1}{z - k\pi} + \frac{1}{z + k\pi} \right). \tag{48}$$

The expansion of a meromorphic function in a series of the principal parts is noteworthy in that it clearly shows the position of all the singular points and also allows us to compute the function on the whole of its domain of definition.

The theory of meromorphic functions has become fundamental for the study of many classes of functions that are of great importance in analysis. In particular, we must emphasize its significance for the equations of mathematical physics. The creation of the theory of integral equations, providing answers to many important questions in the theory of the equations of mathematical physics, was based to a great extent on the fundamental theorems for meromorphic functions.

Since that time the development of that part of functional analysis which is most closely connected with mathematical physics, namely the theory of operators, has very often depended on facts from the theory of analytic functions.

On analytic representation of functions. We saw previously that in a neighborhood of every point where a function is differentiable it may be defined by a power series. For an entire function the power series converges on the whole plane and gives an analytic expression for the function wherever it is defined. In case the function is not entire, the Taylor series, as we know, converges only in a circle whose circumference passes through the nearest singular point of the function. Consequently the power series does not allow us to compute the function everywhere, and so it may happen that an analytic function cannot be given by a power series on its whole domain of definition. For a meromorphic function an analytic expression giving the function on its whole domain of definition is the expansion in principal parts.

If a function is not entire but is defined in some circle or if we have a function defined in some domain but we want to study it only in a circle, then the Taylor series may serve to represent it. But when we study the function in domains that are different from circles, there arises the question of finding an analytic expression for the function suitable for representing it on the whole domain. A power series giving an expression for an analytic function in a circle has as its terms the simplest polynomials $a_n z^n$. It is natural to ask whether we can expand an analytic function in an arbitrary domain in a more general series of polynomials. Then every term of the series can again be computed by arithmetic operations, and we obtain a method for representing functions that is once more based on the simplest operations of arithmetic. The general answer to this question is given by the following theorem.

An analytic function, given on an arbitrary domain, the boundary of which consists of one curve, may be expanded in a series of polynomials

$$f(z) = P_0(z) + P_1(z) + \cdots + P_n(z) + \cdots.$$

The theorem formulated gives only a general answer to the question of expanding a function in a series of polynomials in an arbitrary domain but does not yet allow us to construct the series for a given function, as was done earlier in the case of the Taylor series. This theorem raises rather then solves the question of expanding functions in a series of polynomials. Questions of the construction of the series of polynomials, given the function or some of its properties, questions of the construction of more rapidly converging series or of series closely related to the behavior of the function itself, questions of the structure of a function defined by a given series of polynomials, all these questions represent an extensive development of the theory of approximation of functions by series of polynomials. In the creation of this theory a large role has been played by Soviet mathematicians, who have derived a series of fundamental results.

§5. Uniqueness Properties and Analytic Continuation

Uniqueness properties of analytic functions. One of the most remarkable properties of analytic functions is their uniqueness, as expressed in the following theorem.

If in the domain D two analytic functions are given that agree on some curve C lying inside the domain, then they agree on the entire domain.

The proof of this theorem is very simple. Let $f_1(z)$ and $f_2(z)$ be the two functions analytic in the domain D and agreeing on the curve C. The difference

$$\phi(z) = f_1(z) - f_2(z)$$

will be an analytic function on the domain D and will vanish on the curve C. We now show that $\phi(z) = 0$ at every point of the domain D. In fact, if in the domain D there exists a point z_0 (figure 21) at which $\phi(z_0) \neq 0$, we extend the curve C to the point z_0 and proceed along the extended curve toward z_0 as long as the function remains equal to zero on Γ. Let ζ be the last point of Γ that is accessible in this way. If $\phi(z_0) \neq 0$, then $\zeta \neq z_0$, and on a segment of the curve Γ beyond ζ the function $\phi(z)$, by the definition of the point ζ, will not be equal to zero. We show that this is impossible. In fact, on the part Γ_ζ of the curve Γ up to the point ζ, we have $\phi(z) = 0$. We may compute all derivatives of the function $\phi(z)$ on Γ_ζ using only the values of $\phi(z)$ on Γ_ζ, so that on Γ_ζ all derivatives of $\phi(z)$ are equal to zero. In particular, at the point ζ

$$\phi(\zeta) = \phi'(\zeta) = \cdots = \phi^{(n)}(\zeta) = \cdots = 0.$$

Let us expand the function $\phi(\zeta)$ in a Taylor series at the point ζ. All the coefficients of the expansion vanish, so that we get

$$\phi(z) = 0$$

in some circle with center at the point ζ, lying in the domain D. In

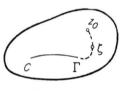

FIG. 21.

particular, it follows that the equation $\phi(z) = 0$ must be satisfied on some segment of the curve Γ lying beyond ζ. The assumption $\phi(z_0) \neq 0$ gives us a contradiction.

This theorem shows that if we know the values of an analytic function on some segment of a curve or on some part of a domain, then the values of the function are uniquely deter-

mined everywhere in the given domain. Consequently, the values of an analytic function in various parts of the argument plane are closely connected with one another.

To realize the significance of this uniqueness property of an analytic function, it is only necessary to recall that the general definition of a function of a complex variable allows any law of correspondence between values of the argument and values of the function. With such a definition there can, of course, be no question of determining the values of a function at any point by its values in another part of the plane. We see that the single requirement of differentiability of a function of a complex variable is so strong that it determines the connection between values of the function at different places.

We also emphasize that in the theory of functions of a real variable the differentiability of a function does not in itself lead to any similar consequences. In fact, we may construct examples of functions that are infinitely often differentiable and agree on some part of the Ox axis but differ elsewhere. For example, a function equal to zero for all negative values of x may be defined in such a manner that for positive x it differs from zero and has continuous derivatives of every order. For this it is sufficient, for example, to set, for $x > 0$

$$f(x) = e^{-1/x}.$$

Analytic continuation and complete analytic functions. The domain of definition of a given function of a complex variable is often restricted by the very manner of defining the function. Consider a very elementary example. Let the function be given by the series

$$f(z) = 1 + z + z^2 + \cdots + z^n + \cdots. \tag{49}$$

This series, as is well known, converges in the unit circle and diverges outside this circle. Thus the analytic function given by formula (49) is defined only in this circle. On the other hand, we know that the sum of the series (49) in the circle $|z| < 1$ is expressed by the formula

$$f(z) = \frac{1}{1 - z}. \tag{50}$$

Formula (50) has meaning for all values of $z \neq 1$. From the uniqueness theorem it follows that expression (50) represents the unique analytic function, agreeing with the sum of the series (49) in the circle $|z| < 1$. So this function, given at first only in the unit circle, has been extended to the whole plane.

If we have a function $f(z)$ defined inside some domain D, and there exists another function $F(z)$ defined in a domain Δ, containing D, and agreeing with $f(z)$ in D, then from the uniqueness theorem the value of $F(z)$ in Δ is defined in a unique manner.

The function $F(z)$ is called the *analytic continuation* of $f(z)$. An analytic function is called *complete* if it cannot be continued analytically beyond the domain on which it is already defined. For example, an entire function, defined for the whole plane, is a complete function. A meromorphic function is also a complete function; it is defined everywhere except at its poles. However there exist analytic functions whose entire domain of definition is a bounded domain. We will not give these more complicated examples.

The concept of a complete analytic function leads to the necessity of considering multiple-valued functions of a complex variable. We show this by the example of the function

$$\operatorname{Ln} z = \ln r + i\phi,$$

where $r = |z|$ and $\phi = \arg z$. If at some point $z_0 = r_0(\cos \phi_0 + i \sin \phi_0)$ of the z-plane we consider some initial value of the function

$$(\operatorname{Ln} z)_0 = \ln r_0 + i\phi_0,$$

then our analytic function may be extended continuously along a curve C.

As was mentioned earlier, it is easy to see that if the point z describes

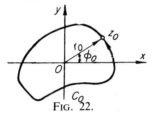

FIG. 22.

a closed path C_0, issuing from the point z_0 and circling around the origin (figure 22), and then returning to the point z_0, we find at the point z_0 the original value of ln r_0 but the angle ϕ is increased by 2π. This shows that if we extend the function Ln z in a continuous manner along the path C, we increase its value by $2\pi i$ in one circuit of the contour C. If the point z moves along this closed contour n times, then in place of the original value

$$(\text{Ln } z)_0 = \ln r_0 + i\phi_0$$

we obtain the new value

$$(\text{Ln } z)_n = \ln r_0 + (2\pi n + \phi_0)i.$$

If the point z describes the contour m times in the opposite direction, we get

$$(\text{Ln } z)_{-m} = \ln r_0 + (-2\pi m + \phi_0)i.$$

These remarks show that on the complex plane we are unavoidably compelled to consider the connection between the various values of Ln z. The function Ln z has infinitely many values. With respect to its multiple-valued character, a special role is played by the point $z = 0$, around which we pass from one value of the function to another. It is easy to establish that if z describes a closed contour not surrounding the origin, the value of Ln z is not changed. The point $z = 0$ is called a branch point of the function Ln z.

In general, if for a function $f(z)$, in a circuit around the point a, we pass from one of its values to another, then the point a is called a *branch point* of the function $f(z)$.

Let us consider a second example. Let

$$w = \sqrt[n]{z}.$$

As noted previously, this function is also multiple-valued and takes on n values

$$\sqrt[n]{r}\left(\cos\frac{\phi}{n} + i\sin\frac{\phi}{n}\right), \qquad \sqrt[n]{r}\left(\cos\frac{\phi + 2\pi}{n} + i\sin\frac{\phi + 2\pi}{n}\right),$$

$$\cdots, \sqrt[n]{r}\left(\cos\frac{\phi + 2\pi(n-1)}{n} + i\sin\frac{\phi + 2\pi(n-1)}{n}\right).$$

All the various values of our function may be derived from the single one

$$w_0 = \sqrt[n]{r_0} \left(\cos \frac{\phi_0}{n} + i \sin \frac{\phi_0}{n} \right)$$

by describing a closed curve around the origin, since for each circuit around the origin the angle ϕ will be increased by 2π.

In describing the closed curve $(n - 1)$ times, we obtain from the first value of $\sqrt[n]{z}$, all the remaining $(n - 1)$ values. Going around the contour the nth time leads back to the value

$$\sqrt[n]{z_0} = \sqrt[n]{r_0} \left(\cos \frac{\phi_0 + 2\pi n}{n} + i \sin \frac{\phi_0 + 2\pi n}{n} \right) = \sqrt[n]{r_0} \left(\cos \frac{\phi_0}{n} + i \sin \frac{\phi_0}{n} \right),$$

i.e., we return to the original value of the root.

Riemann surfaces for multiple-valued functions. There exists an easily visualized geometric manner of representing the character of a multiple-valued function.

We consider again the function Ln z, and on the z-plane we make a cut along the positive part of the axis Ox. If the point z is prevented from crossing the cut, then we cannot pass continuously from one value of Ln z to another. If we continue Ln z from the point z_0, we can arrive only at the same value of Ln z.

The single-valued function found in this manner in the cut z-plane is called a *single-valued branch* of the function Ln z. All the values of Ln z are distributed on an infinite set of single-valued branches

$$\ln r + i\phi, \quad 2\pi n < \phi \leqslant 2\pi(n + 1).$$

It is easy to show that the nth branch takes on the same value on the lower side of the cut as the $(n + 1)$th branch has on the upper side.

To distinguish the different branches of Ln z, we imagine infinitely many examples of the z-plane, each of them cut along the positive part of the axis Ox, and map onto the nth sheet the values of the argument z corresponding to the nth branch. The points lying on different examples of the plane but having the same coordinates will here correspond to one and the same number $x + iy$; but the fact that this number is mapped on the nth sheet shows that we are considering the nth branch of the logarithm.

In order to represent geometrically the fact that the nth branch of the logarithm, on the lower part of the cut of the nth plane, agrees with the

$(n + 1)$th branch of the logarithm on the upper part of the cut in the $(n + 1)$th plane, we paste together the nth plane and the $(n + 1)$th, connecting the lower part of the cut in the nth plane with the upper part of the cut in the $(n + 1)$th plane. This construction leads us to a many-sheeted surface, having the form of a spiral staircase (figure 23). The role of the central column of the staircase is played by the point $z = 0$.

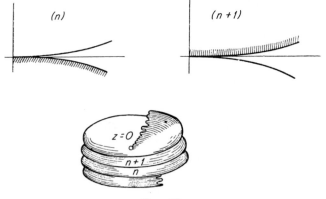

Fig. 23.

If a point passes from one sheet to another, then the complex number returns to its original value, but the function Ln z passes from one branch to another.

The surface so constructed is called the *Riemann surface* of the function Ln z. Riemann first introduced the idea of constructing surfaces representing the character of multiple-valued analytic functions and showed the fruitfulness of this idea.

Let us also discuss the construction of the Riemann surface for the function $w = \sqrt{z}$. This function is double-valued and has a branch point at the origin.

We imagine two examples of the z-plane, placed one on top of the other and both cut along the positive part of the axis Ox. If z starts from z_0 and describes a closed contour C containing the origin, then $\sqrt{z}$ passes from one branch to the other, and thus the point on the Riemann surface passes from one sheet to the other. To arrange this, we paste the lower border of the cut in the first sheet to the upper border of the cut in the second sheet. If z describes the closed contour C a second time, then $\sqrt{z}$ must return to its original value, so that the point in the Riemann surface must return to its original position on the first sheet. To arrange this, we must now attach the lower border of the second sheet to the upper border of the first sheet. As a result we get a two-sheeted surface, intersecting itself along the positive part of the axis Ox. Some idea of this surface may be obtained from figure 24, showing the neighborhood of the point $z = 0$.

In the same way we can construct a many-sheeted surface to represent the character of any given multiple-valued function. The different sheets of such a surface are connected with one another around branch points

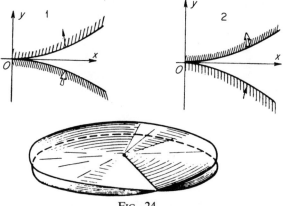

FIG. 24.

of the function. It turns out that the properties of analytic functions are closely connected with the geometric properties of Riemann surfaces. These surfaces are not only an auxiliary means of illustrating the character of a multiple-valued function but also play a fundamental role in the study of the properties of analytic functions and the development of methods of investigating them. Riemann surfaces formed a kind of bridge between analysis and geometry in the region of complex variables, enabling us not only to relate to geometry the most profound analytic properties of the functions but also to develop a whole new region of geometry, namely topology, which investigates those geometric properties of figures which remain unchanged under continuous deformation.

One of the clearest examples of the significance of the geometric properties of Riemann surfaces is the theory of algebraic functions, i.e., functions obtained as the solution of an equation

$$f(z, w) = 0$$

the left side of which is a polynomial in z and w. The Riemann surface of such a function may always be deformed continuously into a sphere or else into a sphere with handles (figure 25). The characteristic property of these surfaces is the number of handles. This number is called the genus of the surface and of the algebraic function from which the surface was obtained. It turns out that the genus of an algebraic function determines its most important properties.

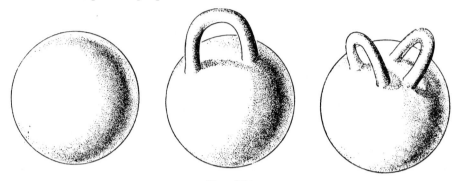

Fig. 25.

§6. Conclusion

The theory of analytic functions arose in connection with the problem of solving algebraic equations. But as it developed it came into constant contact with newer and newer branches of mathematics. It shed light on the fundamental classes of functions occurring in analysis, mechanics, and mathematical physics. Many of the central facts of analysis could at last be made clear only by passing to the complex domain. Functions of a complex variable received an immediate physical interpretation in the important vector fields of hydrodynamics and electrodynamics and provided a remarkable apparatus for the solution of problems arising in these branches of science. Relations were discovered between the theory of functions and problems in the theory of heat conduction, elasticity, and so forth.

General questions in the theory of differential equations and special methods for their solution have always been based to a great extent on the theory of functions of a complex variable. Analytic functions entered naturally into the theory of integral equations and the general theory of linear operators. Close connections were discovered between the theory of analytic functions and geometry. All these constantly widening connections of the theory of functions with new areas of mathematics and science show the vitality of the theory and the continuous enrichment of its range of problems.

In our survey we have not been able to present a complete picture of all the manifold ramifications of the theory of functions. We have tried only to give some idea of the widely varied nature of its problems by indicating the basic elementary facts for some of the various fundamental directions in which the theory has moved. Some of its most important aspects, its connection with the theory of differential equations and special functions, with elliptic and automorphic functions, with the theory of trigonometric series, and with many other branches of mathematics, have been completely ignored in our discussion. In other cases we have had to restrict ourselves to the briefest indications. But we hope that this survey will give the reader a general idea of the character and significance of the theory of functions of a complex variable.

Suggested Reading

R. V. Churchill, *Introduction to complex variables and applications*, McGraw-Hill, New York, 1948.

P. Franklin, *Functions of complex variables*, Prentice-Hall, Englewood Cliffs, N. J., 1958.

G. N. Watson, *Complex integration and Cauchy's theorem*, Hafner, New York, 1960.

PART 4

CHAPTER X

PRIME NUMBERS

§1. The Study of the Theory of Numbers

Whole numbers. As the reader knows from the introduction to Chapter I, mankind had to deal even in the most ancient times with whole numbers, but the passage of many centuries was necessary to produce the concept of the infinite sequence of natural numbers

$$1, 2, 3, 4, 5, \cdots. \tag{1}$$

Nowadays, in the most various questions of practical activity, we are constantly faced with problems involving whole numbers. Whole numbers reflect many quantitative relations in nature; in all questions connected with discrete objects, they form the necessary mathematical apparatus.

Moreover, whole numbers play an important role in the study of the continuous. Thus, for example, in mathematical analysis one considers the expansion of an analytic function in a power series with integral powers of x

$$f(x) = a_0 + a_1 x + a_2 x^2 + \cdots + a_n x^n + \cdots.$$

All computations are essentially carried out with *whole* numbers, as is immediately obvious from even a superficial examination of automatic computing machines or desk calculators, or of mathematical tables, such as tables of logarithms. After these operations on whole numbers have been carried out, decimal points are inserted in well-defined positions, corresponding to the formation of decimal fractions; such fractions, like all rational fractions, represent quotients of two *whole* numbers. In dealing with any *real* number in practical work (for example, π), we replace it in fact by a rational fraction (for example, we assume that $\pi = 22/7$, or that $\pi = 3.14$).

While the establishment of rules for operating on numbers is the concern of arithmetic, the deeper properties of the sequence of natural numbers (1), extended to include zero and the negative integers, are studied in the *theory of numbers*, which is the science of the system of integers and, in an extended sense, also of systems of numbers constructed in some definite manner from the integers (see, in particular, §5 of this chapter). It is understood that the theory of numbers considers integers not as isolated one from another but as interdependent; the theory of numbers studies properties of integers that are defined by certain relations among them.

One of the basic questions in the theory of numbers concerns *divisibility* of one number by another; if the result of dividing the integer a by the integer b (not equal to zero) is an integer, i.e., if

$$a = b \cdot c$$

(a, b, c are integers) then we say that a is *divisible* by b or that b *divides a.* If the result of dividing the integer a by the integer b is a fraction, then we say that a is not divisible by b. Questions of divisibility of numbers are encountered constantly in practice and also play an important role in some questions of mathematical analysis. For example, if the expansion of a function in integer powers of x

$$f(x) = a_0 + a_1 x + a_2 x^2 + \cdots + a_n x^n + \cdots \tag{2}$$

is such that all odd coefficients (with indices not divisible by 2) are equal to zero, i.e., if

$$f(x) = a_0 + a_2 x^2 + \cdots + a_{2k} x^{2k} + \cdots,$$

then the function satisfies the condition

$$f(-x) = f(x);$$

such a function is called an even function, and its graph is symmetric with respect to the axis of ordinates. But if in the expansion (2) all the even coefficients (with indices divisible by 2) are equal to zero, in other words, if

$$f(x) = a_1 x + a_3 x^3 + \cdots + a_{2k+1} x^{2k+1} + \cdots,$$

then

$$f(-x) = -f(x);$$

in this case the function is called odd, and its graph is symmetric with respect to the origin.

Thus, for example

$$\sin x = x - \frac{x^3}{3!} + \frac{x^5}{5!} - \cdots \qquad \text{(odd function)};$$

$$\cos x = 1 - \frac{x^2}{2!} + \frac{x^4}{4!} - \cdots \qquad \text{(even function)}.$$

The geometric question of the possibility of construction of a regular n-polygon with ruler and compass turns out to depend on the arithmetic nature of the number n.*

A *prime number* is any integer (greater than one) that has only the two positive integer divisors, one and itself. One is not considered as a prime number since it does not have two different positive divisors.

Thus the prime numbers are

$$2, 3, 5, 7, 11, 13, 17, 19, 23, 29, \cdots. \qquad (3)$$

Prime numbers play a fundamental role in the theory of numbers because of the basic theorem: Every integer $n > 1$ may be represented as the product of prime numbers (with possible repetition of factors), i.e., in the form

$$n = p_1^{a_1} p_2^{a_2} \cdots p_k^{a_k}, \qquad (4)$$

where $p_1 < p_2 < \cdots < p_k$ are primes and $a_1, a_2, \cdots, a_k$ are integers not less than one; furthermore, the representation of n in the form (4) is unique.

The properties of numbers connected with the representation of numbers as a sum of terms are called *additive*; the properties of numbers relating to their representation in the form of a product are called *multiplicative*. The connection between additive and multiplicative properties of numbers is extraordinarily complicated; it has given rise to a series of basic problems in the theory of numbers.

The existence of these difficult problems in the theory of numbers together with the fact that the whole number is not only the simplest and clearest of all mathematical concepts but is closely related to objective reality have led to the creation, for use in the theory of numbers, of profound new ideas and powerful methods, many of which have become important in other branches of mathematics as well. For example, a vast influence on all developments of mathematics has been exerted by the idea of the infinite sequence of natural numbers, reflecting the infiniteness of the material world in space and time. Of great significance also is the fact the terms in the sequence of natural numbers are ordered. Study of the

---

* See Chapter IV.

operations on integers has led to the concept of an algebraic operation, which plays a basic role in several different branches of mathematics.

Of immense importance in mathematics has been the concept, particularly applicable to arithmetical questions, of an algorithm, a process of solving problems based on the repeated carrying out of a strictly defined procedure; in particular, the role of the algorithm is fundamental to the use of mathematical machines. The essential nature of the algorithmic method for solving a problem is clearly illustrated by the Euclidean algorithm for finding the greatest common divisor of two natural numbers a and b.

Suppose $a > b$. We divide a by b and find the quotient q_1 and, if b does not divide a, the remainder r_2

$$a = bq_1 + r_2, \quad 0 < r_2 < b. \tag{5_1}$$

Further, if $r_2 \neq 0$, we divide b by r_2

$$b = r_2 q_2 + r_3, \quad 0 < r_3 < r_2. \tag{5_2}$$

Then we divide r_2 by r_3 and continue until we get to a zero remainder, which must necessarily happen for a decreasing set of nonnegative integers $r_2, r_3, \cdots$. Let

$$r_{n-2} = r_{n-1} q_{n-1} + r_n, \tag{5_{n-1}}$$

$$r_{n-1} = r_n q_n, \tag{5_n}$$

then r_n is at once seen to be the greatest common divisor of a and b. For if two integers l and m have a common divisor d, then for any integers h and k the number $hl + km$ will also be divisible by d. Let us denote the greatest common divisor of a and b by δ. From equation (5_1) we see that δ is a divisor of r_2; from (5_2) it follows that δ is a divisor of $r_3, \cdots$; from (5_{n-1}) that δ is a divisor of r_n. But r_n itself is a common divisor of a and b, since in (5_n) we see that r_n divides r_{n-1}; from (5_{n-1}) that r_n divides r_{n-2}, etc. Thus δ is identical with r_n and the problem of finding the greatest common divisor of a and b is solved. We have here a well-defined procedure, of the same type for all a and b, which leads us automatically to the desired result and is thus a characteristic example of an algorithm.

The theory of numbers has exerted an influence on the development of many mathematical disciplines: mathematical analysis, geometry, classical and contemporary algebra, the theory of summability of series, the theory of probability, and so forth.

Methods of the theory of numbers. In its methods, the theory of numbers is divided into four parts: elementary, analytic, algebraic, and geometric.

The elementary theory of numbers studies the properties of integers without calling on other mathematical disciplines. Thus, starting from Euler's identity

$$(x_1^2 + x_2^2 + x_3^2 + x_4^2)(y_1^2 + y_2^2 + y_3^2 + y_4^2) = (x_1y_1 + x_2y_2 + x_3y_3 + x_4y_4)^2$$
$$+ (x_1y_2 - x_2y_1 + x_3y_4 - x_4y_3)^2 + (x_1y_3 - x_3y_1 + x_4y_2 - x_2y_4)^2$$
$$+ (x_1y_4 - x_4y_1 + x_2y_3 - x_3y_2)^2, \tag{6}$$

we may very simply prove that every integer $N > 0$ may be expressed as the sum of the squares of four integers; i.e., every integer is representable in the form

$$N = x^2 + y^2 + z^2 + u^2,$$

where x, y, z, and u are integers.*

The analytic theory of numbers makes use of mathematical analysis for problems of the theory of numbers. Its foundations were laid by Euler and it was developed by P. L. Čebyšev, Dirichlet, Riemann, Ramanujan, Hardy, Littlewood, and other mathematicians, its most powerful methods being due to Vinogradov. This part of the theory of numbers is closely connected with the theory of functions of a complex variable (a theory that is very rich in practical applications), and also with the theory of series, the theory of probability, and other branches of mathematics.

The basic concept of the algebraic theory of numbers is the concept of an algebraic number, i.e., a root of the equation

$$a_0x^n + a_1x^{n-1} + a_2x^{n-2} + \cdots + a_{n-1}x + a_n = 0,$$

where a_0, a_1, a_2, $\cdots$, a_n are integers.†

The greatest contributions to this branch of the theory of numbers were made by Lagrange, Gauss, Kummer, E. I. Zolotarev, Dedekind, A. O. Gel'fond, and others.

The basic objects of study in the geometric theory of numbers are "space lattices"; that is, systems consisting entirely of "integral" points, all of whose coordinates in a given rectilinear coordinate system, rectangular or oblique, are integers. Space lattices have great significance in geometry and in crystallography, and are intimately connected with important questions in the theory of numbers; in particular, with the

---

* We have here an example of an indeterminate equation, to be investigated from the point of view of its solvability in integers.

† If $a_0 = 1$, the algebraic number is called an algebraic integer. A number which is not algebraic is called transcendental.

arithmetic theory of quadratic forms, i.e., the theory of quadratic forms with integer coefficients and integer variables. Basic work in the geometric theory of numbers is due to H. Minkowski and G. F. Voronoĭ.

It is·to be noted that the methods of the analytic theory of numbers have important applications in the other two branches, the algebraic and the geometric. Particularly noteworthy is the problem of counting the number of integral points in a given domain, a problem which is important in certain branches of physics. Various means of approach to this problem were indicated by G. F. Voronoĭ and methods for its solution were developed by I. M. Vinogradov.

The deep-lying reason for the power of analytic methods in the theory of numbers is that they enrich our study of the interrelations among discrete integers by summoning to our aid new relations among continuous magnitudes.

We must emphasize that in this chapter we are considering only certain selected questions in the theory of numbers.

§2. The Investigation of Problems Concerning Prime Numbers

The number of primes is infinite. In considering the sequence (3) of prime numbers

$$2, 3, 5, 7, 11, 13, 17, 19, \cdots$$

it is natural to ask the question: Is this sequence infinite? The fact that any integer can be represented in the form (4) does not yet solve the problem, since the exponents $a_1, \cdots, a_k$ may take on an infinite set of values. An affirmative answer to the question was given by Euclid, who proved that the number of primes cannot be equal to any finite integer k.

Let $p_1, p_2, \cdots, p_k$ be primes; then the number

$$m = p_1 p_1 \cdots p_k + 1,$$

since it is an integer greater than one, is either itself a prime or has a prime factor. But m is not divisible by any one of the primes $p_1, p_2, \cdots, p_k$ since, if it were, the difference $m - p_1 p_2 \cdots p_k$ would also be divisible by this number; which is impossible, since this difference is equal to one. Thus, either m itself is a prime or it is divisible by some prime p_{k+1}, different from $p_1, \cdots, p_k$. So the set of primes cannot be finite.

The sieve of Eratosthenes. The Greek mathematician Eratosthenes in the 3rd century B.C. described the following "sieve" method for finding all the primes not exceeding a given natural number N. We write all the integers from 1 through N

$$1, 2, 3, 4, \cdots, N,$$

and then cross out, from the left, first the number 1, then all numbers except 2 that are multiples of 2, then all except 3 that are multiples of 3, and then all except 5 that are multiples of 5 (the multiples of four have already been crossed out), and so forth; the remaining numbers will then be primes. It is worthy of note that the process of crossing out needs to be continued only to the point where we have found all primes less than $\sqrt{N}$, since every composite number (i.e., not prime) that is not greater than N will necessarily have a prime divisor not exceeding $\sqrt{N}$.

Examination of the sequence of prime numbers in the sequence of all positive integers would lead us to believe that the law of distribution of prime numbers must be very complicated; for example, we encounter primes such as 8,004,119 and 8,004,121 (the so-called twin primes) whose difference is two, and also primes that are far from each other, such as 86,629 and 86,677, between which there is no other prime. But the tables show that "on the average" prime numbers occur more and more rarely as we traverse the sequence of integers.

Euler's identity; his proof that the number of primes is infinite. The great 18th century mathematician L. Euler, a member of the Russian Academy of Sciences, introduced the following function, with argument $s > 1$, which at the present time is denoted by $\zeta(s)$:

$$\zeta(s) = 1 + \frac{1}{2^s} + \frac{1}{3^s} + \cdots + \frac{1}{n^s} + \cdots. \tag{7}$$

As we know from Chapter II, this series converges for $s > 1$ (and diverges for $s \leqslant 1$). Euler derived a remarkable identity that plays a very important role in the theory of prime numbers:

$$\sum_{n=1}^{\infty} \frac{1}{n^s} = \prod_p \frac{1}{1 - \frac{1}{p^s}}, \tag{8}$$

where the symbol $\prod_p$ means that we must multiply together the expressions $1/[1 - (1/p^s)]$ for all primes p. To see how the proof of this identity goes, we note that $1/(1 - q) = 1 + q + q^2 + \cdots$ for $|q| < 1$, so that

$$\frac{1}{1 - \frac{1}{p^s}} = 1 + \frac{1}{p^s} + \frac{1}{p^{2s}} + \cdots.$$

Multiplying these series for the various primes p and recalling that every n is uniquely representable as the product of primes, we find that

$$\prod_p \left(1 + \frac{1}{p^s} + \frac{1}{p^{2s}} + \cdots\right) = 1 + \frac{1}{2^s} + \frac{1}{3^s} + \cdots + \frac{1}{n^s} + \cdots.$$

For a rigorous proof, of course, we must establish the validity of our limit process, but this presents no particular difficulty.

From identity (8) we may derive as a corollary the fact that the series $\Sigma_p\, 1/p$, consisting of the reciprocals of all the primes, diverges (this provides a new proof of the fact already known to us that the prime numbers cannot be finite in number), and also that the quotient of the number of prime numbers not exceeding x, divided by x itself, converges to zero for unboundedly increasing x.

The investigations of P. L. Čebyšev on the distribution of the prime numbers in the sequence of natural numbers. We denote by $\pi(x)$, as is now customary, the number of prime numbers not exceeding x; for example, $\pi(10) = 4$, since 2, 3, 5, and 7 are all the primes not exceeding 10, $\pi(\pi) = 2$, since 2 and 3 are all the primes not exceeding π. As noted earlier

$$\lim_{x \to \infty} \frac{\pi(x)}{x} = 0.$$

But just how does the ratio $\pi(x)/x$ decrease; in other words what is the law of growth for $\pi(x)$? May we look for a fairly simple, well-known function that differs only a little from $\pi(x)$? The famous French mathematician Legendre, in considering tables of prime numbers, stated that such a function will be

$$\frac{x}{\ln x - A}, \tag{9}$$

where $A = 1.08\cdots$, but he did not give a proof of this proposition. Gauss, who also considered the question of the distribution of the prime numbers, conjectured that $\pi(x)$ differs comparatively little from $\int_2^x dt/\ln t$ (we note that the following relation holds:

$$\lim_{x \to \infty} \frac{\displaystyle\int_2^x \frac{dt}{\ln t}}{\dfrac{x}{\ln x}} = 1, \tag{10}$$

which is established by integrating by parts and finding estimates for the new integral).

The first mathematician since the time of Euclid to make real progress in the very difficult question of the distribution of the prime numbers was P. L. Čebyšev. In 1848, basing his work on a study of Euler's function $\zeta(s)$ for real s, Čebyšev showed that for arbitrarily large positive n and arbitrarily small positive α there exist arbitrarily large values of x for which

$$\pi(x) > \int_2^x \frac{dt}{\ln t} - \frac{\alpha x}{\ln^n x},$$

and also arbitrarily large x for which

$$\pi(x) < \int_2^x \frac{dt}{\ln t} + \frac{\alpha x}{\ln^n x},$$

which is in good agreement with Gauss's assumption. In particular, taking $n = 1$ and applying (10), Čebyšev established the fact that

$$\lim_{x \to \infty} \frac{\pi(x)}{\dfrac{x}{\ln x}} = 1, \tag{11}$$

provided that the limit in (11) exists.

Čebyšev also refuted Legendre's assumption concerning the value of the constant A which occurs in expression (9) as giving the best approximation to $\pi(x)$; he showed that this value can only be $A = 1$.

The well-known French mathematician Bertrand was led by his investigations in the theory of groups to the following conjecture, which he verified empirically from the tables up to quite large values of n: If $n > 3$, then between n and $2n - 2$ there is at least one prime. All the attempts of Bertrand, and of other mathematicians, to prove this conjecture proved fruitless until 1850, when Čebyšev published his second article on prime numbers, in which he not only proved the conjecture ("Bertrand's postulate") but also showed that for sufficiently large x

$$A_1 < \frac{\pi(x)}{\dfrac{x}{\ln x}} < A_2, \tag{12}$$

where

$$0.92 < A_1 < 1 \text{ and } 1 < A_2 < 1.1.$$

In §3 we give a simplified presentation of Čebyšev's method, which leads, however, to considerably less precise results than those of Čebyšev himself.

Čebyšev's works had a great influence on many mathematicians, in particular Sylvester and Poincaré. In the course of more than forty years a number of scientists busied themselves with the improvement of Čebyšev's inequality (12) (increasing the constant on the left side of the inequality.and decreasing the constant on the right side), but they were unable to establish the existence of the limit

$$\lim_{x \to \infty} \frac{\pi(x)}{\dfrac{x}{\ln x}}$$

(as was pointed out previously, we know from the work of Čebyšev that if this limit exists it is equal to one).

Only in 1896 did Hadamard, using arguments from the theory of functions of a complex variable, prove that the function $\Theta(x)$, introduced by Čebyšev and defined by the equation

$$\Theta(x) = \sum_{p \leqslant x} \ln p,$$

satisfies the condition

$$\lim_{x \to \infty} \frac{\Theta(x)}{x} = 1, \tag{13}$$

from which it is relatively easy to obtain the relation (11) without any further assumptions; this is the so-called asymptotic law for the distribution of primes.

The result (13) was found by Hadamard on the basis of the investigations by the famous German 19th century mathematician Riemann, who studied the $\zeta(s)$ function of Euler (7) for complex values of the variable $s = \sigma + it$ (Čebyšev himself had considered this function only for real values of the argument).*

Riemann showed that the function $\zeta(s)$, defined in the half plane $\sigma > 1$ by the series (7)

$$\zeta(s) = \sum_{n=1}^{\infty} \frac{1}{n^s}$$

has the property that

$$\zeta(s) - \frac{1}{s-1}$$

---

* In 1949 A. Selberg gave an elementary proof (i.e., not using complex variables) of the asymptotic law of distribution of primes.

is an entire transcendental function (for $\sigma \leqslant 1$ the series (7) ceases to converge, but the values of $\zeta(s)$ in the half plane $\sigma \leqslant 1$ are defined by analytic continuation) (see Chapter IX). Riemann made the conjecture ("the Riemann hypothesis") that all roots of $\zeta(s)$ in the strip $0 \leqslant \sigma \leqslant 1$ have real part equal to $\frac{1}{2}$, i.e., lie on the straight line $\sigma = \frac{1}{2}$; the question of the correctness of this assumption remains open to this day.

An important step in the proof of (13) was the establishment of the fact that on the straight line $\sigma = 1$ there are no roots of $\zeta(s)$.

The investigation of the behavior of $\zeta(s)$ led to the development of an elegant theory of entire and meromorphic functions, with important practical applications.

The work of Vinogradov and his students in the theory of prime numbers. From equation (13), which by (10) may be written in the form

$$\lim_{x \to \infty} \frac{\pi(x)}{\displaystyle\int_2^x \frac{dt}{\ln t}} = 1, \tag{14}$$

there arose the question of the degree of exactness with which the function $\int_2^x dt/\ln t$ represents $\pi(x)$. The best results in this direction were found by N. G. Čudakov and were based on Vinogradov's *method of trigonometric sums* (this method will be described in §4), which also allowed Čudakov to decrease considerably the bounds between which we can find at least one prime. Namely, it had been established previously that if we consider the sequence

$$1^{250}, \, 2^{250}, \, 3^{250}, \, \cdots, \, n^{250}, \, (n+1)^{250}, \, \cdots, \tag{15}$$

then, starting with some $n = n_0$, there must exist, between any two adjacent terms, i.e., between n^{250} and $(n+1)^{250}$, at least one prime.

We note that, as follows from the binomial formula

$$(n+1)^{250} - n^{250} > 250n^{249},$$

this difference is very large. N. G. Čudakov succeeded in replacing sequence (15) by

$$1^4, \, 2^4, \, 3^4, \, \cdots, \, n^4, \, (n+1)^4, \, \cdots, \tag{16}$$

whose terms lie considerably closer together than those of the sequence (15) but which also contains at least one prime between every two successive terms, i.e., between n^4 and $(n+1)^4$, beginning at some $n = n_0$. Subsequently, this result has been improved by replacing the fourth powers by cubes.

If k and l are relatively prime, i.e., have no common divisor larger than one, then an arithmetic progression with general term $kt + l$ contains infinitely many prime numbers. This fact, a generalization of the result of Euclid, was established in the 19th century by Dirichlet. But can we find a bound that will certainly not be exceeded by the smallest prime in the progression $kt + l$? The Leningrad mathematician Ju. V. Linnik proved the existence of an absolute constant C with the property that in progression $kt + l$ (k and l relatively prime) there necessarily exists at least one prime less than k^C. Thus Linnik provided an essentially complete solution of the problem, raised many years before, of the least prime in an arithmetic progression; further investigators can only decrease the value of the constant C. Linnik also carried out very important investigations concerning the zeros of the function $\zeta(s)$ and more general functions.

As mentioned previously, the best results with regard to the distribution of primes were found by the method of Vinogradov for estimating trigonometric sums.

A *trigonometric sum* is a sum of the form

$$\sum_{A < x < B} e^{2\pi i f(x)},$$

where $f(x)$ is a real function of x, and x takes on all integral values between A and B, or some specific subset of these values, for example the primes between A and B. Since the modulus of $e^{2\pi i z}$ for real z is equal to one, and the modulus of a sum does not exceed the sum of the moduli of its terms, we have

$$\left| \sum_{x=1}^{p} e^{2\pi i f(x)} \right| \leqslant P. \tag{17}$$

This "trivial" estimate can be improved considerably in a number of cases; the decisive steps in this direction were taken by Vinogradov. For definiteness, let $f(x)$ be a polynomial

$$f(x) = \alpha_n x^n + \alpha_{n-1} x^{n-1} + \cdots + \alpha_1 x + \alpha_0 .$$

If all the α are integers, then $e^{2\pi i f(x)} = 1$ for integral x, and in this case the estimate (17) obviously cannot be improved. But if $\alpha_1 , \cdots, \alpha_n$ are not all integers then, as Vinogradov showed, the estimate (17) may be sharpened by approximating any of these coefficients by rational fractions with denominators not exceeding some bound (it may be shown that any α lying between 0 and 1 is representable in the form $\alpha = a/q + z$, where a and q are relatively prime integers, $q \leqslant \tau$, $|z| \leqslant 1/q^\tau$ and τ is a preassigned integer greater than 1).

The creation of the method of trigonometric sums by Vinogradov allowed him to solve a series of very difficult problems in the theory of numbers. In particular, in 1937 he solved a famous problem stated by Goldbach, by proving that every sufficiently large odd N is representable as the sum of three primes

$$N = p_1 + p_2 + p_3 . \tag{18}$$

This problem arose in 1742 in correspondence between Euler and another member of the Russian Academy of Sciences, C. Goldbach, and remained unsolved for almost two centuries, despite the efforts of a number of eminent mathematicians.

As we have seen, the equation (4) shows that prime numbers play a fundamental role in the *multiplicative* representation of an odd number by means of primes. It is easy to show from (18) that one can represent a sufficiently large even number as the sum of no more than four primes.* In this manner, the Vinogradov-Goldbach theorem established a profound connection between additive and multiplicative properties of numbers.

The significance of the method of trigonometric sums created by Vinogradov is not restricted to the theory of numbers. In particular, it plays an important role in the theory of functions and in the theory of probability. Some idea of Vinogradov's method may be obtained from §4 of this chapter.

Readers who are interested in a more detailed treatment may consult Vinogradov's book "The method of trigonometric sums in the theory of numbers," after a preliminary reading of his book "Foundations of the theory of numbers."

§3. Čebyšev's Method

Čebyšev's Θ function and its estimates. We now give a simplified presentation of Čebyšev's method for computing the number of primes lying with given limits. For brevity we agree to use the following notation: if B is a positive variable quantity that may grow unboundedly, and A is another quantity such that $|A|$ grows "no more rapidly" than CB, where C is a positive constant (more precisely, if there exists a constant $C > 0$ such that starting from some instant we always have $|A|/B \leqslant C$), then we will write

$$A = O(B).$$

---

* The correctness of the conjecture that every sufficiently large *even* number N can be represented as the sum of two primes remains an open question to this day.

This is usually read as: "A is a quantity of the order of B." Thus, for example

$$\sin x = O(1),$$

since everywhere

$$\frac{|\sin x|}{1} \leqslant 1;$$

in exactly the same way

$$5x^3 \cos 2x = O(x^3).$$

We will also denote by $[x]$ the integral part of x, i.e., the largest integer not exceeding x; thus, for example

$$[\pi] = 3, \quad [5] = 5, \quad [-1.5] = -2, \quad [0.999] = 0.$$

We now pose the following question: Let p be a prime, and n a natural number, and let $n!$, as usual, denote the product $1 \cdot 2 \cdot 3 \cdot \cdots \cdot n$; we note incidentally that as n increases the value of $n!$ grows very rapidly. What is the largest power a of the prime p that divides $n!$ with no remainder?

Among the numbers $1, 2, \cdots, n$, there will be precisely $[n/p]$ numbers divisible by p; the number of these which will also be divisible by p^2 is $[n/p^2]$; further, of these there will be $[n/p^3]$ divisible by p^3, etc. Hence it is easy to show that

$$a = \left[\frac{n}{p}\right] + \left[\frac{n}{p^2}\right] + \left[\frac{n}{p^3}\right] + \cdots$$

(where the series terminates, since $[n/p^s] > 0$ only for $n \geqslant p^s$). Thus, in the last sum every factor of the product $1 \cdot 2 \cdot 3 \cdot \cdots \cdot n$ such that the highest power of the number p by which it is divisible is equal to p^m will occur precisely m times, once as a multiple of p, once as a multiple of p^2, once as a multiple of p^3, $\cdots$, and finally once as a multiple of p^m.

From this result and from the representability of any natural number in the form (4) it follows that $n!$ will be the product of powers of the form

$$p^{\left[\frac{n}{p}\right] + \left[\frac{n}{p^2}\right] + \left[\frac{n}{p^3}\right] + \cdots},$$

taken for all primes $p \leqslant n$. Thus $\ln(n!)$ will be the sum of the logarithms of these powers, which can be concisely written in the form

$$\ln n! = \sum_{p \leqslant n} \left(\left[\frac{n}{p}\right] + \left[\frac{n}{p^2}\right] + \left[\frac{n}{p^3}\right] + \cdots \right) \ln p. \quad (19)$$

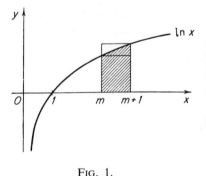

FIG. 1.

We simplify equation (19). Since $y = \ln x$ is an increasing function, we have

$$\ln m = \ln m \int_m^{m+1} dx < \int_m^{m+1} \ln x \, dx < \ln(m + 1) \int_m^{m+1} dx = \ln(m + 1)$$

as is clear from figure 1. Thus

$$\ln n! = \ln 1 + \ln 2 + \cdots + \ln n$$

$$< \int_1^2 \ln x \, dx + \int_2^3 \ln x \, dx + \cdots$$

$$+ \int_{n-1}^n \ln x \, dx + \ln n = \int_1^n \ln x \, dx + \ln n,$$

on the other hand

$$\ln n! > \ln 1 + \int_1^2 \ln x \, dx + \cdots$$

$$+ \int_{n-2}^{n-1} \ln x \, dx + \int_{n-1}^n \ln x \, dx = \int_1^n \ln x \, dx.$$

Using the formula for integration by parts, we find

$$\int_1^n \ln x \, dx = [x \cdot \ln x]_1^n - \int_1^n x \cdot \frac{1}{x} \cdot dx = n \ln n - (n - 1).$$

Thus

$$n \ln n - n + 1 < \ln n! < n \ln n - n + 1 + \ln n,$$

and hence it follows that

$$\ln n! = n \ln n + O(n). \tag{20}$$

We note that $\ln n = O(n)$; further, for $n \to \infty$, the function $\ln n$ increases more slowly than any positive power of n, i.e., for any constant $\alpha > 0$

$$\lim_{n \to \infty} \frac{\ln n}{n^\alpha} = 0, \tag{21}$$

since by the rule for indeterminate forms (cf. Chapter II)

$$\lim_{n \to \infty} \frac{\ln n}{n^\alpha} = \lim_{n \to \infty} \frac{\frac{1}{n}}{\alpha n^{\alpha-1}} = \frac{1}{\alpha} \lim_{n \to \infty} \frac{1}{n^\alpha} = 0.$$

Further, we find

$$\sum_{p \leqslant n} \left(\left[\frac{n}{p^2} \right] + \left[\frac{n}{p^3} \right] + \cdots \right) \ln p \leqslant \sum_{p \leqslant n} \left(\frac{n}{p^2} + \frac{n}{p^3} + \cdots \right) \ln p$$

$$= \sum_{p \leqslant n} \frac{n \ln p}{p^2 \left(1 - \frac{1}{p} \right)} < 2n \sum_{p \leqslant n} \frac{\ln p}{p^2} < 2n \sum_{m=1}^{\infty} \frac{\ln m}{m^2} = 2n C_0 = O(n), \tag{22}$$

where C_0 is the sum of the convergent series $\sum_{m=1}^{\infty} \frac{\ln m}{m^2}$. The absolute convergence of this series is established by using (21), for example, for $\alpha = \frac{1}{2}$, by the comparison test and the so-called integral test for convergence (cf. Chapter II, §14). In view of (20) and (22), equation (19) may be put in the form

$$\sum_{p \leqslant n} \left[\frac{n}{p} \right] \ln p = n \ln n + O(n). \tag{23}$$

We now consider the function introduced by Čebyšev

$$\Theta(n) = \sum_{p \leqslant n} \ln p \tag{24}$$

(the logarithm of the product of all prime numbers not exceeding n).
Equation (23) can be rewritten as:

$$\Theta \left(\frac{n}{1} \right) + \Theta \left(\frac{n}{2} \right) + \Theta \left(\frac{n}{3} \right) + \Theta \left(\frac{n}{4} \right) + \cdots = n \ln n + O(n). \tag{25}$$

In fact, every given $\ln p$ enters into all the sums of the form $\Theta(n/s)$, where $p \leqslant n/s$, i.e., where $s \leqslant n/p$, and the number of such sums $\Theta(n/s)$ is equal to $[n/p]$.

Equation (25) is also valid for any noninteger n. To see this, it is obviously sufficient to prove that it is true for all x under the condition $n < x < n + 1$; and for this it is enough to prove that replacing n by x in the left side of (25) does not change that side, and that the first term in the right side may increase by an amount which is $O(n)$. But the first follows from the fact that such a replacement will not increase the value of any one of the terms of the left-hand side (such an increase would be possible only if n were increased by more than unity) and, of course, the left side is not decreased. The second follows from the fact that by the formula for the increment of a function (cf. Chapter II)

$$f(x) - f(a) = (x - a) f'(\xi), \quad a < \xi < x,$$

we have

$$x \ln x - n \ln n = (x - n) \cdot (\ln \xi + 1), \quad n < \xi < x,$$

and the right side of this last equation is less than $\ln (n + 1) + 1 = O(n)$, since $0 < x - n < 1$. From equation (25) let us subtract twice the equation derived from (25) by replacing n by $n/2$;

$$\Theta \left(\frac{n}{1}\right) + \Theta \left(\frac{n}{2}\right) + \Theta \left(\frac{n}{3}\right) + \Theta \left(\frac{n}{4}\right) + \cdots = n \ln n + O(n),$$

$$2\Theta \left(\frac{n}{2}\right) + 2\Theta \left(\frac{n}{4}\right) + \cdots = 2 \cdot \frac{n}{2} \cdot \ln \frac{n}{2} + O(n),$$

we obtain

$$\Theta \left(\frac{n}{1}\right) - \Theta \left(\frac{n}{2}\right) + \Theta \left(\frac{n}{3}\right) - \Theta \left(\frac{n}{4}\right) + \cdots = n \ln 2 + O(n) < C_1 n,$$

where C_1 is some positive constant. But $\Theta(n/1) - \Theta(n/2)$ is not larger than the whole left side, since the differences, $\Theta(n/3) - \Theta(n/4)$, $\Theta(n/5) - \Theta(n/6)$, $\cdots$ cannot be negative. Thus it follows from this last inequality that

$$\Theta \left(\frac{n}{1}\right) - \Theta \left(\frac{n}{2}\right) < C_1 n.$$

Inserting here the numbers $n/2$, $n/4$, $\cdots$ in place of n, we also get

$$\Theta \left(\frac{n}{2}\right) - \Theta \left(\frac{n}{4}\right) < C_1 \cdot \frac{n}{2},$$

$$\Theta \left(\frac{n}{4}\right) - \Theta \left(\frac{n}{8}\right) < C_1 \cdot \frac{n}{4},$$

$$\cdots \cdots \cdots \cdots \cdots \cdots ,$$

hence, using the fact that $\Theta(n/2^k) = 0$ for sufficiently large k (when $n/2^k < 2$), addition of terms gives

$$\Theta(n) < C_1 \left(n + \frac{n}{2} + \frac{n}{4} + \cdots\right) = 2C_1 n. \tag{26}$$

Returning to equation (23), we find

$$0 \leqslant \sum_{p \leqslant n} \frac{n}{p} \ln p - \sum_{p \leqslant n} \left[\frac{n}{p}\right] \ln p \leqslant \sum_{p \leqslant n} \ln p = \Theta(n) \leqslant 2C_1 n = O(n),$$

so that equation (23) gives

$$\sum_{p \leqslant n} \frac{n}{p} \ln p = n \ln n + O(n),$$

$$\sum_{p \leqslant n} \frac{\ln p}{p} = \ln n + \theta C, \tag{27}$$

where C is a constant greater than zero and θ depends on the number n in such a manner that $|\theta| \leqslant 1$.

An estimate for the number of primes in a given interval. We now show that one may choose a positive constant M in such a manner that between n and Mn there will lie as many primes p as desired, if n is sufficiently large. Namely, we establish simple inequalities for the number T of primes in the interval $n < p \leqslant Mn$. Obviously,

$$\sum_{n<p \leqslant Mn} \frac{\ln p}{p} = \sum_{p \leqslant Mn} \frac{\ln p}{p} - \sum_{p \leqslant n} \frac{\ln p}{p} . \tag{28}$$

From equation (27), replacing n by Mn, we get

$$\sum_{p \leqslant Mn} \frac{\ln p}{p} = \ln (Mn) + \theta'C = \ln M + \ln n + \theta'C, \tag{29}$$

where $|\theta'| \leqslant 1$; thus, in view of equations (28), (29), and (27), we have

$$\sum_{n<p \leqslant Mn} \frac{\ln p}{p} = \ln M + \theta'C - \theta C = \ln M + 2\theta_0 C,$$

where $|\theta_0| \leqslant 1$, i.e.,

$$\ln M - 2C \leqslant \sum_{n<p \leqslant Mn} \frac{\ln p}{p} \leqslant \ln M + 2C. \tag{30}$$

On the other hand, since $y = \ln x/x$ for $x > e$ is a decreasing function (since $y' = (1 - \ln x)/x^2 < 0$ for $\ln x > 1$, i.e., $x > e$), it follows that for $n \geqslant 3$

$$T\frac{\ln Mn}{Mn} \leqslant \sum_{n<p \leqslant Mn} \frac{\ln p}{p} \leqslant T\frac{\ln n}{n} ,$$

hence, from (30), we have

$$T\frac{\ln n}{n} > \ln M - 2C \tag{31}$$

and

$$T \frac{\ln (Mn)}{Mn} < \ln M + 2C. \tag{32}$$

We now choose the constant M such that the right side of (31) is equal to one

$$\ln M - 2C = 1,$$

i.e.,

$$M = e^{2C+1},$$

and we set

$$L = M(\ln M + 2C).$$

Then for the number T of primes lying between n and Mn, we get from (31) and (32) the inequalities

$$\frac{n}{\ln n} < T < L \frac{n}{\ln n}, \tag{33}$$

which it was our purpose to establish. Since $n/\ln n \to \infty$ for unbounded increase in n, it follows that $T \to \infty$ also.

§4. Vinogradov's Method

Vinogradov's method in its application to the solution of Goldbach's problem. We attempt in this section to give some account of Vinogradov's method for the particular case of Goldbach's problem of representing an odd number as the sum of three prime numbers.

An expression in the form of an integral for the number of representations of N as the sum of three primes. Let N be a sufficiently large odd number. We denote by $I(N)$ the number of representations of N as the sum of three primes; in other words, the number of solutions of the equation

$$N = p_1 + p_2 + p_3 \tag{34}$$

in prime numbers p_1, p_2, and p_3.

Goldbach's problem will be solved if it can be established that $I(N) > 0$. Vinogradov's method allows us not only to establish this fact (for sufficiently large N), but also to find an approximating expression for $I(N)$.

$I(N)$ may be written in the following form

$$I(N) = \sum_{p_1 \leqslant N} \sum_{p_2 \leqslant N} \sum_{p_3 \leqslant N} \int_0^1 e^{2\pi i (p_1 + p_2 + p_3 - N)\alpha} \, d\alpha, \tag{35}$$

where the summations are taken over the prime numbers not exceeding N. In fact, for integer $n \neq 0$

$$\int_0^1 e^{2\pi i n \alpha}\, d\alpha = \frac{1}{2\pi n i}\left[e^{2\pi i n \alpha}\right]_0^1 = \frac{1}{2\pi n i}\left(e^{2\pi n i} - e^0\right) = 0,$$

since

$$e^{2\pi i n} = \cos 2\pi n + i \sin 2\pi n = 1;$$

but if $n = 0$, then

$$\int_0^1 e^{2\pi i n \alpha}\, d\alpha = \int_0^1 d\alpha = 1.$$

Thus, every time the primes p_1, p_2, and p_3 have the sum N the integral inside the summation sign in (35) has the value one, and when the sum $p_1 + p_2 + p_3 \neq N$, this integral is equal to zero, which proves the validity of equation (35).

Since $e^{2\pi i a} \cdot e^{2\pi i b} = e^{2\pi i (a+b)}$ and the integral of a sum of terms is equal to the sum of the integrals of these terms, it follows from equation (35) that

$$I(N) = \int_0^1 \left(\sum_{p \leqslant N} e^{2\pi i \alpha p}\right)^3 e^{-2\pi i \alpha N}\, d\alpha.$$

Introducing the notation

$$T_\alpha = \sum_{p \leqslant N} e^{2\pi i \alpha p} \tag{36}$$

we then have

$$I(N) = \int_0^1 T_\alpha^3 e^{-2\pi i \alpha N}\, d\alpha. \tag{37}$$

Decomposition of the interval of integration into basic and complementary intervals. Let h be a quantity, chosen in an appropriate manner depending on N, which increases unboundedly with N but is small in comparison with N and even with $\sqrt[3]{N/2}$, and set $\tau = N/h$. Since the function integrated in (37) has a period equal to one, the interval of integration in (37) may be replaced by the segment from $-(1/\tau)$ to $1 - (1/\tau)$. Thus

$$I(N) = \int_{-1/\tau}^{1-1/\tau} T_\alpha^3 e^{-2\pi i \alpha N}\, d\alpha. \tag{38}$$

We now consider all proper irreducible fractions a/q with denominators not exceeding h, and distinguish in the segment $-(1/\tau) \leqslant \alpha \leqslant 1 - (1/\tau)$ the "basic" intervals corresponding to these fractions

$$\frac{a}{q} - \frac{1}{\tau} \leqslant \alpha \leqslant \frac{a}{q} + \frac{1}{\tau}; \tag{39}$$

for sufficiently large N these intervals, as may be proved,* will have no points in common. In this manner, the segment $-(1/\tau) \leqslant \alpha \leqslant 1 - (1/\tau)$ can be decomposed into basic intervals and "complementary" intervals.

We represent $I(N)$ as the sum of two terms

$$I(N) = I_1(N) + I_2(N), \tag{40}$$

where $I_1(N)$ denotes the sum of the integrals on the basic intervals and $I_2(N)$ is the sum of the integrals on the complementary intervals. As will be seen below, for unbounded growth of odd N we also have unbounded growth of $I_1(N)$, with

$$\lim_{N \to \infty} \frac{I_2(N)}{I_1(N)} = 0. \tag{41}$$

So we see from (40) that the number of representations of an odd N as the sum of three primes grows unboundedly with N, so that, in particular, we have proved Goldbach's conjecture for all sufficiently large odd N.

An expression for the integral on the basic intervals. Let α belong to one of the basic intervals; from (39), $\alpha = a/q + z$, where $1 \leqslant q \leqslant h$ and $|z| \leqslant 1/\tau$. We break up the sum (36)

$$T_\alpha = \sum_{p \leqslant N}' e^{2\pi i p \alpha} = \sum_{p \leqslant N}' e^{2\pi i (a/q+z)p},$$

extended over all primes not exceeding N into partial sums $T_{\alpha,M}$ of the form

$$T_{\alpha,M} = \sum_{M \leqslant p < M'}' e^{2\pi i (a/q+z)p},$$

where M' is so chosen that $e^{2\pi i z p}$ differs "little" from $e^{2\pi i z M}$; since we intend to give only the *idea* of Vinogradov's method, and not a proof of the Goldbach-Vinogradov theorem, we will not state precisely what we mean

---

* If two such intervals surrounding the points a_1/q_1 and a_2/q_2 intersect, then at a common point we will have the equation

$$\frac{a_1}{q_1} + \frac{\theta_1}{\tau} = \frac{a_2}{q_2} + \frac{\theta_2}{\tau}, \quad \text{where} \quad |\theta_1| \leqslant 1, \quad |\theta_2| \leqslant 1,$$

or

$$\frac{a_1 q_2 - a_2 q_1}{q_1 q_2} = \frac{\theta_1 - \theta_2}{\tau}.$$

But the absolute value of the left side of this last equation is not less than $1/q_1 q_2$, i.e., is greater than $1/h^2$, and the right side is not greater than $2/\tau$, i.e., is less than $2h/N$. So if this last equation were true, it would imply the inequality $1/h^2 < 2h/N$ which contradicts the choice of h.

by the expression "differs little"; in his proof Vinogradov deals with rigorously defined inequalities, involving a great deal of calculation. Thus

$$T_{\alpha,M} \approx e^{2\pi i M z} \sum_{M \leqslant p < M'}{}' e^{2\pi i (a/q) p} = e^{2\pi i M z} \, T_{a/q,M} , \qquad (42)$$

where the symbol $\approx$ means that the first of the three expressions on the last relation differs "little" from the second.

We further break up each of the sums

$$T_{a/q,M} = \sum_{M \leqslant p < M'}{}' e^{2\pi i (a/q) p} \qquad (43)$$

into sums $T_{a/q,\,M'l}$, taken over all primes p_l satisfying the relation $M \leqslant p_l < M'$ and belonging to arithmetic progressions $qx + l$, where l takes on all values from 0 to $q - 1$ which are relatively prime to q. But

$$e^{2\pi i (a/q) pl} = e^{2\pi i x + 2\pi i (a/q) l} = e^{2\pi i (a/q) l},$$

and thus

$$T_{a/q,M'l} = e^{2\pi i (a/q) l} \cdot \pi(M, M', l), \qquad (44)$$

where $\pi(M, M', l)$ is the number of primes satisfying the conditions $M \leqslant p < M'$ and belonging to the arithmetic progression $qx + l$. In the development of formula (14) for the number $\pi(x)$ of primes not exceeding x, it was established that $\pi(M, M', l)$, for values of q which are "small" in comparison with the difference $M' - M$, differs little from $1/\phi(q) \int_M^{M'} dx/\ln x$, where $\phi(q)$ is *Euler's function*. This is a number-theoretic function (i.e., a function defined for natural numbers q) representing the number of positive integers not exceeding q and relatively prime to q. From (44) we may thus derive

$$T_{a/q,M'l} \approx e^{2\pi i (a/q) l} \cdot \frac{1}{\phi(q)} \int_M^{M'} \frac{dx}{\ln x} . \qquad (45)$$

In the expression on the right side of (45), only the first factor depends on l, i.e., on the choice of the arithmetic progression $qx + l$ (we now consider q as fixed). After summing on l, we obtain

$$T_{a/q,M} \approx \frac{1}{\phi(q)} \int_M^{M'} \frac{dx}{\ln x} \sum_l e^{2\pi i (a/q) l},$$

and further, from (42),

$$T_{\alpha,M} \approx e^{2\pi i M z} \cdot \frac{1}{\phi(q)} \int_M^{M'} \frac{dx}{\ln x} \cdot \sum_l e^{2\pi i (a/q) l}, \qquad (46)$$

where

$$e^{2\pi i M z} \int_M^{M'} \frac{dx}{\ln x} \approx \int_M^{M'} \frac{e^{2\pi i z x}}{\ln x} \, dx,$$

which allows us to replace (46) by the relation

$$T_{\alpha, M} \approx \int_M^{M'} \frac{e^{2\pi i z x}}{\ln x} \, dx \cdot \frac{1}{\phi(q)} \sum_l e^{2\pi i (a/q) l}. \tag{47}$$

After summing on M it is established that

$$T_\alpha \approx \int_2^N \frac{e^{2\pi i z x}}{\ln x} \, dx \cdot \frac{1}{\phi(q)} \sum_l e^{2\pi i (a/q) l}. \tag{48}$$

The sum

$$\sum_l e^{2\pi i (a/q) l},$$

occuring on the right side of (48), with the summation taken over natural numbers l not exceeding q and relatively prime to q may be expressed as a number-theoretic function $\mu(q)$ defined in the following manner: $\mu(q) = 0$ if q is divisible by the square of an integer greater than one; $\mu(1) = 1$ and $\mu(q) = (-1)^n$ if $q = p_1 p_2 \cdots p_n$ where $p_1, p_2, \cdots, p_n$ are distinct primes. Thus, for relatively prime a and q

$$\sum_l e^{2\pi i (a/q) l} = \mu(q). \tag{49}$$

Thus equation (48) may be written in the form

$$T_\alpha \approx \frac{\mu(q)}{\phi(q)} \int_2^N \frac{e^{2\pi i z x}}{\ln x} \, dx.$$

From the fact $\mu^3(q) = \mu(q)$ we have

$$T_\alpha^3 \approx \frac{\mu(q)}{(\phi(q))^3} \left(\int_2^N \frac{e^{2\pi i z x}}{\ln x} \, dx \right)^3, \tag{50}$$

and from the definition of $I_1(N)$

$$I_1(N) = \sum_{1 \leqslant q < h} \sum_a \int_{a/q - 1/\tau}^{a/q + 1/\tau} T_\alpha^3 e^{-2\pi i \alpha N} \, d\alpha, \tag{51}$$

where for a given q the summation is taken over all nonnegative a less than q. Since $\alpha = a/q = z$, we then have, as a result of (50),

$$I_1(N) \approx \sum_{1 \leqslant q < h} \frac{\mu(q)}{(\phi(q))^3} \sum_a e^{-2\pi i (a/q)N} \int_{-1/\tau}^{1/\tau} \left(\int_2^N \frac{e^{2\pi izx}}{\ln x} \, dx \right)^3 e^{-2\pi izN} \, dz.$$

(52)

We introduce the notation

$$R(N) = \int_{-1/\tau}^{1/\tau} \left(\int_2^N \frac{e^{2\pi izx}}{\ln x} \, dx \right)^3 e^{-2\pi izN} \, dz.$$

(53)

From relation (52) it follows that

$$I_1(N) \approx R(N) \sum_{1 \leqslant q < h} \frac{\mu(q)}{[\phi(q)]^3} \sum_a e^{-2\pi i (a/q)N}.$$

(54)

Here we must draw attention to the fact that $R(N)$ is an analytic expression, which can therefore be calculated approximately; in fact, it runs out that

$$R(N) \approx \frac{N^2}{2(\ln N)^3} \, .$$

(55)

The expression occuring as a factor of $R(N)$ on the right side of (54) differs "little" from the sum of the infinite series

$$S(N) = \sum_{q=1}^{\infty} \frac{\mu(q)}{[\phi(q)]^3} \sum_a e^{-2\pi i (a/q)N},$$

(56)

so that, from (54) and (55), it can be established that

$$I_1(N) \approx \frac{N^2}{2(\ln N)^3} S(N),$$

(57)

or, more precisely,

$$I_1(N) = \frac{N^2}{2(\ln N)^3} [S(N) + \gamma_1(N)],$$

(58)

where

$$\lim_{N \to \infty} \gamma_1(N) = 0.$$

(59)

We note that number-theoretic expression $S(N)$ may be written in the form

$$S(N) = C \prod_p \left(1 - \frac{1}{p^2 - 3p + 3} \right),$$

(60)

where C is a constant, the multiplication is extended over all prime divisors of the number N, and, as the computations show,

$$S(N) > 0.6. \qquad (61)$$

Estimate of the integral on the complementary intervals. We turn now to an estimate of the sum I_2 of the integrals on the complementary intervals. Since the modulus of the integral does not exceed the integral of the modulus of the function being integrated, and since $|e^{-2\pi i \alpha N}| = 1$ for real αN, we have

$$|I_2| < \max |T_\alpha| \cdot \int_{-1/\tau}^{1-1/\tau} |T_\alpha|^2 \, d\alpha, \qquad (62)$$

where $\max |T_\alpha|$ represents the largest value of $|T_\alpha|$ for α belonging to the complementary intervals (we have strengthened the inequality by taking as the factor of $\max |T_\alpha|$ the integral extended over the whole interval $-(1/\tau) \leqslant \alpha \leqslant 1 - 1/\tau$).

But the square of the modulus of a complex number is equal to the product of the number with its complex conjugate, so that

$$|T_\alpha|^2 = T_\alpha \cdot \overline{T}_\alpha,$$

where from (36) we have

$$\overline{T}_\alpha = \sum_{p \leqslant N} e^{-2\pi i \alpha p},$$

since $e^{-2\pi i \alpha p} = \cos 2\pi \alpha p - i \sin 2\pi \alpha p$. Thus, inequality (62) may be rewritten in the form

$$|I_2| < \max |T_\alpha| \cdot \int_{-1/\tau}^{1-1/\tau} \sum_{p \leqslant N} e^{2\pi i \alpha p} \sum_{p_1 \leqslant N} e^{-2\pi i \alpha p_1} \, d\alpha$$

or in the form

$$|I_2| < \max |T_\alpha| \cdot \int_{-1/\tau}^{1-1/\tau} \sum_{p \leqslant N} \sum_{p_1 \leqslant N} e^{2\pi i \alpha (p-p_1)} \, d\alpha. \qquad (63)$$

But the integral in the inequality (63), from what was said at the beginning of the present section, represents the number of U of solutions in primes p, p_1, not exceeding N, of the equation $p - p_1 = 0$, or simply the number of primes not exceeding N, i.e., $\pi(N)$. From the result (12) of Čebyšev we have

$$\pi(N) < B \cdot \frac{N}{\ln N},$$

where B is a constant. In this manner

$$| I_2 | < B \cdot \frac{N}{\ln N} \cdot \max | T_\alpha |, \qquad (64)$$

where, to repeat, $\max | T_\alpha |$ represents the largest value of $| T_\alpha |$ on the complementary intervals. From (58) and (59) it follows that in order to complete the proof of the Goldbach-Vinogradov theorem, we must now show that $\max | T_\alpha |$ has order less than $N/(\ln N)^2$; however, the establishment of this fact presents the greatest difficulty and constitutes the essential part of the whole proof of the theorem.

Every α belonging to a complementary interval can be represented in the form $\alpha = a/q + z$, where $h < q \leqslant \tau$ and $| z | \leqslant 1/q\tau$. The problem thus consists of estimating the modulus of the trigonometric sum

$$T_\alpha = \sum_{p \leqslant N} e^{2\pi i(a/q+z)p}$$

under the given conditions. Vinogradov established, in particular, that

$$\lim_{N \to \infty} \frac{\max T_\alpha}{\dfrac{N}{(\ln N)^3}} = 0 ; \qquad (65)$$

here he made use of a very important identity which he discovered for the function $\mu(n)$ discussed previously.

Unfortunately, it is not possible here to give a proof of equation (65); the interested reader is referred to Chapter X in Vinogradov's book "Methods of trigonometric sums in the theory of numbers."

From (65) and (64), as we noted, it follows that

$$\lim_{N \to \infty} \frac{I_2(N)}{I_1(N)} = 0.$$

In this manner, from (40), (58), and (59) we have

$$I(N) = \frac{N^2}{2(\ln N)^3} [S(N) + \gamma(N)], \qquad (66)$$

where

$$\lim_{N \to \infty} \gamma(N) = 0,$$

and $S(N)$ has the value (60), so that, from (61), $S(N) > 0.6$. This completes the proof of the theorem.

§5. Decomposition of Integers into the Sum of Two Squares; Complex Integers

The importance of the study of prime numbers is chiefly because of the central role they play in most of the laws of number theory: It frequently happens that questions which at first sight seem far removed from divisibility are nevertheless shown by more careful consideration to be intimately connected with the theory of prime numbers. We illustrate this statement by the following example.

One of the problems of number theory consists of finding those natural numbers that can be decomposed into the sum of the squares of two integers (not necessarily different from zero).

The rule for the sequence of numbers that are the sum of two squares is not immediately clear. From 1 to 50, for example, it consists of the numbers 1, 2, 4, 5, 8, 9, 10, 13, 16, 18, 20, 25, 26, 29, 32, 34, 36, 37, 40, 41, 45, 49, 50 a sequence which seems quite erratic. The 17th century French mathematician Fermat noticed that here everything depends on how the number can be represented as the product of primes, i.e., the question is inherently related to the theory of prime numbers.

Prime numbers, other than $p = 2$, are odd, so that division by 4 gives a remainder equal to 1 (for a prime number of the form $4n + 1$) or to 3 (for a prime number of the form $4n + 3$).

We will consider the question of expressing a given number as the sum of two squares under the following three headings.

1. A prime number p is the sum of two squares if and only if $p = 4n + 1$.

The proof of the fact that a number of the form $4n + 3$ cannot be expressed as the sum of two squares is almost obvious: The sum of the squares of two even numbers is divisible by 4, the sum of the square of two odd numbers gives a remainder of 2 when divided by 4, and the sum of the squares of an even and an odd number, when divided by 4, gives a remainder of 1.

Let us now prove a preliminary theorem, namely that if p is a prime, then $(p - 1)! + 1$ is divisible by p. The numbers not divisible by p, when divided by p give the remainder 1, 2, 3, $\cdots$, $p - 1$. We choose an integer r, $1 \leqslant r \leqslant p - 1$ and multiply r by 1, 2, $\cdots$, $p - 1$; when we divide the products so constructed by p we obtain, as is not difficult to prove, all these same remainders, but in general in a different order. In particular, among these remainders will be the number 1, that is to say, for every r one can find an r_1 such that $r \cdot r_1 = 1 + kp$. We note that $r = r_1$ only if $r = 1$ or $r = p - 1$. For if $r^2 = 1 + kp$, then $(r + 1)(r - 1)$ is divisible by p; but for numbers $1 \leqslant r \leqslant p - 1$ this is possible only for $r = 1$ and

$r = p - 1$. Let us find the remainders on dividing $(p - 1)! = 1 \cdot 2 \cdots (p - 1)$ by p. In this product, for every factor r, except 1 and $p - 1$, there occurs a corresponding r_1, distinct from r, such that $r \cdot r_1$ gives the remainder 1. Thus $(p - 1)!$ will give a remainder dividing by p which is the same as if only the two factors 1 and $p - 1$ were present, i.e., it gives the remainder $p - 1$. Thus, $(p - 1)! + 1$ is divisible by p.

Now let $p = 4n + 1$. Further, we write

$$(p - 1)! + 1 = \left\{ 1 \cdot 2 \cdots \frac{p - 1}{2} \right\} \cdot \left\{ \left(p - \frac{p - 1}{2} \right) \cdots (p - 2)(p - 1) \right\} + 1.$$

The second expression in braces, when divided by p, will leave the remainder $(-1)^{p-1/2} [(p - 1)/2]!$. But $(p - 1)/2 = 2n$ is an even number, so that in this case $[(p - 1)/2]!^2 + 1$ is also divisible by p. We denote by A the remainder on dividing $[(p - 1)/2]!$ by p. It is obvious that $A^2 + 1$ is also divisible by p.

We consider the expression $x - Ay$, in which x and y range independently over the numbers 0, 1, $\cdots$, $[\sqrt{p}]$; (here $[x]$ denotes the largest integer not exceeding x). We thus obtain $([\sqrt{p}] + 1)^2 \geqslant p + 1$ numerical values for $x - Ay$, which may be distinct or may in some cases coincide. Since the various remainders on dividing by p can only be $p(0, 1, 2, \cdots, p - 1)$, while we here have at least $p + 1$ values for $x - Ay$, there must exist two distinct pairs (x_1, y_1) and (x_2, y_2) such that $x_1 - Ay_1$ and $x_2 - Ay_2$ leave the same remainder on dividing by p; i.e., $(x_1 - x_2) - A(y_1 - y_2)$ is divisible by p. We set $x_0 = x_1 - x_2$, $y_0 = y_1 - y_2$. Obviously, $|x_0| < \sqrt{p}, |y_0| < \sqrt{p}$. Since $A^2 + 1$ is divisible by p, it follows that $y_0^2(A^2 + 1) = (Ay_0)^2 + y_0^2$ is divisible by p; but since $x_0 - Ay_0$ is divisible by p, the number $x_0^2 - (Ay_0)^2 = (x_0 - Ay_0)(x_0 + Ay_0)$ is divisible by p. Thus the quantity $x_0^2 + y_0^2$, which is equal to $(x_0^2 - (Ay_0)^2 + (Ay_0)^2 + y_0^2)$, is divisible by p. But $|x_0| < \sqrt{p}$, $|y_0| < \sqrt{p}$. Hence $x_0^2 + y_0^2 = 0$ or $x_0^2 + y_0^2 = p$. The first is impossible, since the pairs (x_1, y_1) and (x_2, y_2) were distinct. Thus a prime number of the form $4n + 1$ is representable as the sum of two squares.

2. We turn to the decomposition of an arbitrary integer into the sum of two squares. It is easy to establish the identity

$$(a^2 + b^2)(c^2 + d^2) = (ac - bd)^2 + (ad + bc)^2.$$

This identity shows that the product of two integers that are the sum of two squares is again the sum of two squares. Hence the product of any powers of prime numbers of the form $4n + 1$ (or which are equal to 2) is the sum of two squares. Since multipliying the sum of two squares by a square gives the sum of two squares, any number in which the prime factors of the $4n + 3$ occur in even powers is the sum of two squares.

3. We now show that if a prime number of the form $4n + 3$ enters into a number in an odd power, the number cannot be expressed as the sum of two squares. The original question will then be completely settled.

We will consider complex numbers of the form $a + bi$, where a and b are ordinary integers. Such a complex number will be called a *complex integer*. If an integer N is the sum of two squares $N = a^2 + b^2$, then $N = (a + bi)(a - bi) = \alpha \cdot \bar{\alpha}$ (where $\bar{\alpha}$ denotes the complex conjugate of the number α), i.e., N is factored in the domain of complex integers into complex conjugate factors.

In this domain of complex integers, we may construct a theory of divisibility completely analogous to the theory of divisibility in the domain of ordinary integers. We will say that the complex integer α is divisible by the complex integer β, if α/β is again a complex integer. There exist only four complex integers α which divide 1, namely 1, -1, i, and $-i$. We will say that a complex integer α is a prime, if it does not have any divisors other than 1, -1, i, $-i$, α, $-\alpha$, αi, $-\alpha i$. But now the problem solved under the first heading above will have a different meaning; it will now turn out that numbers of the form $4n + 1$ (or equal to 2) which in the previous case were prime will cease to be prime in the domain of complex integers, while it is easy to prove that primes of the form $4n + 3$ remain prime.

For, if $p = \alpha\beta$, then $p = \bar{\alpha}\bar{\beta}$ and $p^2 = \alpha\bar{\alpha}\beta\bar{\beta}$. But $\alpha\bar{\alpha}$ and $\beta\bar{\beta}$ are ordinary positive integers; and $p \neq \alpha\bar{\alpha}$, since prime numbers of the form $4n + 3$ are not the sum of two squares. This means that $\alpha\bar{\alpha} = 1$; thus α can be only ± 1 or $\pm i$, so that p has no divisors other than the obvious ones.

For complex integers the theorem on the unique decomposition into prime factors still holds. Uniqueness here means, of course, that the order of multiplication is ignored and also all factors of the form 1, -1, i, $-i$.

Let N be the sum of two squares, $N = \alpha\bar{\alpha}$. Let p be a prime number of the form $4n + 3$. Let us calculate what power of p appears in the number N. From the fact that p remains a prime in the complex domain, it is sufficient to calculate what power of p appears in α and in $\bar{\alpha}$. But these powers are equal, so that p necessarily appears in N to an even power, which proves the proposition.

The discovery that a rich theory of divisibility is possible elsewhere than in the domain of whole rational numbers greatly extended the field of vision of 19th century mathematicians. The development of these ideas called for the creation of new general concepts in mathematics, such as, for example, rings and ideals. The significance of these concepts at the present time has far outgrown the frame of number theory.

Suggested Reading

H. Davenport, *The higher arithmetic: an introduction to the theory of numbers*, Harper Brothers, New York, 1960.

T. Estermann, *Introduction to modern prime number theory*, Cambridge University Press, New York, 1952.

A. A. Fraenkel, *Integers and theory of numbers*, Scripta Mathematica, New York, 1955.

G. H. Hardy and F. M. Wright, *An introduction to the theory of numbers*, 2nd ed., Clarendon Press, Oxford, 1945.

A. Ia. Khinchin, *Three pearls of number theory*, Graylock Press, Rochester, N. Y., 1952.

O. Ore, *Number theory and its history*, McGraw-Hill, New York, 1948.

I. M. Vinogradov, *An introduction to the theory of numbers*, Pergamon Press, New York, 1955.

CHAPTER XI

THE THEORY
OF PROBABILITY

§1. The Laws of Probability

The simplest laws of natural science are those that state the conditions under which some event of interest to us will either certainly occur or certainly not occur; i.e., these conditions may be expressed in one of the following two forms:

1. If a complex (i.e., a set or collection) of conditions S is realized, then event A certainly occurs;

2. If a complex of conditions S is realized, then event A cannot occur.

In the first case the event A, with respect to the complex of conditions S, is called a "certain" or "necessary" event, and in the second an "impossible" event. For example, under atmospheric pressure and at temperature t between $0°$ and $100°$ (the complex of conditions S) water necessarily occurs in the liquid state (the event A_1 is certain) and cannot occur in a gaseous or solid state (events A_2 and A_3 are impossible).

An event A, which under a complex of conditions S sometimes occurs and sometimes does not occur, is called random with respect to the complex of conditions. This raises the question: Does the randomness of the event A demonstrate the absence of any law connecting the complex of conditions S and the event A? For example, let it be established that lamps of a specific type, manufactured in a certain factory (condition S) sometimes continue to burn more than 2,000 hours (event A), but sometimes burn out and become useless before the expiration of that time. May it not still be possible that the results of experiments to see whether a given lamp will or will not burn for 2,000 hours will serve to evaluate the production of the factory? Or should we restrict ourselves to indicating only the period (say 500 hours) for which in practice all lamps work without fail, and the period (say 10,000 hours) after which in practice all lamps do not work? It is clear that to describe the working life of a lamp by an inequality of the form $500 \leqslant T \leqslant 10,000$ is of little help to the consumer. He will receive much more valuable information if we tell him that in approximately 80% of the cases the lamps work for no less than 2,000 hours. A still more complete evaluation of the quality of the lamps will consist of showing for any T the percent $v(T)$ of the lamps which work for no less than T hours, say in the form of the graph in figure 1.

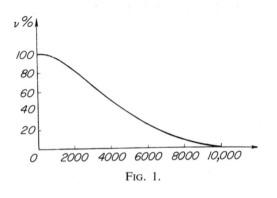

FIG. 1.

The curve $v(T)$ is found in practice by testing with a sufficiently large sample (100-200) of the lamps. Of course, the curve found in such a manner is of real value only in those where it truly represents an actual law governing not only the given sample but all the lamps manufactured with a given quality of material and under given technological conditions; that is, only if the same experiments conducted with another sample will give approximately the same results (i.e., the new curve $v(T)$ will differ little from the curve derived from the first sample). In other words, the statistical law expressed by the curves $v(T)$ for the various samples is only a reflection of the law of probability connecting the useful life of a lamp with the materials and the technological conditions of its manufacture.

This law of probability is given by a function $P(T)$, where $P(T)$ is the probability that a single lamp (made under the given conditions) will burn no less than T hours.

The assertion that the event A occurs under conditions S with a definite probability

$$P(A/S) = p$$

amounts to saying that in a sufficiently long series of tests (i.e., realizations of the complex of conditions S) the frequencies

$$v_r = \frac{\mu_r}{n_r}$$

of the occurrence of the event A (where n_r is the number of tests in the rth series, and μ_r is the number of tests of this series for which event A occurs) will be approximately identical with one another and will be close to p.

The assumption of the existence of a constant $p = \mathbf{P}(A/S)$ (objectively determined by the connection between the complex of conditions S and the event A) such that the frequencies ν get closer "generally speaking" to p as the number of tests increases, is well borne out in practice for a wide class of events. Events of this kind are usuaully called *random* or *stochastic*.

This example belongs to the laws of probability for mass production. The reality of such laws cannot be doubted, and they form the basis of important practical applications in statistical quality control. Of a similar kind are the laws of probability for the scattering of missiles, which are basic in the theory of gunfire. Since this is historically one of the earliest applications of the theory of probability to technical problems, we will return below to some simple problems in the theory of gunfire.

What was said about the "closeness" of the frequency ν to the probability p for a large number n of tests is somewhat vague; we said nothing about how small the difference $\nu - p$ may be for any n. The degree of closeness of ν to p is estimated in §3. It is interesting to note that a certain indefiniteness in this question is quite unavoidable. The very statement itself that ν and p are close to each other has only a probabilistic character, as becomes clear if we try to make the whole situation precise.

§2. The Axioms and Basic Formulas of the Elementary Theory of Probability

Since it cannot be doubted that statistical laws are of great importance, we turn to the question of methods of studying them. First of all one thinks of the possibility of proceeding in a purely empirical way. Since a law of probability exhibits itself only in mass processes, it is natural to imagine that in order to discover the law we must conduct a mass experiment.

Such an idea, however, is only partly right. As soon as we have established certain laws of probability by experiment, we may proceed to deduce from them new laws of probability by logical means or by computation, under certain general assumptions. Before showing how this is done, we must enumerate certain basic definitions and formulas of the theory of probability.

From the representation of probability as the standard value of the frequency $\nu = m/n$, where $0 \leqslant m \leqslant n$, and thus $0 \leqslant \nu \leqslant 1$, it follows that the probability $P(A)$ of any event A must be assumed to lie between zero and one*

$$0 \leqslant P(A) \leqslant 1. \tag{1}$$

Two events are said to be mutually exclusive if they cannot both occur (under the complex of conditions S). For example, in throwing a die, the the occurrence of an even number of spots and of a three are mutually exclusive. An event A is called the *union* of events A_1 and A_2 if it consists of the occurrence of at least one of the events A_1, A_2. For example, in throwing a die, the event A, consisting of rolling 1, 2, or 3, is the union of the events A_1 and A_2, where A_1 consists of rolling 1 or 2 and A_2 consists of rolling 2 or 3. It is easy to see that for the number of occurrences m_1, m_2, and m of two mutually exclusive events A_1 and A_2 and their union $A = A_1 \cup A_2$, we have the equation $m = m_1 + m_2$, or for the corresponding frequencies $\nu = \nu_1 + \nu_2$.

This leads naturally to the following axiom for the addition of probabilities:

$$P(A_1 \cup A_2) = P(A_1) + P(A_2), \tag{2}$$

if the events A_1 and A_2 are mutually exclusive and $A_1 \cup A_2$ denotes their union.

Further, for an event U which is certain, we naturally take

$$P(U) = 1. \tag{3}$$

The whole mathematical theory of probability is constructed on the basis of simple axioms of the type (1), (2), and (3). From the point of view of pure mathematics, *probability* is a numerical function of "events," with a number of properties determined by axioms. The properties of probability, expressed by formulas (1), (2), and (3), serve as a sufficient basis for the construction of what is called the elementary theory of probability, if we do not insist on including in the axiomatization the concepts of an event itself, the union of events, and their intersection, as defined later. For the beginner it is more useful to confine himself to an intuitive understanding of the terms "event" and "probability," but to realize that although the meaning of these terms in practical life cannot be completely formalized, still this fact does not affect the complete formal precision of an axiomatized, purely mathematical presentation of the theory of probability.

The union of any given number of events A_1, A_2, $\cdots$, A_s is defined as the event A consisting of the occurrence of at least one of these events.

---

* For brevity we now change $P(A/S)$ to $P(A)$.

From the axiom of addition, we easily obtain for any number of pairwise mutually exclusive events A_1, A_2, $\cdots$, A_s and their union A,

$$\mathbf{P}(A) = \mathbf{P}(A_1) + \mathbf{P}(A_2) + \cdots + \mathbf{P}(A_s)$$

(the so-called *theorem of the addition of probabilities*).

If the union of these events is an event that is certain (i.e., under the complex of conditions S one of the events A_k must occur), then

$$\mathbf{P}(A_1) + \mathbf{P}(A_2) + \cdots + \mathbf{P}(A_s) = 1.$$

In this case the system of events A_1, $\cdots$, A_s is called a *complete system* of events.

We now consider two events A, and B, which, generally speaking, are not mutually exclusive. The event C is the intersection of the events A and B, written $C = AB$, if the event C consists of the occurrence of both A and B.*

For example, if the event A consists of obtaining an even number in the throw of a die and B consists of obtaining a multiple of three, then the event C consists of obtaining a six.

In a large number n of repeated trials, let the event A occur m times and the event B occur l times, in k of which B occurs together with the event A. The quotient k/m is called the conditional frequency of the event B under the condition A. The frequencies k/m, m/n, and k/n are connected by the formula

$$\frac{k}{m} = \frac{k}{n} : \frac{m}{n}$$

which naturally gives rise to the following definition:

The conditional probability $\mathbf{P}(B/A)$ of the event B under the condition A is the quotient

$$\mathbf{P}(B/A) = \frac{\mathbf{P}(AB)}{\mathbf{P}(A)}.$$

Here it is assumed, of course, that $\mathbf{P}(A) \neq 0$.

If the events A and B are in no way essentially connected with each other, then it is natural to assume that event B will not appear more often, or less often, when A has occurred than when A has not occurred, i.e., that approximately $k/m \sim l/n$ or

$$\frac{k}{n} = \frac{k}{m}\frac{m}{n} \sim \frac{l}{n}\frac{m}{n}.$$

---

* Similarly, the intersection C of any number of events A_1, A_2, $\cdots$, A_s consists of the occurrence of all the given events.

In this last approximate equation $m/n = \nu_A$ is the frequency of the event A, and $l/n = \nu_B$ is the frequency of the event B and finally $k/n = \nu_{AB}$ is the frequency of the intersection of the events A and B.

We see that these frequencies are connected by the relation

$$\nu_{AB} \sim \nu_A \nu_B .$$

For the probabilities of the events A, B and AB, it is therefore natural to accept the corresponding exact equation

$$\mathbf{P}(AB) = \mathbf{P}(A) \cdot \mathbf{P}(B). \tag{4}$$

Equation (4) serves to define the *independence* of two events A and B.

Similarly, we may define the independence of any number of events. Also, we may give a definition of the independence of any number of experiments, which means, roughly speaking, that the outcome of any part of the experiments do not depend on the outcome of the rest.*

We now compute the probability P_k of precisely k occurrences of a certain event A in n independent tests, in each one of which the probability p of the occurrence of this event is the same. We denote by $\bar{A}$ the event that event A does not occur. It is obvious that

$$\mathbf{P}(\bar{A}) = 1 - \mathbf{P}(A) = 1 - p.$$

From the definition of the independence of experiments it is easy to see that the probability of any specific sequence consisting of k occurrences of A and $n - k$ nonoccurrences of A is equal to

$$p^k(1 - p)^{n-k}. \tag{5}$$

Thus, for example, for $n = 5$ and $k = 2$ the probability of getting the sequence $A\bar{A}A\bar{A}\bar{A}$ will be $p(1 - p) p(1 - p) (1 - p) = p^2(1 - p)^3$,

By the theorem on the addition of probabilities, P_k will be equal to the sum of the probabilities of all sequences with k occurrences and $n - k$ nonoccurrences of the event A, i.e., P_k will be equal from (5) to the product of the number of such sequences by $p^k(1 - p)^{n-k}$. The number of such

---

* A more exact meaning of *independent experiments* is the following. We divide the n experiments in any way into two groups and let the event A consist of the result that all the experiments of the first group have certain preassigned outcomes, and the event B that the experiments of the second group have preassigned outcomes. The experiments are called independent (as a collection) if for arbitrary decomposition into two groups and arbitrarily preassigned outcomes the events A and B are independent in the sense of (4).

We will return in §4 to a consideration of the objective meaning in the actual world of the independence of events.

sequences is obviously equal to the number of combinations of n things taken k at a time, since the k positive outcomes may occupy any k places in the sequence of n trials.

Finally we get

$$P_k = C_n^k p^k (1 - p)^{n-k} \quad (k = 0, 1, 2, \cdots, n) \tag{6}$$

(which is called a binomial distribution).

In order to see how the definitions and formulas are applied, we consider an example that arises in the theory of gunfire.

Let five hits be sufficient for the destruction of the target. What interests us is the question whether we have the right to assume that 40 shots will insure the necessary five hits. A purely empirical solution of the problem would proceed as follows. For given dimensions of the target and for a given range, we carry out a large number (say 200) of firings, each consisting of 40 shots, and we determine how many of these firings produce at least five hits. If this result is achieved, for example, by 195 firings out of the 200, then the probability P is approximately equal to

$$P = \frac{195}{200} = 0.975.$$

If we proceed in this purely empirical way, we will use up 8,000 shells to solve a simple special problem. In practice, of course, no one proceeds in such a way. Instead, we begin the investigation by assuming that the scattering of the shells for a given range is independent of the size of the target. It turns out that the longitudinal and lateral deviations, from the mean point of landing of the shells, follow a law with respect to the frequency of deviations of various sizes that is illustrated in figure 2.

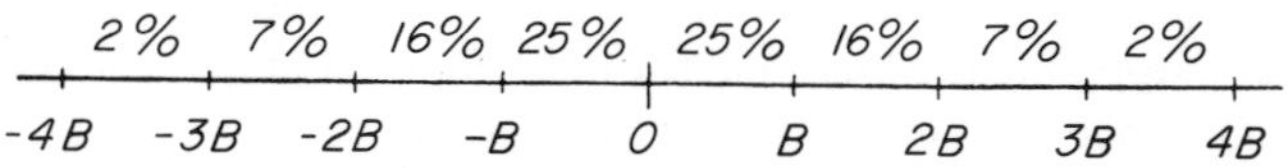

FIG. 2.

The letter B here denotes what is called the probable deviation. The probable deviation, generally speaking, is different for longitudinal and for lateral deviations and increases with increasing range. The probable deviations for different ranges for each type of gun and of shell are found empirically in firing practice on an artillery range. But the subsequent solution of all possible special problems of the kind described is carried out by calculations only.

For simplicity, we assume that the target has the form of a rectangle, one side of which is directed along the line of fire and has a length of two probable longitudinal deviations, while the other side is perpendicular to the line of fire and is equal in length to two probable lateral deviations. We assume further that the range has already been well established, so that the mean trajectory of the shells passes through its center (figure 3).

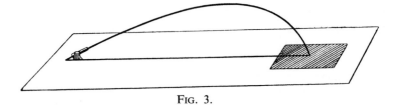

FIG. 3.

We also assume that the lateral and longitudinal deviations are independent.* Then for a given shell to fall on the target, it is necessary and sufficient that its longitudinal and lateral deviations do not exceed the corresponding probable deviations. From figure 2 each of these events will be observed for about 50% of the shells fired, i.e., with probability $\frac{1}{2}$. The intersection of the two events will occur for about 25% of the shells fired; i.e., the probability that a specific shell will hit the target will be equal to

$$p = \frac{1}{2} \cdot \frac{1}{2} = \frac{1}{4},$$

and the probability of a miss for a single shell will be

$$q = 1 - p = 1 - \frac{1}{4} = \frac{3}{4}.$$

Assuming that hits by the individual shells represent independent events, and applying the binomial formula (6), we find that the probability for getting exactly k hits in 40 shots will be

$$P_k = C_{40}^k p^k q^{40-k} = \frac{40 \cdot 39 \cdots (39 - k)}{1 \cdot 2 \cdots k} \left(\frac{1}{4}\right)^k \left(\frac{3}{4}\right)^{40-k}.$$

What concerns us is the probability of getting no less than five hits, and this is now expressed by the formula

$$P = \sum_{k=5}^{40} P_k.$$

---

* This assumption of independence is borne out by experience.

But it is simpler to compute this probability from the formula $P = 1 - Q$, where

$$Q = \sum_{k=0}^{4} P_k$$

is the probability of getting less than five hits.

We may calculate that

$$P_0 = \left(\frac{3}{4}\right)^{40} \sim 0.00001,$$

$$P_1 = 40 \left(\frac{3}{4}\right)^{39} \frac{1}{4} \sim 0.00013,$$

$$P_2 = \frac{40 \cdot 39}{2} \left(\frac{3}{4}\right)^{38} \left(\frac{1}{4}\right)^{2} \sim 0.00087,$$

$$P_3 = \frac{40 \cdot 39 \cdot 38}{2 \cdot 3} \left(\frac{3}{4}\right)^{37} \left(\frac{1}{4}\right)^{3} \sim 0.0037,$$

$$P_4 = \frac{40 \cdot 39 \cdot 38 \cdot 37}{2 \cdot 3 \cdot 4} \left(\frac{3}{4}\right)^{36} \left(\frac{1}{4}\right)^{4} \sim 0.0113,$$

so that

$$Q = 0.016, \quad P = 0.984.$$

The probability P so obtained is somewhat closer to certainty than is usually taken to be sufficient in the theory of gunfire. Most often it is considered permissible to determine the number of shells needed to guarantee the result with probability 0.95.

The previous example is somewhat schematized, but it shows in sufficient detail the practical importance of probability calculations. After establishing by experiment the dependence of the probable deviations on the range (for which we did not need to fire a large number of shells), we were then able to obtain, by simple calculation, the answers to questions of the most diverse kind. The situation is the same in all other domains where the collective influence of a large number of random factors leads to a statistical law. Direct examination of the mass of observations makes clear only the the very simplest statistical laws; it uncovers only a few of the basic probabilities involved. But then, by means of the laws of the theory of probability, we use these simplest probabilities to compute the probabilities of more complicated occurrences and deduce the statistical laws that govern them.

Sometimes we succeed in completely avoiding massive statistical material, since the probabilities may be defined by sufficiently convincing considerations of symmetry. For example, the traditional conclusion that a die, i.e., a cube made of a homogeneous material will fall, when thrown to a sufficient height, with equal probability on each of its faces was reached long before there was any systematic accumulation of data to verify it by observation. Systematic experiments of this kind have been carried out in the last three centuries, chiefly by authors of textbooks in the theory of probability, at a time when the theory of probability was already a well-developed science. The results of these experiments were satisfactory, but the question of extending them to analogous cases scarcely arouses interest. For example, as far as we know, no one has carried out sufficiently extensive experiments in tossing homogeneous dice with twelve sides. But there is no doubt that if we were to make 12,000 such tosses, the twelve-sided die would show each of its faces approximately a thousand times.

The basic probabilities derived from arguments of symmetry or homogeneity also play a large role in many serious scientific problems, for example in all problems of collision or near approach of molecules in random motion in a gas; another case where the successes have been equally great is the motion of stars in a galaxy. Of course, in these more delicate cases we prefer to check our theoretical assumptions by comparison with observation or experiment.

§3. The Law of Large Numbers and Limit Theorems

It is completely natural to wish for greater quantitative precision in the proposition that in a "long" series of tests the frequency of an occurrence comes "close" to its probability. But here we must form a clear notion of the delicate nature of the problem. In the most typical cases in the theory of probability, the situation is such that in an arbitrarily long series of tests it remains theoretically possible that we may obtain either of the two extremes for the value of the frequency

$$\frac{\mu}{n} = \frac{n}{n} = 1 \quad \text{and} \quad \frac{\mu}{n} = \frac{0}{n} = 0.$$

Thus, whatever may be the number of tests n, it is impossible to assert with complete certainty that we will have, say, the inequality

$$\left| \frac{\mu}{n} - p \right| < \frac{1}{10}.$$

For example, if the event A is the rolling of a six with a die, then in n trials, the probability that we will turn up a six on all n trials is $(\frac{1}{6})^n > 0$, in other words, with probability $(\frac{1}{6})^n$ we will obtain a frequency of rolling a six which is equal to *one*; and with probability $(1 - \frac{1}{6})^n > 0$ a six will not come up at all, i.e., the frequency of rolling a six will be equal to *zero*.

In all similar problems any nontrivial estimate of the closeness of the frequency to the probability cannot be made with complete certainty, but only with some probability less than one. For example, it may be shown that in independent tests,* with constant probability p of the occurrence of an event in each test the inequality

$$\left| \frac{\mu}{n} - p \right| < 0.02 \tag{7}$$

for the frequency μ/n will be satisfied, for $n = 10,000$ (and any p), with probability

$$P > 0.9999. \tag{8}$$

Here we wish first of all to emphasize that in this formulation the quantitative estimate of the closeness of the frequency μ/n to the probability p involves the introduction of a new probability P.

The practical meaning of the estimate (8) is this: If we carry out N sets of n tests each, and count the M sets in which inequality (7) is satisfied, then for sufficiently large N we will have approximately

$$\frac{M}{N} \approx P > 0.9999. \tag{9}$$

But if we wish to define the relation (9) more precisely, either with respect to the degree of closeness of M/N to P, or with respect to the confidence with which we may assert that (9) will be verified, then we must have recourse to general considerations of the kind introduced previously in discussing what is meant by the closeness of μ/n and p. Such considerations may be repeated as often as we like, but it is clear that this procedure will never allow us to be free of the necessity, at the last stage, of referring to probabilities in the primitive imprecise sense of this term.

It would be quite wrong to think that difficulties of this kind are peculiar in some way to the theory of probability. In a mathematical investigation of actual events, we always make a model of them. The discrepancies between the actual course of events and the theoretical model can, in its turn, be made the subject of mathematical investigation. But for these discrepancies we must construct a model that we will use without formal mathematical analysis of the discrepancies which again would arise in it in actual experiment.

---

* The proof of the estimate (8) is discussed later in this section.

We note, moreover, that in an actual application of the estimate*

$$\mathbf{P}\left\{\left|\frac{\mu}{n} - p\right| < 0.02\right\} > 0.9999 \tag{10}$$

to one series of n tests we are already depending on certain considerations of symmetry: inequality (10) shows that for a very large number N of series of tests, relation (7) will be satisfied in no less than 99.99% of the cases; now it is natural to expect with great confidence that inequality (7) will apply in particular to that one of the sequence of n tests which is of interest to us, but we may expect this only if we have some reason for assuming that the position of this sequence among the others is a regular one, that is, that it has no special features.

The probabilities that we may decide to neglect are different in different practical situations. We noted earlier that our preliminary calculations for the expenditure of shells necessary to produce a given result meet the standard that the problem is to be solved with probability 0.95, i.e., that the neglected probabilities do not exceed 0.05. This standard is explained by the fact that if we were to make calculations neglecting a probability of only 0.01, let us say, we would necessarily require a much greater expenditure of shells, so that in practice we would conclude that the task could not be carried out in the time at our disposal, or with the given supply of shells.

In scientific investigations also, we are sometimes restricted to statistical methods calculated on the basis of neglecting probabilities of 0.05, although this practice should be adopted only in cases where the accumulation of more extensive data is very difficult. As an example of such a method let us consider the following problem. We assume that under specific conditions the customary medicine for treating a certain illness gives positive results 50% of the time, i.e., with probability 0.5. A new preparation is proposed, and to test its advantages we plan to use it in ten cases, chosen without bias from among the patients suffering from the illness. Here we agree that the advantage of the new preparation will be considered as proved if it gives a positive result in no less than eight cases out of the ten. It is easy to calculate that such a procedure involves the neglect of probabilities of the order of 0.05 of getting a wrong result, i.e., of indicating an advantage for the new preparation when in fact it is only equally effective or even worse than the old. For if in each of the ten experiments, the probability of a positive outcome is equal to p, then the

---

* This is the accepted notation for estimate (8) of the probability of inequality (7).

probability of obtaining in ten experiments 10, 9, or 8 positive outcomes, is equal respectively to

$$P_{10} = p^{10}, \quad P_9 = 10p^9(1-p), \quad P_8 = 45p^8(1-p)^2.$$

For the case $p = \frac{1}{2}$ the sum of these is

$$P = P_{10} + P_9 + P_8 = \frac{56}{1024} \sim 0.05.$$

In this way, under the assumption that in fact the new preparation is exactly as effective as the old, we risk with probability of order 0.05 the error of finding that the new preparation is better than the old. To reduce this probability to about 0 01, without increasing the number of experiments $n = 10$, we will need to agree that the advantage of the new preparation is proved if it gives a positive result in no less than nine cases out of the ten. If this requirement seems too severe to the advocates of the new preparation, it will be necessary to make the number of experiments considerably larger than 10. For example, for $n = 100$, if we agree that the advantage of the new preparation is proved for $\mu > 65$, then the probability of error will only be $P \approx 0.0015$.

For serious scientific investigations a standard of 0.05 is clearly insufficient; but even in such academic and circumstantial matters as the treatment of astronomical observations, it is customary to neglect probabilities of error of 0.001 or 0.003. On the other hand, some of the scientific results based on the laws of probability are considerably more reliable even than that; i.e., they involve the neglect of smaller probabilities. We will return to this question later.

In the previous examples, we have made use of particular cases of the binomial formula (6)

$$P_m = C_n^m p^m (1-p)^{n-m}$$

for the probability of getting exactly m positive results in n independent trials, in each one of which a positive outcome has probability p. Let us consider, by means of this formula, the question raised at the beginning of this section concerning the probability

$$P = \mathbf{P} \left\{ \left| \frac{\mu}{n} - p \right| < \epsilon \right\}, \tag{11}$$

where μ is the actual number of positive results.* Obviously, this prob-

---

* Here μ takes the values $m = 0, 1, \cdots, n$, with probability P_m; i.e.,
$$\mathbf{P}(\mu = m) = P_m .$$

ability may be written as the sum of those P_m for which m satisfies the inequality

$$\left| \frac{m}{n} - p \right| < \epsilon, \tag{12}$$

i.e., in the form

$$P = \sum_{m=m_1}^{m_2} P_m, \tag{13}$$

where m_1 is the smallest of the values of m satisfying inequality (12), and m_2 is the largest.

Formula (13) for fairly large n is hardly convenient for immediate calculation, a fact which explains the great importance of the asymptotic formula discovered by de Moivre for $p = \frac{1}{2}$ and by Laplace for general p. This formula allows us to find P_m very simply and to study its behavior for large n. The formula in question is

$$P_m \sim \frac{1}{\sqrt{2\pi np(1-p)}} e^{-(m-np)^2/2np(1-p)}. \tag{14}$$

If p is not too close to zero or one, it is sufficiently exact even for n of the order of 100. If we set

$$t = \frac{m - np}{\sqrt{np(1-p)}}, \tag{15}$$

then formula (14) becomes

$$P_m \sim \frac{1}{\sqrt{2\pi np(1-p)}} e^{-t^2/2}. \tag{16}$$

From (13) and (16) one may derive an approximate representation of the probability (11)

$$P \sim \frac{1}{\sqrt{2\pi}} \int_{-T}^{T} e^{-t^2/2} \, dt = F(T), \tag{17}$$

where

$$T = \epsilon \sqrt{\frac{n}{p(1-p)}}. \tag{18}$$

The difference between the left and right sides of (17) for fixed p, different from zero or one, approaches zero uniformly with respect to ϵ, as $n \to \infty$. For the function $F(T)$ detailed tables have been constructed. Here is a small excerpt from them

T	1	2	3	4
F	0.68269	0.95450	0.99730	0.99993

For $T \to \infty$ the values of the function $F(T)$ converge to one.

From formula (17) we derive an estimate of the probability

$$\mathbf{P}\left\{\left|\frac{\mu}{n} - p\right| < 0.02\right\}$$

for $n = 10,000$. Since

$$T = \frac{2}{\sqrt{p(1 - p)}},$$

we have

$$P \approx F\left(\frac{2}{\sqrt{p(1 - p)}}\right).$$

Since the function $F(T)$ is monotonic increasing with increasing T, it follows for an estimate of P from the following which is independent of p, we must take the smallest possible (for the various p) value of T. Such a smallest value occurs for $p = \frac{1}{2}$ and is equal to 4. Thus, approximately

$$P \geqslant F(4) = 0.99993. \tag{19}$$

In equality (19) no account is taken of the error arising from the approximate character of formula (17). By estimating the error involved here, we may show that in any case $P > 0.9999$.

In connection with this example of the application of formula (17), one should note that the estimates of the remainder term in formula (17) given in theoretical works on the theory of probability were for a long time unsatisfactory. Thus the applications of (17) and similar formulas to calculations based on small values of n, or with probabilities p very close to 0 or 1 (such probabilities are frequently of particular importance) were often based on experimental verification only of results of this kind for a restricted number of examples, and not on any valid estimates of the possible error. Also, it was shown by more detailed investigation that in many important practical cases the asymptotic formulas introduced previously require not only an estimate of the remainder term but also certain further refinements (without which the remainder term would be too large). In both directions the most complete results are due to S. N. Bernšteĭn.

Relations (11), (17), and (18) may be rewritten in the form

$$\mathbf{P}\left\{\left|\frac{\mu}{n} - p\right| < t\sqrt{\frac{p(1 - p)}{n}}\right\} \sim F(t). \tag{20}$$

For sufficiently large t the right side of formula (20), which does not contain n, is arbitrarily close to one, i.e., to the value of the probability which gives complete certainty. We see, in this way, that, *as a rule, the deviation of the frequency* μ/n *from the probability p is of order* $1/\sqrt{n}$. Such a proportionality between the exactness of a law of probability and the square root of the number of observations is typical for many other questions. Sometimes it is even said in popular simplifications that "the law of the square root of *n*" is the basic law of the theory of probability. Complete precision concerning this idea was attained through the introduction and systematic use by the great Russian mathematician P. L. Čebyšev of the concepts of "mathematical expectation" and "variance" for sums and arithmetic means of "random variables."

A *random variable* is the name given to a quantity which under given conditions *S* may take various values with specific probabilities. For us it is sufficient to consider random variables that may take on only a finite number of different values. To give the *probability distribution*, as it is called, of such a random variable ξ, it is sufficient to state its possible values x_1, x_2, $\cdots$, x_n and the probabilities

$$P\{ = \mathbf{P}\{\xi = x_r\}.$$

The sum of these probabilities for all possible values of the variable ξ is always equal to one:

$$\sum_{r=1}^{s} P_r = 1.$$

The number investigated above of positive outcomes in *n* experiments may serve as an example of a random variable.

The *mathematical expectation* of the variable ξ is the expression

$$\mathbf{M}(\xi) = \sum_{r=1}^{s} P_r x_r ,$$

and the *variance* of ξ is the mathematical expectation of the square of the deviation $\xi - \mathbf{M}(\xi)$, i.e., the expression

$$\mathbf{D}(\xi) = \sum_{r=1}^{s} P_r [x_r - \mathbf{M}(\xi)]^2 .$$

The square root of the variance

$$\sigma\xi = \sqrt{\mathbf{D}(\xi)}$$

is called the *standard deviation* (of the variable from its mathematical expectation $\mathbf{M}(\xi)$).

At the basis of the simplest applications of variance and standard deviation lies the famous inequality of Čebyšev

$$\mathbf{P}\{|\,\xi - \mathbf{M}(\xi)| \leqslant t\,\sigma_\xi\} \geqslant 1 - \frac{1}{t^2}. \qquad (21)$$

It shows that deviations of ξ from $\mathbf{M}(\xi)$ significantly greater than σ_ξ are rare.

As for the sum of random variables

$$\xi = \xi^{(1)} + \xi^{(2)} + \cdots + \xi^{(n)},$$

their mathematical expectations always satisfy the equation

$$\mathbf{M}(\xi) = \mathbf{M}(\xi^{(1)}) + \mathbf{M}(\xi^{(2)}) + \cdots + \mathbf{M}(\xi^{(n)}). \qquad (22)$$

But the analogous equation for the variance

$$\mathbf{D}(\xi) = \mathbf{D}(\xi^{(1)}) + \mathbf{D}(\xi^{(2)}) + \cdots + \mathbf{D}(\xi^{(n)}) \qquad (23)$$

is true only under certain restrictions. For the validity of equation (23) it is sufficient, for example, that the variables $\xi^{(i)}$ and $\xi^{(j)}$ with different indices not be "correlated" with one another, i.e., that for $i \neq j$ the equation*

$$\mathbf{M}\{[\xi^{(i)} - \mathbf{M}(\xi^{(i)})]\,[\xi^{(j)} - \mathbf{M}(\xi^{(j)})]\} = 0 \qquad (24)$$

be satisfied.

In particular, equation (24) holds if the variables $\xi^{(i)}$ and $\xi^{(j)}$ are independent of each other.† Consequently, for mutually independent terms equation (23) always holds. For the arithmetic mean

$$\zeta = \frac{1}{n}(\xi^{(1)} + \xi^{(2)} + \cdots + \xi^{(n)})$$

it follows from (23) that

$$\mathbf{D}(\zeta) = \frac{1}{n^2}[\mathbf{D}(\xi^{(1)}) + \mathbf{D}(\xi^{(2)}) + \cdots + \mathbf{D}(\xi^{(n)})]. \qquad (25)$$

---

* The *correlation coefficient* between the variables $\xi^{(i)}$ and $\xi^{(j)}$ is the expression

$$R = \frac{M\{[\xi^{(i)} - M(\xi^{(i)})][\xi^{(j)} - M(\xi^{(j)})]\}}{\sigma_{\xi^{(i)}}\sigma_{\xi^{(j)}}}.$$

If $\sigma_{\xi^{(i)}} > 0$ and $\sigma_{\xi^{(j)}} > 0$, then condition (24) is equivalent to saying that $R = 0$. The correlation coefficient R characterizes the degree of dependence between random variables. $|R| \leqslant 1$ always, and $R = \pm 1$ only for a linear relationship

$$\eta = a\xi + b \qquad (a \neq 0).$$

For independent variables $R = 0$.

† The independence of two random variables ξ and η, which may assume, respectively, the values $x_1, x_2, \cdots, x_m$ and $y_1, y_2, \cdots, y_n$, is defined to mean that for any i and j the events $A_i = \{\xi = x_i\}$ and $B_j = \{\eta = y_j\}$ are independent in the sense of the definition given in §2.

We now assume that for each of these terms the variance does not exceed a certain constant

$$\mathbf{D}(\xi^{(i)}) \leqslant C^2.$$

Then from (25)

$$\mathbf{D}(\zeta) \leqslant \frac{C^2}{n},$$

and from Čebyšev's inequality for any t

$$\mathbf{P} \left\{ | \zeta - \mathbf{M}(\zeta)| \leqslant \frac{tC}{\sqrt{n}} \right\} \geqslant 1 - \frac{1}{t^2}. \qquad (26)$$

Inequality (26) expresses what is called the law of large numbers, in the form established by Čebyšev: If the variables $\xi^{(i)}$ are mutually independent and have bounded variance, then for increasing n the arithmetic mean ζ will deviate more and more rarely from the mathematical expectation $\mathbf{M}(\zeta)$.

More precisely, the *sequence of variables*

$$\xi^{(1)}, \ \xi^{(2)}, \ \cdots, \ \xi^{(n)}, \ \cdots$$

is said to obey the law of large numbers if for the corresponding arithmetic means ζ and for any constant $\epsilon > 0$

$$\mathbf{P}\{ \ | \ \zeta - \mathbf{M}(\zeta)| \leqslant \epsilon\} \to 1 \qquad (27)$$

for $n \to \infty$.

In order to pass from inequality (26) to the limiting relation (27) it is sufficient to put

$$t = \epsilon \frac{\sqrt{n}}{C}.$$

A large number of investigations of A. A. Markov, S. N. Bernšteĭn, A. Ja. Hinčin, and others were devoted to the question of widening as far as possible the conditions under which the limit relation (27) is valid, i.e., the conditions for the validity of the law of large numbers. These investigations are of basic theoretical significance, but still more important is an exact study of the probability distribution for the variable $\zeta - \mathbf{M}(\zeta)$.

One of the greatest services rendered by the classical Russian school of mathematicians to the theory of probability is the establishment of the fact that under very wide conditions the equation

$$\mathbf{P}\{t_1\sigma_\zeta < \zeta - \mathbf{M}(\zeta) < t_2\sigma_\zeta\} \sim \frac{1}{\sqrt{2\pi}} \int_{t_1}^{t_2} e^{-t^2/2} \, dt \qquad (28)$$

is asymptotically valid (i.e., with greater and greater exactness as n increases beyond all bounds).

Čebyšev gave an almost complete proof of this formula for the case of independent and bounded terms. Markov closed a gap in Čebyšev's argument and widened the conditions of applicability of formula (28). Still more general conditions were given by Ljapunov. The applicability of formula (28) to the sum of mutually dependent terms was studied with particular completeness by S. N. Bernšteĭn.

Formula (28) embraces such a large number of particular cases that it has long been called the central limit theorem in the theory of probability. Even though it has been shown lately to be included in a series of more general laws its value can scarcely be overrated even at the present time.

If the terms are independent and their variances are all the same, and are equal to

$$\mathbf{D}(\xi^{(i)}) = \sigma^2,$$

then it is convenient, using relation (25), to put formula (28) into the form

$$\mathbf{P}\left\{\frac{t_1\sigma}{\sqrt{n}} < \zeta - \mathbf{M}(\zeta) < \frac{t_2\sigma}{\sqrt{n}}\right\} \sim \frac{1}{\sqrt{2\pi}} \int_{t_1}^{t_2} e^{-t^2/2}\, dt. \tag{29}$$

Let us show that relation (29) contains the solution of the problem, considered earlier, of evaluating the deviation of the frequency μ/n from the probability p. For this we introduce the random variables $\xi^{(i)}$, defined as follows:

$$\xi^{(i)} = \begin{cases} 0, \text{ if the } i\text{th test has a negative outcome,} \\ 1, \text{ if the } i\text{th test has a positive outcome.} \end{cases}$$

It is easy to verify that then

$$\mu = \xi^{(1)} + \xi^{(2)} + \cdots + \xi^{(n)}, \qquad \frac{\mu}{n} = \zeta,$$

$$\mathbf{M}(\xi^{(i)}) = p, \quad \mathbf{D}(\xi^{(1)}) = p(1-p), \quad \mathbf{M}(\zeta) = p,$$

and formula (29) gives

$$\mathbf{P}\left\{t_1\sqrt{\frac{p(1-p)}{n}} < \frac{\mu}{n} - p < t_2\sqrt{\frac{p(1-p)}{n}}\right\} \sim \frac{1}{\sqrt{2\pi}} \int_{t_1}^{t_2} e^{-t^2/2}\, dt,$$

which for $t_1 = -t$, $t_2 = t$ leads again to formula (20).

§4. Further Remarks on the Basic Concepts of the Theory of Probability

In speaking of random events, which have the property that their frequencies tend to become stable, i.e., in a long sequence of experiments repeated under fixed conditions, their frequencies are grouped around some *standard level*, called their probability $\mathbf{P}(A/S)$, we were guilty, in §1, of a certain vagueness in our formulations, in two respects. In the first place, we did not indicate how long the sequence of experiments n_r must be in order to exhibit beyond all doubt the existence of the supposed stability; in other words, we did not say what deviations of the frequencies μ_r/n_r from one another or from their standard level p were allowable for sequences of trials $n_1, n_2, \cdots, n_s$ of given length. This inexactness in the first stage of formulating the concepts of a new science is unavoidable. It is no greater than the well-known vagueness surrounding the simplest geometric concepts of point and straight line and their *physical* meaning. This aspect of the matter was made clear in §3.

More fundamental, however, is the second lack of clearness concealed in our formulations; it concerns the manner of forming the sequences of trials in which we are to examine the stability of the frequency of occurrence of the event A.

As stated earlier, we are led to statistical and probabilistic methods of investigation in those cases in which an exact specific prediction of the course of events is impossible. But if we wish to create in some artificial way a sequence of events that will be, as far as possible, purely random, then we must take special care that there shall be no methods available for determining in advance those cases in which A is likely to occur with more than normal frequency.

Such precautions are taken, for example, in the organization of government lotteries. If in a given lottery there are to be M winning tickets in a drawing of N tickets, then the probability of winning for an individual ticket is equal to $p = M/N$. This means that in whatever manner we select, in advance of the drawing, a sufficiently large set of n tickets, we can be practically certain that the ratio μ/n of the number μ of winning tickets in the chosen set to the whole number n of tickets in this set will be close to p. For example, people who prefer tickets labeled with an even number will not have any systematic advantage over those who prefer tickets labeled with odd numbers, and in exactly the same way there will be no advantage in proceeding on the principle, say, that it is always better to buy tickets with numbers having exactly three prime factors, or tickets whose numbers are close to those that were winners in the preceding lottery, etc.

Similarly, when we are firing a well-constructed gun of a given type, with a well-trained crew and with shells that have been subjected to a standard quality control, the deviation from the mean position of the points of impact of the shells will be less than the previously determined probable deviation B in approximately *half* the cases. This fraction remains the same in a series of successive trials, and also in case we count separately the number of deviations that are less than B for even-numbered shots (in the order of firing) or for odd-numbered. But it is completely possible that if we were to make a selection of particularly homogeneous shells (with respect to weight, etc.), the scattering would be considerably decreased, i.e., we would have a sequence of firings for which the fraction of the deviations which are greater than the standard B would be considerably less than a half.

Thus, to say that an event A is "random" or "stochastic" and to assign it a definite probability

$$p = \mathbf{P}(A/S)$$

is possible only when we have already determined the class of allowable ways of setting up the series of experiments. The nature of this class will be assumed to be included in the conditions S.

For *given* conditions S the properties of the event A of being random and of having the probability $p = \mathbf{P}(A/S)$ express the objective character of the connection between the condition S and the event A. In other words, there exists no event which is absolutely random; an event is random or is predetermined depending on the connection in which it is considered, but under specific conditions an event may be random in a completely non-subjective sense, i.e., independently of the state of knowledge of any observer. If we imagine an observer who can master all the detailed distinctive properties and particular circumstances of the flight of shells, and can thus predict for each one of them the deviation from the mean trajectory, his presence would still not prevent the shells from scattering in accordance with the laws of the theory of probability, provided, of course, that the shooting was done in the usual manner, and not according to instructions from our imaginary observer.

In this connection we note that the formation of a series of the kind discussed earlier, in which there is a tendency for the frequencies to become constant in the sense of being grouped around a normal value, namely the probability, proceeds in the actual world in a manner completely independent of our intervention. For example, it is precisely by virtue of the random character of the motion of the molecules in a gas that the number of molecules which, even in a very small interval of time, strike an arbitrarily preassigned small section of the wall of the container (or of the surface of bodies situated in the gas) proves to be proportional with very great exactness to the area of this small piece of the wall and to the length of the interval of time. Deviations from this proportionality in cases where the number of hits is not large also follow the laws of the

theory of probability and produce phenomena of the type of Brownian
motion, of which more will be said later.

We turn now to the objective meaning of the concept of independence.
We recall that the conditional probability of an event A under the condition
B is defined by the formula

$$P(A/B) = \frac{P(AB)}{P(B)}. \tag{30}$$

We also recall that events A and B are called independent if, as in (4),

$$P(AB) = P(A)\,P(B).$$

From the independence of the events A and B and the fact that $P(B) > 0$
it follows that

$$P(A/B) = P(A).$$

All the theorems of the mathematical theory of probability that deal
with independent events apply to any events satisfying the condition (4),
or to its generalization to the case of the mutual independence of several
events. These theorems will be of little interest, however, if this definition
bears no relation to the properties of objective events which are independent in the causal sense.

It is known, for example, that the probability of giving birth to a boy is,
with sufficient stability, $P(A) = 22/43$. If B denotes the condition that the
birth occur on a day of the conjunction of Jupiter with Mars, then under
the assumption that the position of the planets does not influence the fate
of individuals, the conditional probability $P(A/B)$ has the same value:
$P(A/B) = 22/43$; i.e., the actual calculation of the frequency of births
of boys under such special astrological conditions would give just the same
frequency 22/43. Although such a calculation has probably never been
carried out on a sufficiently large scale, still there is no reason to doubt
what the result would be.

We give this example, from a somewhat outmoded subject, in order to
show that the development of human knowledge consists not only in
establishing valid relations among phenomena, but also in refuting
imagined relations, i.e., in establishing in relevant cases the thesis of the
independence of any two sets of events. This unmasking of the meaningless
attempts of the astrologers to connect two sets of events that are not in
fact connected is one of the classic examples.

Naturally, in dealing with the concept of independence, we must not
proceed in too absolute a fashion. For example, from the law of universal
graviation, it is an undoubted fact that the motions of the moons of Jupiter
have a certain effect, say, on the flight of an artillery shell. But it is also

obvious that in practice this influence may be ignored. From the philosophical point of view, we may perhaps, in a given concrete situation, speak more properly not of the independence but of the insignificance of the dependence of certain events. However that may be, the independence of events in the cited concrete and relative sense of this term in no way contradicts the principle of the universal interconnection of all phenomena; it serves only as a necessary supplement to this principle.

The computation of probabilities from formulas derived by assuming the independence of certain events is still of practical interest in cases where the events were originally independent but became interdependent as a result of the events themselves. For example, one may compute probabilities for the collision of particles of cosmic radiation with particles of the medium penetrated by the radiation, on the assumption that the motion of the particles of the medium, up to the time of the appearance near them of a rapidly moving particle of cosmic radiation, proceeds independently of the motion of the cosmic particle. One may compute the probability that a hostile bullet will strike the blade of a rotating propeller, on the assumption that the position of the blade with respect to the axis of rotation does not depend on the trajectory of the bullet, a supposition that will of course be wrong with respect to the bullets of the aviator himself, since they are fired between the blades of the rotating propeller. The number of such examples may be extended without limit.

It may even be said that wherever probabilistic laws turn up in any clear-cut way we are dealing with the influence of a large number of factors that, if not entirely independent of one another, are interconnected only in some weak sense.

This does not at all mean that we should uncritically introduce assumptions of independence. On the contrary, it leads us, in the first place, to be particularly careful in the choice of criteria for testing hypotheses of independence, and second, to be very careful in investigating the borderline cases where dependence between the facts must be assumed but is of such a kind as to introduce complications into the relevant laws of probability. We noted earlier that the classical Russian school of the theory of probability has carried out far-reaching investigations in this direction.

To bring to an end our discussion of the concept of independence, we note that, just as with the definition of independence of two events given in formula (4), the formal definition of the independence of several random variables is considerably broader than the concept of independence in the practical world, i.e., the absence of causal connection.

Let us assume, for example, that the point ξ falls in the interval [0, 1] in such a manner for

$$0 \leqslant a \leqslant b \leqslant 1$$

the probability that it belongs to the segment $[a, b]$ is equal to the length of this segment $b - a$. It is easy to prove that in the expansion

$$\xi = \frac{\alpha_1}{10} + \frac{\alpha_2}{100} + \frac{\alpha_3}{1000} + \cdots$$

of the abscissa of the point ξ in a decimal fraction, the digits α_k will be mutually independent, although they are interconnected by the way they are produced.* (From this fact follow many theoretical results, some of which are of practical interest.)

Such flexibility in the formal definition of independence should not be considered as a blemish. On the contrary it merely extends the domain of applicability of theorems established for one or another assumption of independence. These theorems are equally applicable in cases where the independence is postulated on the basis of practical considerations and in cases where the independence is proved by computation proceeding from previous assumptions concerning the probability distributions of the events and the random variables under study.

In general, investigation of the formal structure of the mathematical apparatus of the theory of probability has led to interesting results. It turns out that this apparatus occupies a very definite and clear-cut place in the classification, which nowadays is gradually becoming clear in outline, of the basic objects of study in contemporary mathematics.

We have already spoken of the concepts of intersection AB and union $A \cup B$ of the events A and B. We recall that events are called mutually exclusive if their intersection is empty, i.e., if $AB = N$, where N is the symbol for an impossible event.

The basic axiom of the elementary theory of probability consists of the requirement (cf. §2) that under the condition $AB = N$ we have the equation

$$\mathbf{P}(A \cup B) = \mathbf{P}(A) + \mathbf{P}(B).$$

The basic concepts of the theory of probability, namely random events and their probabilities, are completely analogous in their properties to plane figures and their areas. It is sufficient to understand by AB the intersection (common part) of two figures, by $A \cup B$ their union, by N the conventional "empty" figure, and by $\mathbf{P}(A)$ the area of the figure A, whereupon the analogy is complete.

---

* This is also valid, for any n, for the digits α_k in the expansion of the number ξ in the fraction

$$\xi = \frac{\alpha_1}{n} + \frac{\alpha_2}{n^2} + \frac{\alpha^3}{n^3} + \cdots.$$

The same remarks apply to the volumes of three-dimensional figures.

The most general theory of entities of such a type, which contains as special cases the theory of volume and area, is now usually called *measure theory*, discussed in Chapter XV in connection with the theory of functions of a real variable.

It remains only to note that in the theory of probability, in comparison with the general theory of measure or in particular with the theory of area and volume, there is a certain special feature: A probability is never greater than one. This maximal probability holds for a necessary event U.

$$\mathbf{P}(U) = 1.$$

The analogy is by no means superficial. It turns out that the whole mathematical theory of probability from the formal point of view may be constructed as a theory of measure, making the special assumption that the measure of "the entire space" U is equal to one.*

Such an approach to the matter has produced complete clarity in the formal construction of the mathematical theory of probability and has also led to concrete progress not only in this theory itself but in other theories closely related to it in their formal structure. In the theory of probability success has been achieved by refined methods developed in the metric theory of functions of a real variable and at the same time probabilistic methods have proved to be applicable to questions in neighboring domains of mathematics not "by analogy," but by a formal and strict transfer of them to the new domain. Wherever we can show that the axioms of the theory of probability are satisfied, the results of these axioms are applicable, even though the given domain has nothing to do with randomness in the actual world.

The existence of an axiomatized theory of probability preserves us from the temptation "to define" probability by methods that claim to construct a strict, purely formal mathematical theory on the basis of features of probability that are immediately suggested by the natural sciences. Such definitions roughly correspond to the "definition" in geometry of a point as the result of trimming down a physical body an infinite number of times, each time decreasing its diameter by a factor of 2.

With definitions of this sort, probability is taken to be the limit of the frequency as the number of experiments increases beyond all bounds. The very assumption that the experiments are probabilistic, i.e., that the frequencies tend to cluster around a constant value, will remain valid (and

---

* Nevertheless, because of the nature of its problems, the theory of probability remains an independent mathematical discipline; its basic results (presented in detail in §3) appear artificial and unnecessary from the point of view of pure measure theory.

the same is true for the "randomness" of any particular event) only if certain conditions are kept fixed for an unlimited time and with absolute exactness. Thus the exact passage to the limit

$$\frac{\mu}{n} \to p$$

cannot have any objective meaning. Formulation of the principle of stability of the frequencies in such a limit process demands that we define the allowable methods of setting up an infinite sequence of experiments, and this can only be done by a mathematical fiction. This whole conglomeration of concepts might deserve serious consideration if the final result were a theory of such distinctive nature that no other means existed of putting it on a rigorous basis. But, as was stated earlier, the mathematical theory of probability may be based on the theory of measure, in its present-day form, by simply adding the condition

$$\mathbf{P}(U) = 1.$$

In general, for any practical analysis of the concept of probability, there is no need to refer to its formal definition. It is obvious that concerning the purely formal side of probability, we can only say the following: The probability $\mathbf{P}(A/S)$ is a number around which, under conditions S determining the allowable manner of setting up the experiments, the frequencies have a tendency to be grouped, and that this tendency will occur with greater and greater exactness as the experiments, always conducted in such a way as to preserve the original conditions, become more numerous, and finally that the tendency will reach a satisfactory degree of reliability and exactness during the course of a practicable number of experiments.

In fact, the problem of importance, in practice, is not to give a formally precise definition of randomness but to clarify as widely as possible the conditions under which randomness of the cited type will occur. One must clearly understand that, in reality, hypotheses concerning the probabilistic character of any phenomenon are very rarely based on immediate statistical verification. Only in the first stage of the penetration of probabilistic methods into a new domain of science has the work consisted of purely empirical observation of the constancy of frequencies. From §3, we see that statistical verification of the constancy of frequencies with an exactness of ϵ requires a series of experiments, each consisting of $n = 1/\epsilon^2$ trials. For example, in order to establish that in a given concrete problem the probability is defined with an exactness of 0.0001, it is necessary to carry out a series of experiments containing approximately 100,000,000 trials in each.

The hypothesis of probabilistic randomness is much more often introduced from considerations of symmetry or of successive series of events, with subsequent verification of the hypothesis in some indirect way. For example, since the number of molecules in a finite volume of gas is of the order of 10^{20} or more, the number $\sqrt{n}$, corresponding to the probabilistic deductions made in the kinetic theory of gases, is very large, so that many of these deductions are verified with great exactness. Thus, the pressures on the opposite sides of a plate suspended in still air, even if the plate is of microscopic dimensions, turn out exactly the same, although an excess of pressure on one side of the order of a thousandth of one per cent can be detected in a properly arranged experiment.

§5. Deterministic and Random Processes

The principle of causal relation among phenomena finds its simplest mathematical expression in the study of physical processes by means of differential equations as demonstrated in a series of examples in §1 of Chapter V.

Let the state of the system under study be defined at the instant of time t by n parameters

$$x_1, x_2, \cdots, x_n.$$

The rates of change of these parameters are expressed by their derivatives with respect to time

$$\dot{x}_k = \frac{dx_k}{dt}.$$

If it is assumed that these rates are functions of the values of the parameters, then we get a system of differential equations

$$\dot{x}_1 = f_1(x_1, x_2, \cdots, x_n),$$
$$\dot{x}_2 = f_2(x_1, x_2, \cdots, x_n),$$
$$\cdots\cdots\cdots\cdots\cdots\cdots\cdots\cdots\cdots$$
$$\dot{x}_n = f_n(x_1, x_2, \cdots, x_n).$$

The greater part of the laws of nature discovered at the time of the birth of mathematical physics, beginning with Galileo's law for falling bodies, are expressed in just such a manner. Galileo could not express his discovery in this standard form, since in his time the corresponding mathematical concepts had not yet been developed, and this was first done by Newton.

In mechanics and in any other fields of physics, it is customary to express these laws by differential equations of the second order. But no new principles are involved here; for if we denote the rates $\dot{x}_k$ by the new symbols

$$v_k = \dot{x}_k ,$$

we get for the second derivative of the quantities x_k the expressions

$$\frac{d^2 x_k}{dt^2} = \dot{v}_k ,$$

and the equations of the second order for the n quantities $x_1 , x_2 , \cdots , x_n$ become equations of the first order for the $2n$ quantities $x_1 , \cdots , x_n ,$ $v_1 , v_2 , \cdots , v_n .$

As an example, let us consider the fall of a heavy body in the atmosphere of the earth. If we consider only short distances above the surface, we may assume that the resistance of the medium depends only on the velocity and not on the height. The state of the system under study is characterized by two parameters: the distance z of the body from the surface of the earth, and its velocity v. The change of these two quantities with time is defined by the two differential equations

$$\dot{z} = -v,$$
$$\dot{v} = g - f(v), \tag{31}$$

where g is the acceleration of gravity and $f(v)$ is some "law of resistance" for the given body.

If the velocity is not great and the body is sufficiently massive, say a stone of moderate size falling from a height of several meters, the resistance of the air may be neglected and equations (31) are transformed into the equations

$$\dot{z} = -v,$$
$$\dot{v} = g. \tag{32}$$

If it is assumed that at the initial instant of time t_0 the quantities z and v have values z_0 and v_0, then it is easy to solve equations (32) to obtain the formula

$$z = z_0 - v(t - t_0) - g \left(\frac{t - t_0}{2} \right)^2 ,$$

which describes the whole process of falling. For example, if $t_0 = 0$, $v_0 = 0$ we get

$$z = z_0 - \frac{g t^2}{2} ,$$

found by Galileo.

In the general case, the integration of equations (31) is more difficult, although the basic result, with very general restrictions on the function $f(v)$, remains the same: Given the values z_0 and v_0 at the initial instant t_0, the values of z and v for all further instants t are computed uniquely, up to the time that the falling body hits the surface of the earth. Theoretically, this last restriction may also be removed, if we assume that the fall is extended to negative values of z. For problems set up in this manner, the following may be established: If the function $f(v)$ is monotone for increasing v and tends to infinity for $v \to \infty$, then if the fall continues unchecked, i.e., for unbounded growth of the variable t, the velocity v tends to a constant limiting value c, which is the solution of the equation

$$g = f(c).$$

From the intuitive point of view, this result of the mathematical analysis of the problem is quite understandable: The velocity of fall increases up to the time that the accelerative force of gravity is balanced by the resistance of the air. For a jump with an open parachute, the stationary velocity v of about five meters per second is attained rather quickly.* For a long jump with unopened parachute the resistance of the air is less, so that the stationary velocity is greater and is attained only after the parachutist has fallen a very long way.

For the falling of light bodies like a feather tossed into the air or a bit of fluff, the initial period of acceleration is very short, often quite unobservable. The stationary rate of falling is established very quickly, and to a standard approximation we may consider that throughout the fall $v = c$. In this case we have only one differential equation

$$\dot{z} = -c,$$

which is integrated very simply:

$$z = z_0 - c(t - t_0).$$

This is how a bit of fluff will fall in perfectly still air.

This deterministic conception is treated in a completely general way in the contemporary theory of dynamical systems, to which is dedicated a series of important works by Soviet mathematicians, N. N. Bogoljubov, V. V. Stepanov, and many others. This general theory also includes as special cases the mathematical formulation of physical phenomena in which the state of a system is not defined by a finite number of parameters

---

* This statement is to be taken in the sense that in practice v soon gets quite close to c.

as in the earlier case, but by one or more functions, for example, in the mechanics of continuous media. In such cases the elementary laws for change of state in "infinitely small" intervals of time are given not by ordinary but by partial differential equations or by some other means. But the features common to all deterministic mathematical formulations of actual processes are: first, that the state of the system under study is considered to be completely defined by some mathematical entity ω (a set of n real numbers, one or more functions, and so forth); and second, that the later values for instants of time $t > t_0$ are uniquely determined by the value ω_0 at the initial instant t_0

$$\omega = F(t_0, \omega_0, t).$$

For phenomena described by differential equations the process of finding the function ϕ consists, as we have seen, in integrating these differential equations with the initial conditions $\omega = \omega_0$ for $t = t_0$.

The proponents of mechanistic materialism assumed that such a formulation is an exact and direct expression of the deterministic character of the actual phenomena, of the physical principle of causation. According to Laplace, the state of the world at a given instant is defined by an infinite number of parameters, subject to an infinite number of differential equations. If some "universal mind" could write down all these equations and integrate them, it could then predict with complete exactness, according to Laplace, the entire evolution of the world in the infinite future.

But in fact this quantitative mathematical infinity is extremely coarse in comparison with the qualitatively inexhaustible character of the real world. Neither the introduction of an infinite number of parameters nor the description of the state of continuous media by functions of a point in space is adequate to represent the infinite complexity of actual events.

As was emphasized in §3 of Chapter V, the study of actual events does not always proceed in the direction of increasing the number of parameters introduced into the problem; in general, it is far from expedient to complicate the ω which describes the separate "states of the system" in our mathematical scheme. The art of the investigation consists rather in finding a very simple space Ω (i.e., a set of values of ω or in other words, of different possible states of the system),* such that if we replace the actual process by varying the point ω in a determinate way over this space, we can include all the *essential* aspects of the actual process.

---

* In the example given earlier of a falling body, the phase space is the system of pairs of numbers (z, v), i.e., a plane. For phase spaces in general, see Chapters XVII and XVIII.

But if from an actual process we abstract its essential aspects, we are left with a certain residue which we must consider to be random. The neglected random factors always exercise a certain influence on the course of the process. Very few of the phenomena that admit mathematical investigation fail, when theory is compared with observation, to show the influence of ignored random factors. This is more or less the state of affairs in the theory of planetary motion under the force of gravity: The distance between planets is so large in comparison with their size that the idealized representation of them as material points is almost perfectly satisfactory; the space in which they are moving is filled with such dispersed material that its resistance to their motion is vanishingly small; the masses of the planets are so large that the pressure of light plays almost no role in their motions. These exceptional circumstances explain the fact that the mathematical solution for the motion of a system of n material points, whose "states" are described by $6n$ parameters* which take into account only the force of gravity, agrees so astonishingly well with observation of the motion of the planets.

Somewhat similar to the case of planetary motion is the flight of an artillery shell under gravity and resistance of the air. This is also one of the classical regions in which mathematical methods of investigation were comparatively easy and quickly produced great success. But here the role of the perturbing random factors is significantly larger and the scattering of the shells, i.e., their deviation from the theoretical trajectory reaches tens of meters, or for long ranges even hundreds of meters. These deviations are caused partly by random deviations in the initial direction and velocity, partly by random deviations in the mass and the coefficient of resistance of the shell, and partly by gusts and other irregularities in the wind and the other random factors governing the extraordinarily complicated and changing conditions in the actual atmosphere of the earth.

The scattering of shells is studied in detail by the methods of the theory of probability, and the results of this study are essential for the practice of gunnery.

But what does it mean, properly speaking, to study random events? It would seem that, when the random "residue" for a given formulation of a phenomenon proves to be so large that it can not be neglected, then the only possible way to proceed is to describe the phenomenon more accurately by introducing new parameters and to make a more detailed study by the same method as before.

But in many cases such a procedure is not realizable in practice. For example, in studying the fall of a material body in the atmosphere, with

---

* The three coordinates and the three components of the velocity of each point.

account taken of an irregular and gusty (or, as one usually says, turbulent) wind flow, we would be required to introduce, in place of the two parameters z and v, an altogether unwieldy mathematical apparatus to describe this structure completely.

But in fact this complicated procedure is necessary only in those cases where for some reason we must determine the influence of these residual "random" factors in all detail and separately for each individual factor. Fortunately, our practical requirements are usually quite different; we need only estimate the total effect exerted by the random factors for a long interval of time or for a large number of repetitions of the process under study.

As an example, let us consider the shifting of sand in the bed of a river, or in a hydroelectric construction. Usually this shifting occurs in such a way that the greater part of the sand remains undisturbed, while only now and then a particularly strong turbulence near the bottom picks up individual grains and carries them to a considerable distance, where they are suddenly deposited in a new position. The purely theoretical motion of each grain may be computed individually by the laws of hydrodynamics, but for this it would be necessary to determine the initial state of the bottom and of the flow in every detail and to compute the flow step by step, noting those instants when the pressure on any particular grain of sand becomes sufficient to set it in motion, and tracing this motion until it suddenly comes to an end. The absurdity of setting up such a problem for actual scientific study is obvious. Nevertheless the average laws or, as they are usually called, the statistical laws of shifting of sand over river bottoms are completely amenable to investigation.

Examples of this sort, where the effect of a large number of random factors leads to a completely clear-cut statistical law, could easily be multiplied. One of the best known and at the same time most fascinating of these, in view of the breadth of its applications, is the kinetic theory of gases, which shows how the joint influence of random collisions of molecules gives rise to exact laws governing the pressure of a gas on the wall, the diffusion of one gas through another, and so forth.

§6. Random Processes of Markov Type

To A. A. Markov is due the construction of a probabilistic scheme which is an immediate generalization of the deterministic scheme of §5 described by the equation

$$\omega = F(t_0, \omega_0, t).$$

It is true that Markov considered only the case where the phase space of the system consists of a finite number of states $\Omega = (\omega_1, \omega_2, \cdots, \omega_n)$ and studied the change of state of the system only for changes of time t in discrete steps. But in this extremely schematic model he succeeded in establishing a series of fundamental laws.

Instead of a function F, uniquely defining the state ω at time $t > t_0$ corresponding to the state ω_0 at time t_0, Markov introduced the probabilities

$$(t_0, \omega_i; t, \omega_j)$$

of obtaining the state ω_j at time t under the condition that at time t_0 we had the state ω_i. These probabilities are connected for any three instants of time

$$t_0 < t_1 < t_2$$

by a relation, introduced by Markov, which may be called the basic equation for a Markov process

$$\mathbf{P}(t_0, \omega_i; t_2, \omega_j) = \sum_{k=1}^{n} \mathbf{P}(t_0, \omega_i; t_1, \omega_k)\mathbf{P}(t_1, \omega_k; t_2, \omega_j). \quad (33)$$

When the phase space is a continuous manifold, the most typical case is that a *probability density* $p(t_0, \omega_0; t, \omega)$ exists for passing from the state ω_0 to the state ω in the interval of time (t_0, t). In this case the probability of passing from the state ω_0 to any of the states ω belonging to a domain G in the phase space Ω is written in the form

$$\mathbf{P}(t_0, \omega_0; t, G) = \int_G p(t_0, \omega_0; t, \omega)\, d\omega, \quad (34)$$

where $d\omega$ is an element of volume in the phase space.* For the probability density $p(t_0, \omega_0; t, \omega)$, the basic equation (33) takes the form

$$p(t_0, \omega_0; t_2, \omega_2) = \int_\Omega p(t_0, \omega_0; t_1, \omega)\, p(t_1, \omega; t_2, \omega_2)\, d\omega. \quad (35)$$

Equation (35) is usually difficult to solve, but under known restrictions we may deduce from it certain partial differential equations that are easy to investigate. Some of these equations were derived from nonrigorous physical considerations by the physicists Fokker and Planck. In its complete form this theory of so-called stochastic differential equations

---

*Properly speaking, equation (34) serves to define the probability density. The quantity $p\, d\omega$ is equal (up to an infinitesimal of higher order) to the probability of passing in the time from t_0 to t from the state ω_0 to the element of volume $d\omega$.

was constructed by Soviet authors, S. N. Bernšteĭn, A. N. Kolmogorov, I. G. Petrovskiĭ, A. Ja. Hinčin, and others.

We will not give these equations here.

The method of stochastic differential equations allows us, for example, to solve without difficulty the problem of the motion in still air of a very small body, for which the mean velocity c of its fall is significantly less than the velocity of the "Brownian motion" arising from the fact, because of the smallness of the particle, its collisions with the molecules of the air are not in perfect balance on its various sides.

Let c be the mean velocity of fall, and D be the so-called coefficient of diffusion. If we assume that a particle does not remain on the surface of the earth ($z = 0$) but is "reflected", i.e., under the influence of the Brownian forces it is again sent up into the atmosphere, and if we also assume that at the instant t_0 the particle is at height z_0, then the probability density $p(t_0, z_0; t, z)$ of its being at height z at the instant t is expressed by the formula

$$p(t_0, z_0; t, z) = \frac{1}{2\sqrt{\pi D(t - t_0)}}$$

$$\times \left[e^{-\frac{(z-z_0)^2}{4D(t-t_0)}} + e^{-\frac{(z+z_0)^2}{4D(t-t_0)}} \right] e^{-\frac{(cz-z_0)}{2D} - \frac{c^2(t-t_0)}{4D}}$$

$$+ \frac{c}{D\sqrt{5}} e^{-cz/D} \int_{\frac{z+z_0-c(t-t_0)}{2\sqrt{D(t-t_0)}}}^{\infty} e^{-z^2}\, dz.$$

In figure 4 we illustrate how the curves $p(t_0, z_0; t, z)$ may change for a sequence of instants t.

We see that in the mean the height of the particle increases, and its position is more and more indefinite, more "random." The most interesting aspect of the situation is that for any t_0 and z_0 and for $t \to \infty$

$$p(t_0, z_0; t, z) \to \frac{c}{D} e^{-cz/D}; \tag{36}$$

i.e., there exists a limit distribution for the height of the particle, and the mathematical expectation for this height with increasing t tends to a positive limit

$$z^* = \frac{c}{D} \int_0^\infty z e^{-cz/D}\, dz = \frac{D}{c}. \tag{37}$$

So in spite of the fact that as long as our particle is above the surface of the earth, it will always tend to fall because of the force of gravity, nevertheless, as this process (wandering in the atmosphere) continues, the particle will be found on the average at a definite positive height. If we take the initial z_0 smaller than z^*, it will turn out that in a sufficiently great interval of time the mean position of the particle will be higher than its initial position, as is shown in figure 5, where $z_0 = 0$.

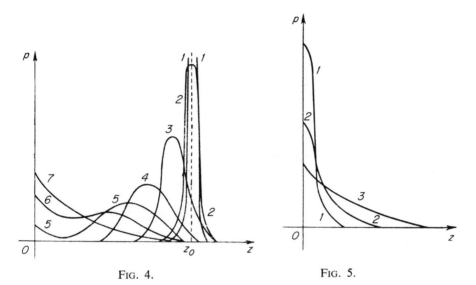

FIG. 4.   FIG. 5.

For individual particles the mean values z^* under discussion here are only mathematical expectations, but from the law of large numbers it follows that for a large number of particles they will actually be realized: The density of the distribution in height of such particles will follow from the indicated laws, and, in particular, after a sufficient interval of time this density will become stable in accordance with formula (36).

What has been said so far is immediately applicable only to gases, to smoke and the like, which occur in the air in small concentrations, since the quantities c and D were assumed to be defined by a preassigned state of the atmosphere. However with certain complications, the theory is applicable to the mutual diffusion of the gases that compose the atmosphere, and to the distribution in height of their densities arising from this mutual diffusion.

The quotient c/D increases with the size of the particles, so that the character of the motion changes from diffusion to regular fall in accordance with the laws considered in §5. The theory allows us to trace all transitions between purely diffusive motion and such laws of fall.

The problem of motion of particles suspended in a turbulent atmosphere is more difficult, but in principle it may be handled by similar probabilistic methods.

Suggested Reading

H. Cramer, *The elements of probability theory and some of its applications*, Wiley, New York, 1955.

W. K. Feller, *An introduction to probability theory and its applications*, 2nd ed., Wiley, New York, 1957.

B. V. Gnedenko and A. Ya. Khinchin, *An elementary introduction to the theory of probability*, W. H. Freeman and Co., San Francisco, Calif., 1961.

M. Kac, *Statistical independence in probability, analysis and number theory*, Wiley, New York, 1959.

J. G. Kemeny and J. L. Snell, *Finite Markov chains*, Van Nostrand, New York, 1960.

A. N. Kolmogorov, *Foundations of the theory of probability*, Chelsea, New York, 1950.

M. Loève, *Probability theory: foundations, random sequences*, Van Nostrand, New York, 1955.

E. Parzen, *Modern probability theory and its applications*, Wiley, New York, 1960.

W. A. Whitworth, *Choice and chance*, Stechert, New York, 1942.

CHAPTER **XII**

APPROXIMATIONS
OF FUNCTIONS

§1. Introduction

In practical life we are constantly faced with the problem of approximating certain numbers by means of others. For example, our measurements of various concrete magnitudes, length, area, temperature, and so forth, lead us to numbers that are only approximations. In practice we use only rational numbers, i.e., numbers of the form p/q, where p and $q(q \neq 0)$ are integers. But, in addition to the rational numbers, the irrational numbers also exist, and although we do not use them in measuring, still our theoretical arguments often lead to them. We know, for example, that the length of the circumference of a circle of radius $r = \frac{1}{2}$ is equal to the irrational number π, and the length of the hypotenuse of a right triangle with unit sides is equal to $\sqrt{2}$. In actual computations with irrational numbers, one first of all approximates them by rational numbers with a required degree of exactness, usually by means of a terminating decimal fraction.

The same situation also occurs for functions. The quantitative laws of nature are expressed in mathematics by means of functions, not with absolute exactness, but approximately, with various degrees of precision. Further, in a vast number of cases we find it necessary, even for functions defined by completely mathematical rules, to approximate them by other functions with specified exactness so as to be able to compute them in practice.

However, these remarks do not refer to computations only. The problem of defining a function by means of other functions has great theoretical importance. Let us illustrate in a few words. The development of mathematical analysis has led to the discovery and study of very important classes of approximating functions that under known conditions have proved to be the natural means of approximating other more or less arbitrary functions. These classes turned out to be, above all, the algebraic and trigonometric polynomials, and also their various generalizations. It was shown that from the properties of the function to be approximated we may estimate, under certain conditions, the character of its deviation from a specific sequence of functions approximating it. Conversely, if we know how it deviates from its approximation by a sequence of functions, we can establish certain properties of the function. In this direction a theory of functions has been constructed that is based on their approximate representation by various classes of approximating functions. There is a similar theory in the theory of numbers. In it the properties of irrational numbers are studied on the basis of their approximations by rational numbers.

In Chapter II the reader has already met one very important method of approximation, namely Taylor's formula. With its help a function satisfying certain conditions is approximated by another function of the form $P(x) = a_0 + a_1 x + \cdots + a_n x^n$, which is called an algebraic polynomial. Here the a_k are constants, independent of x.

An algebraic polynomial has a very simple structure; in order to compute it for given coefficients a_k and given values of x we need to apply only the three arithmetic operations, addition, subtraction, and multiplication. The simplicity of this computation is extremely important in practice and is one of the reasons why algebraic polynomials are the most widespread means of approximating functions (another important reason is discussed later). It is sufficient to point out that especially at the present time technical computations must be carried out on computing machines on a massive scale. In their present state of perfection computing machines work very rapidly and tirelessly. However, machines can perform only relatively simple operations. They may be set to perform arithmetic operations on very large numbers, but never, for example, the infinite process of passage to the limit. A machine cannot compute log x exactly, but we can approximate log x by a polynomial $P(x)$ with any required degree of accuracy, and then compute the polynomial by a machine.

In addition to Taylor's formula, there are others of great practical importance in the approximation of functions by algebraic polynomials. Among them are the various interpolation formulas, which are widely used, in particular, in approximate computation of integrals, and also in approximate integration of differential equations. Well known also is the method of approximation in the sense of the mean square, which is very widely used with other functions as well as algebraic polynomials. For certain practical questions great importance is attached to the method of best uniform (or Čebyšev) approximation, originated by the great Russian mathematician Čebyšev, a method which arose, as we will see, from the solution of a problem connected with the construction of mechanisms.

Our present purpose is to give the reader some idea of these methods and, as far as possible, to state the conditions under which one method is preferable to another. No one of them is absolutely the best. Every method can be seen to be better than the others under certain conditions. For example, if we have a physical problem to solve, then some one method of approximating the functions that occur in the problem is particularly indicated by the character of the problem itself or, as one says, by physical considerations. Also we will see later that under well-known conditions one method of approximation may be applicable, and another not.

Each of the methods of computation arose in its own time and has its own characteristic theory and history. Newton was already familiar with a formula for interpolation and gave it a very convenient form for practical computation with what are called difference quotients. The method of approximation in the sense of the mean square is at least 150 years old. But, for a long time these methods did not give rise to a connected theory. They were only various practical methods of approximating functions, and furthermore, the restrictions on their applicability were not clear.

The present theory of approximations to functions arose from the work of Čebyšev, who introduced the important concept of best approximation, in particular best uniform approximation, made systematic use of it in practical applications and developed its theoretical basis. Best approximation is the fundamental concept in the contemporary theory of approximation. After Čebyšev, his ideas were developed further by his students E. I. Zolotarev, A. N. Korkin, and the brothers A. A. and V. A. Markov. In the Čebyšev period of the theory of approximation of functions, not only were the fundamental concepts introduced, but basic methods were found for obtaining the best approximations to arbitrary individual functions, methods which are in wide use at the present time; also, there were basic investigations of the properties of the approximating classes, particularly of algebraic and trigonometric polynomials, from the point of view of the requirements arising from practical problems.

The further development of the theory of approximation of functions was influenced by an important mathematical discovery, made at the end of the last century by the German mathematician Weierstrass. With complete rigor he proved the theoretical possibility of approximating an arbitrary continuous function by an algebraic polynomial with any given degree of accuracy. This is the second reason why algebraic polynomials are a universal means of approximating functions. The mere simplicity of construction of algebraic polynomials is not sufficient; we also require the possibility of approximating any continuous function by a polynomial with arbitrary prescribed error. This possibility was proved by Weierstrass.

The profound ideas of Čebyšev on best approximation and the theorem of Weierstrass served as a basis, at the beginning of the present century, of the present-day development in the theory of approximation. In this connection let us mention the names of S. N. Bernšteĭn, Borel, Jackson, Lebesgue, and de la Vallée-Poussin. Briefly, this development may be described as follows. Up to the time of Čebyšev (the beginning of the present century), the problems usually consisted of approximation of individual functions, but the characteristic problem of the present-day period is the approximation, by polynomials or otherwise, of entire classes of functions, analytic, differentiable, and the like.

The Russian school, and now the Soviet school, of the theory of approximation has played a leading role in this theory. Important contributions have been made by S. N. Bernšteĭn, A. N. Kolmogorov, M. A. Lavrent'ev, and their students. At the present time the theory has developed into an essentially distinct branch of the theory of functions.

In addition to algebraic polynomials, another very important means of approximation consists of the trigonometric polynomials. A *trigonometric polynomial* of order n is a function of the form

$$u_n(x) = \alpha_0 + \alpha_1 \cos x + \beta_1 \sin x + \alpha_2 \cos 2x + \beta_2 \sin 2x + $$
$$\cdots + \alpha_n \cos nx + \beta_n \sin nx,$$

or more concisely

$$u_n(x) = \alpha_0 + \sum_{k=1}^{n} (\alpha_k \cos kx + \beta_k \sin kx),$$

where α_k and β_k are constants.

There are various particular methods of approximation by trigonometric polynomials, which are usually connected in a rather simple way with the corresponding methods of approximation by algebraic polynomials. Among these methods an especially important role is played by the expansion of functions in a Fourier series (see §7). These series are known by the name of the French mathematician Fourier, who at the beginning of the last century made several theoretical discoveries concerning them, in his study of the conduction of heat. However, it should be noted that trigonometric series were investigated as early as the middle of the 18th century by the great mathematicians Leonhard Euler and Daniel Bernoulli. In Euler's work they were related to his researches in astronomy, and in Bernoulli's to his study of the oscillating string. We may remark that Euler and Bernouilli raised the fundamentally significant question of the possibility of representing a more or less arbitrary function by a trigonometric series, a question which was finally answered only in the middle of the last century. Its affirmative answer, discussed later, was anticipated by Bernoulli.

Fourier series are of great importance in physics, but we will give little attention to this aspect of them, since it has been considered in Chapter VI. In that chapter also the reader will find examples of physical problems that naturally lead to the expansion of a given function in series other than the trigonometric series but with great similarly to them. We refer to the so-called series of orthogonal functions.

Fourier series have had a history of two hundred years. So it is not surprising that by now their theory is extraordinarily broad, subtle, and profound and constitutes an independent discipline in mathematics. An especially remarkable role in this theory has been played by the Moscow school of the theory of functions of a real variable, N. N. Luzin, A. N. Kolmogorov, D. E. Men'šov, and others.

We note also that the significance of trigonometric polynomials in contemporary mathematics is hardly exhausted by their role as methods of approximation. For example, in Chapter X the reader became acquainted with the fundamental results of I. M. Vinogradov in the theory of numbers, which were derived on the basis of a suitably devised apparatus of trigonometric sums (polynomials).

§2. Interpolation Polynomials

A special case of the construction of interpolating polynomials. In practical computations the interpolation method of approximating a function is widely used. To introduce the reader to a range of questions of this type, we consider the following elementary problem.

Let the function $y = f(x)$ be given on the interval $[x_0, x_2]$, with graph as illustrated in figure 1. The appearance of this graph is reminiscent of an arc of a parabola. So if we wish to approximate our function by a simple function, it is natural to choose a polynomial of the second degree

$$P(x) = a_0 + a_1 x + a_2 x^2, \tag{1}$$

the graph of which is a parabola.

The interpolation method consists of the following. In the interval $[x_0, x_2]$ we choose an interior point x_1. The points x_0, x_1, x_2 give corresponding values of our function

$$y_0 = f(x_0), y_1 = f(x_1), y_2 = f(x_2).$$

We construct a polynomial (1) such that at the points x_0, x_1, x_2 it agrees with the function in question (its graph is shown by the dashed curve in figure 1). In other words, we must choose the coefficients a_0, a_1, a_2 in the polynomial (1) so that they satisfy the equations

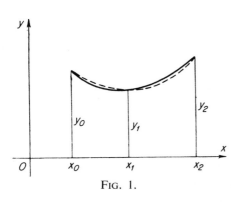

FIG. 1.

$$P(x_0) = y_0, P(x_1) = y_1,$$

$$P(x_2) = y_2. \qquad (2)$$

We note that our function $f(x)$ may be defined otherwise than by a formula; for example, its values may be given empirically as shown by the graph in figure 1. To solve the interpolation problem, we choose an approximating function in the form of an analytic expression, namely the polynomial $P(x)$. If the exactness of the approximation is satisfactory, the polynomial so chosen has the advantage over the original function that we can compute its intermediate values.

This interpolation problem could be solved as follows: We could set up the three equations

$$y_0 = a_0 + a_1 x_0 + a_2 x_0^2,$$

$$y_1 = a_0 + a_1 x_1 + a_2 x_1^2,$$

$$y_2 = a_0 + a_1 x_2 + a_2 x_2^2,$$

solve them for a_0, a_1, a_2 and substitute the values of these coefficients in equation (1). But let us solve it in a somewhat different way. We begin by constructing the polynomial $Q_0(x)$ of the second degree such that it satisfies the three conditions: $Q_0(x_0) = 1$, $Q_0(x_1) = 0$, $Q_0(x_2) = 0$. From the last two conditions it follows that this polynomial must have the form $A(x - x_1)(x - x_2)$, and from the first condition that

$$A = \frac{1}{(x_0 - x_1)(x_0 - x_2)}.$$

So, the desired polynomial has the form

$$Q_0(x) = \frac{(x - x_1)(x - x_2)}{(x_0 - x_1)(x_0 - x_2)}.$$

Similarly the polynomials

$$Q_1(x) = \frac{(x - x_0)(x - x_2)}{(x_1 - x_0)(x_1 - x_2)}, \qquad Q_2(x) = \frac{(x - x_0)(x - x_1)}{(x_2 - x_0)(x_2 - x_1)}$$

satisfy the conditions

$$Q_1(x_0) = Q_1(x_2) = 0, \quad Q_1(x_1) = 1,$$
$$Q_2(x_0) = Q_2(x_1) = 0, \quad Q_2(x_2) = 1.$$

Further, it is obvious that the polynomial $y_0 Q_0(x)$ has the value y_0 for $x = x_0$ and vanishes for $x = x_1$ and $x = x_2$, and corresponding properties hold for the polynomials $y_1 Q_1(x)$ and $y_2 Q_2(x)$.

Hence it readily follows that the desired interpolating polynomial is given by the formula

$$P(x) = y_0 Q_0(x) + y_1 Q_1(x) + y_2 Q_2(x)$$

$$= y_0 \frac{(x - x_1)(x - x_2)}{(x_0 - x_1)(x_0 - x_2)} + y_1 \frac{(x - x_0)(x - x_2)}{(x_1 - x_0)(x_1 - x_2)}$$

$$+ y_2 \frac{(x - x_0)(x - x_1)}{(x_2 + x_0)(x_2 - x_1)}. \tag{3}$$

We note that the polynomial so obtained is the unique polynomial of the second degree which solves our interpolation problem. For if we assume that some other polynomial $P_1(x)$ of the second degree is also a solution of the problem, then the difference $P_1(x) - P(x)$, which is also a polynomial of the second degree, vanishes at the three points $x = x_0$, x_1, x_2. But we know from algebra that if a polynomial of the second degree vanishes for three values of x, then it is identically zero. So the polynomials $P(x)$ and $P_1(x)$ agree identically.

It is clear that in general the polynomial so obtained agrees with the given function only at the points x_0, x_1, x_2 and differs from it for other values of x.

If we take x_1 at the center of the interval $[x_0, x_2]$ and put $x_2 - x_1 = x_1 - x_0 = h$, then formula (3) is somewhat simplified:

$$P(x) = \frac{1}{2h^2} [y_0(x - x_1)(x - x_2) - 2y_1(x - x_0)(x - x_2) + y_2(x - x_0)(x - x_1)].$$

As an example let us interpolate the sine curve $y = \sin x$ (figure 2) by a polynomial of degree two, agreeing with it at the points $x = 0, \pi/2, \pi$. Obviously, the desired polynomial has the form

$$P(x) = \frac{4}{\pi^2} x(\pi - x) \approx \sin x.$$

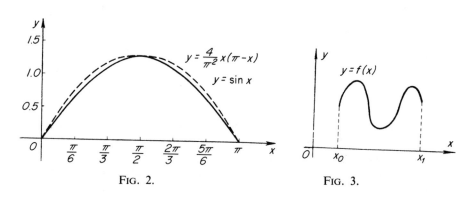

FIG. 2.   FIG. 3.

Let us compare $\sin x$ and $P(x)$ at two intermediate points:

$$P\left(\frac{\pi}{4}\right) = 0.75, \quad \text{while} \quad \sin\frac{\pi}{4} = \frac{\sqrt{2}}{2} \approx 0.71,$$

$$P\left(\frac{\pi}{6}\right) = \frac{10}{18}, \quad \text{while} \quad \sin\frac{\pi}{6} = \frac{9}{18}.$$

In this way we have approximated $\sin x$ on the interval $[0, \pi]$ with an accuracy* of about 0.05. On the other hand, the expansion of $\sin x$ in a Taylor series around the point $\pi/2$ gives

$$\sin x = \cos\left(\frac{\pi}{2} - x\right) = 1 - \frac{\left(\frac{\pi}{2} - x\right)^2}{2!} + \frac{\left(\frac{\pi}{2} - x\right)^4}{4!} - \cdots.$$

If we stop at the second term of the expansion, we have at the point $x = 0$, the approximation $\sin 0 = 1 - \pi^2/8 \approx 0.234$, i.e., an error greater than 0.2.

We see that our interpolation method has produced an approximation to $\sin x$ on the whole interval $[0, \pi]$ by a polynomial of degree two that

---

* However, for a complete justification of this statement, we need to prove that the difference $(4x/\pi^2)(\pi - x) - \sin x$ does not exceed in value 0.05, not only for $x = \pi/4$ and $x = \pi/6$, but also for all x on the interval $[0, \pi]$; we will not do this.

is more satisfactory than the Taylor expansion of second degree. However, we must not forget that Taylor's formula gives a very exact approximation close to the point $x = \pi/2$ around which it is taken, more exact in this neighborhood than the approximation obtained by interpolating.

The general solution of the problem. It is clear that a more complicated function $y = f(x)$, as illustrated in figure 3, is hardly suitable for approximation by a polynomial of degree two, since no parabola of degree two could follow all the bends of the curve $y = f(x)$. In this case it is natural to try an interpolation of the function with a polynomial of higher degree (not less than the fourth).

The general problem of interpolation consists of constructing a polynomial $P(x) = a_0 + a_1x + a_2x^2 + \cdots + a_nx^n$ of degree n which agrees with a given function at $n + 1$ equations:

$$P(x_0) = f(x_0), \ P(x_1) = f(x_1), \cdots, P(x_n) = f(x_n).$$

The points at which it is required that the function agree with its approximating polynomial are called the *points of interpolation*.

Reasoning in the same way as for a second-degree polynomial, we can easily prove that the desired polynomial may be written in the form

$$P_n(x) = \sum_{k=0}^{n} \frac{(x - x_0)(x - x_1) \cdots (x - x_{k-1})(x - x_{k+1}) \cdots (x - x_n)}{(x_k - x_0)(x_k - x_1)\cdots(x_k - x_{k-1})(x_k - x_{k+1})\cdots(x_k - x_n)} f(x_k),$$

$$(4)$$

and further that this polynomial (of degree n) is unique. The formula so written is known as *Lagrange's formula*. It may also be put in various other forms; for example, it is widely used in practice in the form involving Newton's difference quotients.

The deviation of the interpolation polynomial from the generating function. The method of interpolation is a universal means of approximating functions. In principle, the function is not required to have any particular properties for interpolation to be possible; for example, it is not required to have derivatives over the whole interval of approximation. In this respect the method of interpolation has an advantage over Taylor's formula. It is interesting to note that there are cases when the function is even analytic at every point on an interval but cannot be approximated by its Taylor's formula over the interval. Suppose, for example, that we require a good approximation of the function $1/(1 + x^2)$ on the interval

[—2, 2] by means of an algebraic polynomial. At first glance it is natural to try its expansion in a Taylor series about the point $x = 0$

$$\frac{1}{1 + x^2} = 1 - x^2 + x^4 - x^6 + \cdots.$$

But it is easy to see that this series is convergent only in the interval $-1 < x < 1$. Outside the interval [—1, 1], it diverges and consequently cannot approximate $1/(1 + x^2)$ on the whole interval [—2, 2]. Nevertheless, the interpolation method is completely applicable here.

Of course, the question arises in each case of choosing the number and distribution of the points of interpolation in such a way that the error will satisfy certain requirements. For functions with derivatives of sufficiently high order, the answer to this question of the possible magnitude of error is given by the following classical result, which we introduce without proof.

If on the interval $[x_0, x_n]$ the function $f(x)$ has a continuous derivative of order $n + 1$, then for any intermediate value of x the deviation of $f(x)$ from the Lagrange interpolation polynomial $P(x)$ with points of interpolation $x_0 < x_1 < \cdots < x_n$ is given by the formula

$$f(x) - P(x) = \frac{(x - x_0)(x - x_1) \cdots (x - x_n)}{n!} f^{(n+1)}(c),$$

where c is an intermediate point between x_0 and x_n. This formula is reminiscent of the corresponding formula for the remainder term in the Taylor expansion and is essentially a generalization of it. So, if it is known that the derivative $f^{(n+1)}(x)$ of order $n + 1$ on the interval $[x_0, x_n]$ nowhere exceeds the number M in absolute value, then the error of the approximation for any value of x on this interval is bounded by the following estimate:

$$|f(x) - P_n(x)| \leqslant \frac{|x - x_0| \cdots |x - x_n|}{n!} M.$$

The contemporary theory of approximation provides many other methods of estimating the error in interpolation. This question has been carefully studied and some interesting, completely unexpected facts have been discovered.

Consider, for example, a smooth function $y = f(x)$, defined on the interval [—1, 1], i.e., one whose graph is a continuous curve with a continuously varying tangent. Our choice of the interval with specific end points —1 and 1 is unimportant; the facts described here remain valid for an arbitrary interval $[a, b]$ with inconsequential changes.

We assume now that on the interval $[-1, 1]$ we have chosen a system of $n + 1$ points

$$-1 \leqslant x_0 < x_1 < \cdots < x_n \leqslant 1 \qquad (5)$$

and have then constructed the polynomial $P(x) = a_0 + a_1 x + \cdots + a_n x^n$ of degree n that agrees with $f(x)$ at these points. We will assume temporarily that the points of the system (5) are equally spaced along the interval. If n increases indefinitely, then the corresponding interpolating polynomial $P_n(x)$ will agree with $f(x)$ at a greater and greater number of points, and we might think that at an intermediate point x, not belonging to the system (5), the difference $f(x) - P_n(x)$ would converge to zero as $n \to \infty$. This opinion was held even at the end of the last century, but it was afterwards discovered that the facts are far otherwise. It has been shown that for many smooth (even analytic) functions $f(x)$, in the case of evenly spaced points of division x_k, the interpolating polynomials $P_n(x)$ do not at all converge to $f(x)$ as $n \to \infty$. The graph of the interpolating polynomial certainly agrees with $f(x)$ at the given points of interpolation, but in spite of this it deviates strongly for large n from the graph of $f(x)$ at intermediate values of x and the deviation increases with increasing n. As further investigation showed, this situation may be avoided, at least for smooth functions, if the points of interpolation are distributed more sparsely near the center of the interval and more densely near the ends. Indeed, it has been shown that in a well-known sense the best distribution of the points of interpolation is the one in which the points x_k occur at the zeros* of the Čebyšev polynomials $\cos [(n + 1) \arccos x]$ defined by the formula

$$x_k = \cos \frac{2k + 1}{2(n + 1)} \pi \qquad (k = 0, 1, \cdots, n).$$

The polynomials (called Čebyšev polynomials) which correspond to these points of interpolation have the property that they are uniformly convergent to the function which generated them, provided the latter is smooth, i.e., is itself continuous and has a continuous first derivative. The graph of such a function is a continuous curve with a continuously varying tangent. Figure 4 shows the distribution of the zeros of the Čebyšev polynomial for the case $n = 5$.

---

* A zero of the function $f(x)$ is a value x_k for which $f(x_k) = 0$. For details on Čebyšev polynomials see §5.

As for arbitrary nonsmooth continuous functions, the situation is worse; it can be shown that in general there is no sequence of points of interpolation such that the interpolating process will converge for any continuous function (Faber's theorem). In other words, however we may divide the interval [—1, 1] into parts, with the number of points of interpolation approaching infinity, we can always find a function $f(x)$, continuous in the interval, such that the

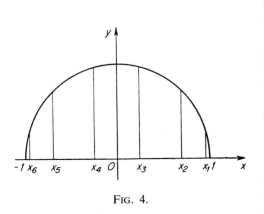

FIG. 4.

successive polynomials with these points of interpolation will not converge to the function. Even for the mathematicians of the middle of the last century, this fact, had it been known, would have sounded paradoxical. Of course, the explanation is that among the continuous nonsmooth functions there are some extraordinarily "bad" ones, for example those which do not have a derivative at any point of the interval on which they are defined, and these supply examples for which a given interpolation process will not converge. Effective methods of approximation to these functions by polynomials can be suggested by making some changes in the previous interpolation process, but we will not take the time to do this here.

In conclusion we note that algebraic polynomials are not the only means available for interpolation. There are methods for interpolation by trigonometric polynomials, for example, which are well developed from the practical and also from the theoretical point of view.

§3. Approximation of Definite Integrals

Interpolation of functions has wide application in questions related to the approximate computation of integrals. As an example, we introduce an approximate formula for a definite integral, namely Simpson's rule, which is widely used in applied analysis.

Let it be required to compute an approximation to the definite integral on the interval $[a, b]$ of the function $f(x)$, whose graph is illustrated in figure 5. The exact value is given by the area of the curvilinear trapezoid $aABb$. Let C be the point of the graph with abscissa $c = (a + b)/2$.

Through the points A, B, and C, we pass a parabola of degree two. As we know from the preceding section, this parabola is the graph of a polynomial of the second degree, defined by the equation

$$P(x) = \frac{1}{2h^2}[(x - c)(x - b)y_0$$

$$- 2(x - a)(x - b)y_1$$

$$+ (x - a)(x - c)y_2],$$

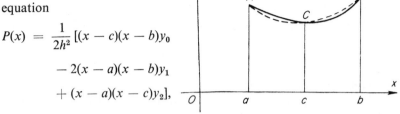

FIG. 5.

where

$$h = \frac{b - a}{2} \quad y_0 = f(a), \quad y_1 = f(c), \quad y_2 = f(b).$$

In the terminology of the preceding section, we may say that the second-degree polynomial $P(x)$ interpolates $f(x)$ at the points with abscissas a, c, b. If the graph of the function $f(x)$ on the interval $[a, b]$ does not change too violently and the interval is not large, then the polynomial $P(x)$ will everywhere differ little from $f(x)$; this, in turn, implies that their integrals taken over $[a, b]$ will also differ little from each other. On this basis we may assume these integrals are approximately equal,

$$\int_a^b f(x)\, dx \approx \int_a^b P(x)\, dx,$$

or, as it is customarily stated, the second integral is an approximation to the first. Simple computations, which we leave to the reader, show that

$$\int_a^b (x - c)(x - b)\, dx = \frac{2}{3}h^3, \quad -\int_a^b (x - a)(x - b)\, dx = \frac{4}{3}h^3,$$

$$\int_a^b (x - a)(x - c)\, dx = \frac{2}{3}h^3.$$

Hence

$$\int_a^b P(x)\, dx = \frac{h}{3}[f(a) + 4(fc) + f(b)].$$

Thus the definite integral may be computed by the following approximation formula:

$$\int_a^b f(x)\, dx \approx \frac{h}{3}[f(a) + 4f(c) + f(b)].$$

This is Simpson's formula.

As an example, let us use this formula to compute the integral of $\sin x$ on the interval $[0, \pi]$. In this case

$$h = \frac{\pi}{2}, \quad f(a) = \sin 0 = 0, \quad f(c) = \sin\frac{\pi}{2} = 1, \quad f(b) = \sin \pi = 0,$$

and consequently $(h/3)[f(a) + 4f(c) + f(b)] = \frac{2}{3}\pi = 2.09 \cdots$. On the other hand the integral can be found exactly

$$\int_0^\pi \sin x \, dx = - \cos x \Big|_0^\pi = 2.$$

The error does not exceed 0.1.

If the interval $[0, \pi]$ is decomposed into two equal parts and on each of these our formula is applied separately, then we get

$$\int_0^{\pi/2} \sin x \, dx \approx \frac{\pi}{12}\left[\sin 0 + 4\sin\frac{\pi}{4} + \sin\frac{\pi}{2}\right] = \frac{\pi}{12}\left(4\frac{\sqrt{2}}{2} + 1\right) \approx 1.001,$$

$$\int_{\pi/2}^\pi \sin x \, dx \approx 1.001.$$

In this manner

$$\int_0^\pi \sin x \, dx \approx 2.002 \, ;$$

and now the error is considerably less than 0.002.

In practice, in order to compute approximately the definite integral of a function $f(x)$ on $[a, b]$ we divide the interval into an even number n of parts by the points $a = x_0 < x_1 < \cdots < x_n = b$ and successively apply Simpson's rule to the segment $[x_0, x_2]$, and then to the segment $[x_2, x_4]$ and so forth. As a result we have the following general formula of Simpson:

$$\int_a^b f(x) \, dx \approx \frac{b-a}{3n}[f(x_0) + 4f(x_1) + 2f(x_2) + 4f(x_3) + \cdots + f(x_n)].$$
(6)

Let us now give without proof the classical estimate for the error. If on the interval $[a, b]$ the function $f(x)$ has a fourth derivative which satisfies the inequality $|f^{IV}(x)| \leq M$, then the following estimate holds

$$\left| \int_a^b f(x) \, dx - L(f) \right| \leq \frac{M(b-a)^5}{180n^4}.$$
(7)

Here by $L(f)$ we denote the right side of formula (6). In this case the error will be of order n^{-4}.*

---

* If a certain quantity α_n, depending on $n = 1, 2, \cdots$, satisfies the inequality $|\alpha_n| < C/n^k$, where C is constant independent of n, then we say that it is of order n^{-k}.

We could have decomposed the interval $[a, b]$ into n equal parts and taken as our approximation to the integral the sum of the areas of the rectangles drawn in figure 6. Then we would get an approximation formula from the rectangles*

$$\int_a^b f(x)\, dx \approx \frac{b-a}{n}\left[f(x_0) + f(x_1) + \cdots + f(x_{n-1}) \right]. \tag{8}$$

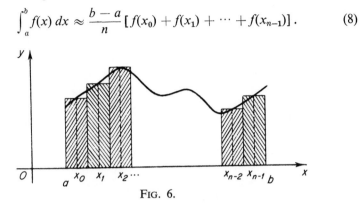

FIG. 6.

It may be shown that the order of error here is n^{-2}, provided the function has a second derivative that is bounded on the interval $[a, b]$. We may also take as an approximation the sum of the areas of the trapezoids drawn in figure 7 and get the trapezoidal formula

$$\int_a^b f(x)\, dx \approx \frac{b-a}{2n}\left[f(x_0) + 2f(x_1) + \cdots + 2f(x_{n-1}) + f(x_n) \right] \tag{9}$$

with order of error n^{-2}, provided the function has a bounded second derivative.

It is usually said that Simpson's formula is more exact than the trapezoidal and rectangular formulas. This statement requires amplifi-

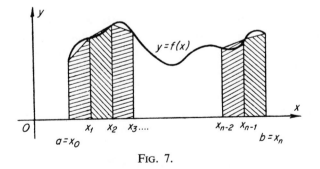

FIG. 7.

---

* In this case x_0, x_1, $\cdots$, x_{n-1} are the centers of the equal parts of the interval $[a, b]$, and not points of division as in formulas (6) and (9).

cation, without which it will not be true. If we know only that a function has a first derivative, then the guaranteed order of approximation for each of the three methods is alike equal to n^{-1}; in this case Simpson's formula has no essential advantage over the rectangular and trapezoidal formulas. For functions that have a second derivative, it is guaranteed that the approximations by the trapezoidal formula and by Simpson formulas are each of order n^{-2}. But if the function has a third and fourth derivative, then the order of the error is still equal to n^{-2} for the rectangular and trapezoidal formulas, but for Simpson's formula it is equal to n^{-3} and n^{-4} respectively. But the order n^{-4} for Simpson's formula proves in its turn to be the best possible result; in other words, for functions that have derivatives of higher order than the fourth, the order of error remains equal to n^{-4}. Thus, if we are given a function that has a derivative of fifth order and wish to make use of this fact to obtain an approximation of order n^{-5}, we need a new method of approximation to the definite integral, different from Simpson's formula. To explain how it must be constructed, we note the following.

The trapezoidal and rectangular formulas, as is easily shown, are exact for polynomials of the first degree; this means that substitution in (9) of the function $A + Bx$, where A and B are constants, leads to exact equality. In the same way Simpson's formula proves to be exact for polynomials of the third degree $A + Bx + Cx^2 + Dx^3$. The gist of the matter lies in this fact. Let us suppose that we have divided the interval $[a, b]$ into n equal parts and on each part have used a method of approximation, the same on each part, which is exact for polynomials $A + Bx + \cdots + Fx^{m-1}$ of degree $m - 1$. Then the error of the approximation for every function which has a bounded mth derivative will be of order n^{-m}, and if this function is not a polynomial of degree $m - 1$, then this order cannot be increased even for functions which have derivatives of much higher order.

Our present remarks emphasize the importance of finding the simplest possible approximate methods of integration that are exact for polynomials of a given degree. This question, on which the present-day literature is quite large, has interested mathematicians for a long time. Here we can only refer to certain classical results.

Let the function $p(x)$ be given. We are asked how to distribute on the interval $[-1, 1]$ the points of division $x_1, \cdots, x_m$ and how to choose the number K, so as to satisfy the equation

$$\int_{-1}^{1} f(x)\, p(x)\, dx = K \sum_{1}^{m} f(x_i),$$

for every polynomial $f(x)$ of degree m.

It can be shown that for $p(x) = (1 - x^2)^{-\frac{1}{2}}$ the problem is solved if $K = \pi/m$, and x_i are the zeros of the Čebyšev polynomial $\cos m \arccos x$ (cf. §5).

For $p(x) = 1$, Čebyšev gave a solution of the problem for $m = 1, 2, \cdots, 7$. For $m = 8$ the problem has no solution: the points of division may be found but they are complex. For $m = 9$ it again has a solution. However, as S. N. Bernšteĭn showed, for any $m > 9$ the problem has no solution (the points of division lie outside the interval $[-1, +1]$).

A quadrature formula that is exact for polynomials of degree n can be constructed very simply by means of Lagrange's formula (4). If we integrate its left and right sides on the interval $[a, b]$, we obtain

$$\int_a^b P_n(x)\,dx = \sum_{k=0}^n p_k f(x_k), \tag{10}$$

where

$$p_k = \int_a^b \frac{(x - x_0) \cdots (x - x_{k-1})(x - x_{k+1}) \cdots (x - x_n)}{(x_k - x_0) \cdots (x_k - x_{k-1})(x_k - x_{k+1}) \cdots (x_k - x_n)}\,dx$$

$$(k = 0, 1, \cdots, n).$$

Consequently, equation (10) is valid for all polynomials of degree n, and thus the quadrature formula

$$\int_a^b f(x)\,dx \approx \sum_0^n p_k f(x_k)$$

is exact for all polynomials of degree n.

When

$$x_0 = a, \qquad x_1 = \frac{a + b}{2}, \qquad x_2 = b,$$

this formula reduces, as we have seen earlier, to Simpson's formula.

The distribution of the points of interpolation x_k ($k = 0, 1, \cdots, n$) in the interval $[a, b]$ may be changed. For every distribution of the points there will be a corresponding quadrature formula.

Gauss, the famous German mathematician of the last century, showed that the interpolation points x_k may be distributed in such a manner that the formula will be exact for all polynomials not only of degree n, but also of degree $2n + 1$.

The polynomial

$$A_{n+1}(x) = (x - x_0)(x - x_1) \cdots (x - x_n)$$

of degree $n + 1$, arising from Gauss's points of division x_k, has a remarkable property: For any polynomial $P(x)$ of degree less than $n + 1$, we have the equation

$$\int_a^b A_{n+1}(x) \, P(x) \, dx = 0.$$

In other words, the polynomial $A_{n+1}(x)$ is orthogonal on the interval $[a, b]$ to all polynomials of degree not greater than n. The polynomials $A_{n+1}(x)$ we call the *Legendre polynomials* (corresponding to the interval $[a, b]$).

§4. The Čebyšev Concept of Best Uniform Approximation

Statement of the question. Čebyšev came to the idea of best uniform approximation from a purely practical problem, since he was not only one of the greatest mathematicians of the last century, creating the basis for a number of mathematical disciplines that are widely developed at present, but was also a leading engineer of his time. In particular, Čebyšev was very much interested in questions of the construction of mechanisms producing a given trajectory of motion. We will now explain this idea.

Let the curve $y = f(x)$ be given on the interval $a \leqslant x \leqslant b$. We wish to construct, subject to specific technical requirements, a mechanism such that a certain one of its points will describe this curve as exactly as possible when the mechanism is in operation. Čebyšev solved the problem as follows. First of all, looking for the solution as an engineer, he constructed the required mechanism in such a manner as to get a rough approximation to the required trajectory. Thus, a certain point A of the mechanism, admittedly not yet in its final form, would describe the curve

$$y = \phi(x), \tag{11}$$

resembling the required curve $y = f(x)$ only in its general features. The mechanism so constructed consists of separate parts, gears, levers of various kinds, and the like. All of these have specific measurements

$$\alpha_0, \alpha_1, \alpha_2, \cdots, \alpha_m, \tag{12}$$

which completely describe the mechanism, and consequently the curve (11). They are the parameters of the mechanism and of the curve (11).* Thus

---

* Details of the calculations for mechanisms of this sort may be found in the publication "The Scientific Heritage of P. L. Čebyšev," Volume II, Academy of Sciences of the USSR, 1945.

the curve (11) depends not only on the argument x, but also on the parameters (12). To any assigned system of values of the parameters will correspond a specific curve, whose equation may be conveniently written in the form

$$y = \phi(x; \alpha_0, \alpha_1, \cdots, \alpha_m). \tag{13}$$

It is customary to say in such cases that we have obtained a family of functions (13), defined on the interval $a \leqslant x \leqslant b$ and depending on the $m + 1$ parameters (12).

For the further solution of his problem Čebyšev worked as a pure mathematician. He proposed, in a perfectly natural way, to take as the measure of the deviation of the function $f(x)$ from the approximating function $\phi(x; \alpha_0, \alpha_1, \cdots, \alpha_m)$ the magnitude

$$\|f - \phi\| = \max_{a \leqslant x \leqslant b} |f(x) - \phi(x; \alpha_0, \alpha_1, \cdots, \alpha_m)|, \tag{14}$$

equal to the maximum of the absolute value of the difference $f(x) - \phi(x; \alpha_0, \alpha_1, \cdots, \alpha_m)$ on the interval $a \leqslant x \leqslant b$ (figure 8). This quantity is obviously a certain function

$$\|f - \phi\| = F(\alpha_0, \alpha_1, \cdots, \alpha_m) \tag{15}$$

of the parameters $\alpha_0, \alpha_1, \cdots, \alpha_m$. The problem is now to find those values of the parameters for which the function (15) is a minimum. These values define a function ϕ, which it is customary to describe as the best uniform approximation of the given function $y = f(x)$ among all possible functions of the given family (11). The magnitude $F(\alpha_0, \alpha_1, \cdots, \alpha_m)$ for these values of the parameters is called the *best uniform approximation of the function* $f(x)$ on the interval $[a, b]$ by means of the functions of the family (13). It is usually denoted by the sym-

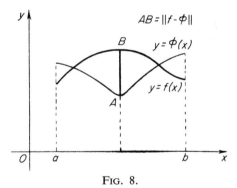

FIG. 8.

bol $E_m(f)$. The term "uniform" is often replaced, especially in non-Soviet literature, by the term "Čebyšev." They both emphasize the specific character of the approximation, since other types of approximation are of course possible; for example, one may speak of the best approximation to $f(x)$ by functions from a given family in the sense of the mean square. This subject will be discussed in §8.

Čebyšev first discovered the various laws which hold for the type of approximation we are discussing here and found that in many cases the function ϕ which is the best uniform approximation to $f(x)$ on the interval $[a, b]$ has the remarkable property that for it the maximum (15) of the absolute value of the difference

$$f(x) - \phi(x; \alpha_0, \alpha_1, \cdots, \alpha_m)$$

is attained for at least $m + 2$ points of the interval $[a, b]$ with successively alternating signs (figure 9).

We have no space here for an exact formulation of the conditions under which this proposition is valid and refer our better prepared readers to the article of V. L. Gončarov "The theory of the best approximation of functions" ("The Scientific Heritage of Čebyšev," Volume I).

The case of approximation of functions by polynomials. The cited investigations of Čebyšev are especially important for the general theory of approximation when applied to the question of approximating an arbitrary function $f(x)$ on a given interval $[a, b]$ by polynomials $P_n(x) = a_0 + a_1 x + a_2 x^2 + \cdots + a_n x^n$ of given degree n. The polynomials $P_n(x)$ of degree n constitute a family of functions depending on the $n + 1$ coefficients as parameters. As may be shown, the theory of Čebyšev is fully applicable to polynomials, so that if we wish to make the best uniform approximation to the function $f(x)$ on the segment $[a, b]$ by a polynomial $P_n(x)$ chosen from all possible polynomials of the given degree n, then we need only find all those values of x on this interval for which the function $|f(x) - P_n(x)|$ assumes its maximum L on $[a, b]$. If among them we can find $n + 2$ values $x_1, x_2, \cdots, x_{n+2}$, such that the difference $f(x) - P_n(x)$ successively changes sign

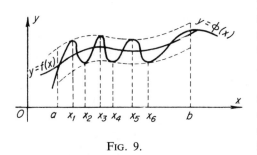

FIG. 9.

$$f(x_1) - P_n(x_1) = \pm L,$$

$$f(x_2) - P_n(x_2) = \pm L,$$

$$\cdots\cdots\cdots\cdots\cdots\cdots\cdots\cdots\cdots\cdots\cdots\cdots$$

$$f(x_{n+2}) - P_n(x_{n+2}) = \pm (-1)^{n+1} L,$$

then $P_n(x)$ is the best polynomial, and otherwise not. For example, the solution of the problem of best uniform approximation by polynomials $P_1(x) = p + qx$ of the first degree to the function $f(x)$ illustrated in figure 10 consists of the polynomial $p_0 + q_0 x$ whose graph is a straight line parallel to the chord AB and dividing into equal parts the parallelogram enclosed between the chord and the tangent CD to the curve

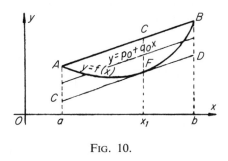

FIG. 10.

$y = f(x)$ which is parallel to that chord, since the absolute value of the difference $f(x) - (p_0 + q_0 x)$ obviously assumes its maximum for the values $x_0 = a$, x_1, and $x_2 = b$, where x_1 is the abscissa of the point of tangency F, and for these values the difference itself successively changes sign. To avoid misunderstanding, we note that we are speaking of a curve that is convex downward and has a tangent at every point. In this example $E_1(f)$ is equal to half the length of any one of the (equal) segments AC, BD, or GF.

§5. The Čebyšev Polynomials Deviating Least from Zero

Let us consider the following problem. It is required to find a polynomial $P_{n-1}(x)$ of degree $n - 1$ which is the best uniform approximation on the interval $[-1, 1]$ to the function x^n.

It turns out that the desired polynomial satisfies the equation

$$x^n - P_{n-1}(x) = \frac{1}{2^{n-1}} \cos n \, \text{arc} \cos x. \tag{16}$$

This fact follows directly from Čebyšev's theorem, if we prove, first that the right side of (16) is an algebraic polynomial of degree n with the coefficient of x^n equal to one; second, that its absolute value on the interval $[-1, +1]$ assumes its maximum, equal to $L = 1/2^{n-1}$, at the $n + 1$ points $x_k = \cos k\pi/n$ $(k = 0, 1, \cdots, n)$; and third, that it changes sign successively at these points.

The fact that the right side of (16) is a polynomial of degree n with coefficient of x^n equal to one may be proved as follows.

Let us assume that for a given natural number n we have already proved that

$$\cos n \, \text{arc} \cos x = 2^{n-1}[x^n - Q_{n-1}(x)];$$

$$-\sqrt{1 - x^2} \sin n \, \text{arc} \cos x = 2^{n-1}[x^{n+1} - Q_n(x)],$$

where Q_{n-1} and Q_n are algebraic polynomials of degree $n-1$ and n, respectively. Then similar equations will also be valid for $n+1$, as is easily established by consideration of the following formulas:

$$\cos (n+1) \text{ arc cos } x = x \cos n \text{ arc cos } x - \sqrt{1-x^2} \sin n \text{ arc cos } x \, ;$$

$$-\sqrt{1-x^2} \sin (n+1) \text{ arc cos } x$$

$$= -x\sqrt{1-x^2} \sin n \text{ arc cos } x + (x^2-1) \cos n \text{ arc cos } x.$$

But our equations for $n=1$ are true, since

$$\cos \text{ arc cos } x = x,$$

$$-\sqrt{1-x^2} \sin \text{ arc cos } x = x^2 - 1.$$

Consequently, they are true for any n.

The right side of (16) is called the *Čebyšev polynomial of degree n deviating least from zero*, since Čebyšev was the first to state and solve this problem. The first few of these polynomials are

$$T_0(x) = 1,$$
$$T_1(x) = x,$$
$$T_2(x) = \tfrac{1}{2}(2x^2 - 1),$$
$$T_3(x) = \tfrac{1}{4}(4x^3 - 3x),$$
$$T_4(x) = \tfrac{1}{8}(8x^4 - 8x^2 + 1),$$
$$T_5(x) = \tfrac{1}{16}(16x^5 - 20x^3 + 5x).$$

We have already seen the important role of the Čebyšev polynomials in questions of interpolation and of approximate methods of integration. Let us make some further remarks on interpolation.

From the fact that the difference $f(x) - P_n(x)$ between an arbitrary function $f(x)$ and its best approximating polynomial $P_n(x)$ changes sign at $n+2$ points, it follows from the properties of continuous functions that $P_n(x)$ agrees with $f(x)$ at $n+1$ specific points of the interval $[a, b]$; i.e., $P_n(x)$ is an interpolating polynomial of degree n for $f(x)$ with a certain choice of points of interpolation.

In this way the problem of the best uniform approximation of a continuous function $f(x)$ becomes one of choosing, on the interval $[-1, 1]$, a system $x_0, x_1, \cdots, x_n$ of points of interpolation such that the corresponding interpolating polynomial of degree n will have a deviation $\|f - Q\| = \max_x f(x) - Q(x)$ of least possible value. Unfortunately, the required points of division are often difficult to find in practice. Usually it is necessary to solve the problem in some approximate way, and here the Čebyšev polynomials play a special role. It turns out that if, in particular, the points of interpolation are taken to be zeros of the polynomial cos $(n + 1)$ arc cos x (i.e., the points where this polynomial is equal to zero), then the corresponding interpolating polynomial, at least for large n, will give a uniform deviation from the function (if it is sufficiently smooth) which differs little from the corresponding deviation of the best uniform approximation to the function by a polynomial. The somewhat vague expression "differs little" can be replaced, in a number of important characteristic cases, by very exact quantitative estimates, which we will not establish here.

Returning to the Čebyšev polynomial, let us consider it in the form $T_n(x) = M \cos n$ arc cos x $(-1 \leqslant x \leqslant 1)$, where M is some positive number. Obviously, on the interval $[-1, 1]$ its absolute value does not exceed the number M. Its derivative is

$$T_n'(x) = - \frac{nM \sin n \text{ arc cos } x}{\sqrt{1 - x^2}},$$

which on the interval $[-1, 1]$ satisfies the inequality

$$|T_n'(x)| \leqslant \frac{nM}{\sqrt{1 - x^2}}.$$

It turns out that this inequality is true for all polynomials $P_n(x)$ of degree n which do not exceed the number M in absolute value on the interval $[-1, 1]$; i.e., for the derivative of any such polynomial on the interval $[-1, 1]$ we have the inequality

$$|P_n'(x)| \leqslant \frac{nM}{\sqrt{1 - x^2}}.$$

This inequality is to be credited to A. A. Markov, since it follows directly from results of his which even go somewhat further. Markov himself obtained it in connection with a question suggested to him by D. I. Mendeleev.

In 1912, S. N. Bernšteĭn obtained a similar inequality, which bears his name, for trigonometric polynomials and by using these inequalities first showed how to establish the differentiability properties of a function if one knows how fast it is approached by its sequence of best approximations. Results of this kind concerning differentiable functions are given in §§6 and 7.

§6. The Theorem of Weierstrass; the Best Approximation to a Function as Related to Its Properties of Differentiability

The Weierstrass theorem. If we apply the general definition, given in §4, of best approximation to a function to the case of approximating polynomials, we are led to the following definition. The best uniform approximation to the function $f(x)$ on the interval $[a, b]$ by polynomials of degree n occurs when the (nonnegative) number $E_n(f)$, is equal to the minimum of the expression

$$\max_{a \leqslant x \leqslant b} |f(x) - P_n(x)| = \| f - P_n \|,$$

taken over all possible polynomials $P_n(x)$ of degree n.

Independently of whether or not we are able to find the exact polynomial that best approximates the given function $f(x)$, it is of great practical and theoretical interest to estimate the quantity $E_n(f)$ as closely as possible. In fact, if we wish to approximate the function f by a polynomial with accuracy δ, in other words, in such a way that

$$|f(x) - P_n(x)| \leqslant \delta \tag{17}$$

for all x in the given interval, then there is no sense in choosing it from the polynomials of degree n for which $E_n(f) > \delta$, since for this n there will certainly not be any polynomial P_n for which (17) holds. On the other hand, if it is known that $E_n(f) < \delta$, then it makes sense for such n to look for a polynomial $P_n(x)$ which will approximate $f(x)$ with accuracy δ, since such polynomials evidently exist.

The properties of the best approximating functions of various classes have been the subject of deep and careful study. First of all we note the following important fact.

If a function $f(x)$ is continuous on the interval $[a, b]$, then its best approximation $E_n(f)$ tends to zero as n increases to infinity.

This is the theorem proved by Weierstrass at the end of the last century. It has great significance, since it guarantees the possibility of approximating an arbitrary continuous function by a polynomial with any desired accuracy. As a result, the set of all polynomials of any degree bears to the set of all continuous functions defined on the interval exactly the same relation as the collection R of rational numbers bears to the collection H of all real (rational and irrational) numbers. In fact, for every irrational number α and arbitrarily small positive number ϵ, one can always find a rational number r satisfying the inequality $| \alpha - r | < \epsilon$. On the other hand, if $f(x)$ is a function continuous on $[a, b]$ and ϵ is an arbitrarily small positive number, then by Weierstrass's theorem there will exist an algebraic polynomial $P_n(x)$ such that for all x from the interval $[a, b]$ we have $|f(x) - P_n(x)| < \epsilon$. Consequently, the best approximation $E_n(f)$ to a continuous function tends to zero for $n \to \infty$.

Let us illustrate the theorem of Weierstrass in the following way. Given the graph of an arbitrary continuous function (figure 9) defined on the interval $[a, b]$, and an arbitrarily small positive number ϵ, let us surround our graph with a strip of height 2ϵ in such a way that the graph passes through the center of the strip. Then it is always possible to choose an algebraic polynomial

$$P_n(x) = a_0 + a_1 x + \cdots + a_n x^n,$$

of sufficiently high degree such that its graph lies entirely inside the strip.

We make the following remark. As before, let $f(x)$ be an arbitrary function continuous on $[a, b]$, and let $P_n(x)$ $(n = 1, 2, \cdots)$ be the polynomials which are the best uniform approximation to it. It is easy to see that the function $f(x)$ may be represented in the form of a series $f(x) = P_1(x) + [P_2(x) - P_1(x)] + [P_3(x) - P_2(x)] + \cdots$, which is uniformly convergent to $f(x)$ on $[a, b]$. This follows from the fact that the sum of the first n terms of the series is equal to $P_n(x)$, and

$$\max_{a \leqslant x \leqslant b} |f(x) - P_n(x)| = E_n(f),$$

while $E_n(f) \to 0$ as $n \to \infty$.

As a result we have a new formulation of Weierstrass's theorem:

Every function continuous on the interval $[a, b]$ may be represented by a series of algebraic polynomials converging uniformly to the function.

This result has great theoretical significance. It guarantees the possibility of representing an arbitrary continuous function, however originally given (for example, by means of a graph), in the form of an analytic expression. (By an analytic expression we mean an elementary function or else a function derived from a sequence of elementary functions by means of a limit process.) Historically this result finally destroyed the notion of analytic expression that had existed in mathematics almost up to the middle of the last century. We say "finally," since Weierstrass's theorem had been preceded by a series of general results of similar type, relating chiefly to Fourier series. Until these results were obtained, it had been assumed that analytic expressions were the means of representing the especially desirable properties that were characteristic of analytic functions. For example, it was usually taken for granted that analytic expressions were infinitely differentiable and could even be expanded in power series. But these ideas all proved to be without foundation. A function may have no derivative anywhere in its interval of definition and yet be representable by an analytic expression.

Fom a methodological point of view, the value of this discovery lies in the fact that it enables us to realize with complete clarity that at least in principle the methods of mathematics are applicable to an immeasurably wider class of laws than had been realized before.

At the present time many different proofs of Weierstrass's theorem are known. For the most part they reduce to the construction of a sequence of polynomials for a given continuous function f, which approximate f uniformly as their degree increases. The simply constructed polynomial

$$B_n(x) = \sum_{k=1}^{n} C_n^k x^k (1 - x)^{n-k} f\left(\frac{k}{n}\right),$$

will approximate a continuous function $f(x)$ on the interval $[0, 1]$. It is called the *Bernšteĭn polynomial*. With increasing n this polynomial converges uniformly on the interval $[0, 1]$ to the function which generated it.* Here C_n^k is the number of combinations of n elements taken k at a time.

We note that a theorem similar to Weierstrass's holds in the complex domain. Exhaustive results in this direction are due to M. A. Lavrent'ev, M. V. Keldyš, and S. N. Mergeljan.

The connection between the order of the best uniform approximation of a function and its differentiability properties. We note further the following results. If a function $f(x)$ on the interval $[a, b]$ has a derivative $f^{(r)}(x)$ of order r which does not exceed the number K in absolute value, then its best approximation $E_n(f)$ satisfies the inequality

$$E_n(f) \leqslant \frac{c_r K}{n^r}, \tag{18}$$

where c_r is a constant, depending only on r (Jackson's theorem). From inequality (18) it can be seen that with increasing n the quantity $E_n(f)$ converges to zero more rapidly for functions with derivatives of higher order. In other words, the better (smoother) the function, the faster the convergence to zero of its best approximation. Bernšteĭn proved that in a certain sense the converse to this proposition is also true.

Still better in this respect than the differentiable functions are the

---

* It must be remarked that, in spite of their simplicity, the Bernšteĭn polynomials are little used in practice. The explanation is that they converge very slowly, even for functions with good differentiability properties.

analytic functions. Bernšteǐn proved that for such functions, $E_n(f)$ satisfies the inequality

$$E_n(f) \leqslant cq^n, \tag{19}$$

where c and q are constants depending on the function f, and $0 < q < 1$; i.e., $E_n(f)$ converges to zero more rapidly than a certain decreasing progression. He also proved that conversely the inequality (19) implies that the function f is analytic on $[a, b]$.

We have given certain very important results that were discovered at the beginning of this century and have been characteristic of the direction taken by contemporary research in the theory of approximation of functions. The practical value of these results may be seen from the following example.

If $Q_n(x)$ is a polynomial of degree n, which interpolates the function $f(x)$ on the interval $[-1, 1]$ at the $n + 1$ points of interpolation which are the zeros of the Čebyšev polynomial $\cos (n + 1)$ arc $\cos x$, then on this interval one has the inequality $|f(x) - Q_n(x)| < c \ln n \, E_n(f)$, where c is a constant independent of n, and $E_n(f)$ is the best approximation to the function f on $[-1, 1]$. In this inequality we may replace $E_n(f)$ by the larger expressions, occurring in (18) or (19), provided f is sufficiently smooth, and obtain a good estimate of the approximation of our interpolating polynomial. Since $\ln n$ increases very slowly with increasing n, the order of the estimate in the given case differs little from the order of convergence to zero of $E_n(f)$. The advantage of interpolation by the Čebyšev points consists of the fact that for other points of interpolation the factor $c \ln n$ in the corresponding inequality is replaced by a more rapidly increasing factor; this is particularly true in the case of equally spaced points of interpolation.

§7. Fourier Series

The origin of Fourier series. Fourier series arose in connection with the study of certain physical phenomena, in particular, small oscillations of elastic media. A characteristic example is the oscillation of a musical string. Indeed, the investigation of oscillating strings was the origin historically of Fourier series and determined the direction in which their theory developed.

Let us consider (figure 11) a tautly stretched string, the ends of which are fixed at the points $x = 0$ and $x = l$ of the axis Ox. If we displace the string from its position of equilibrium, it will oscillate.

We will follow the motion of a specific point of the string, with abscissa x_0. Its deviation vertically from the position of equilibrium is a function

$\phi(t)$ of time. It can be shown that one can always give the string an initial position and velocity at $t = 0$ such that as a result the point which we have agreed to follow will perform harmonic oscillations in the vertical direction, defined by the function

$$\phi = \phi(t) = A \cos \alpha k t + B \sin \alpha k t. \tag{20}$$

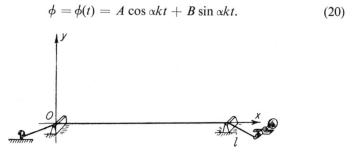

Fig. 11.

Here α is a constant depending only on the physical properties of the string (on the density, tension, and length), k is an arbitrary number, and A and B are constants.

We note that our discussion relates only to small oscillations of the string. This gives us the right to assume approximately that every point x_0 is oscillating only in the vertical direction, displacements in the horizontal direction being ignored.* We also assume that the friction arising from the oscillation of the string is so small that we may ignore it. As a result of these approximate assumptions, the oscillations will not die out.

The possibilities of oscillation for the point x_0 are of course, not exhausted by the periodic motions defined by the harmonic functions (20), but these functions do have the following remarkable property. Experiments and their accompanying theory show that every possible oscillation of the point x_0 is the result of combining certain harmonic oscillations of the form (20). Relatively simple oscillations are obtained by combining a finite number of such oscillations; i.e., they are described by functions of the form

$$\phi(t) = A_0 + \sum_{k=1}^{n} (A_k \cos \alpha k t + B_k \sin \alpha k t),$$

---

* This question is directly connected with the differential equation of the oscillating string

$$\frac{\partial^2 u}{\partial t^2} = a^2 \frac{\partial^2 u}{\partial x^2} \left(a = \frac{l}{\pi}\alpha\right),$$

which was discussed in Chapter VI.

where A_k and B_k are corresponding constants. These functions are called trigonometric polynomials. In more complicated cases, the oscillation will be the result of combining an infinite number of oscillations of the form (20), corresponding to $k = 1, 2, 3, \cdots$ and with suitably chosen constants A_k and B_k, depending on the number k. Consequently, we arrive at the necessity of representing a given function $\phi(t)$ of period $2\pi/\alpha$, which describes an arbitrary oscillation of the point x_0 in the form of a series

$$\phi(t) = A_0 + \sum_{k=1}^{\infty} (A_k \cos \alpha k t + B_k \sin \alpha k t). \tag{21}$$

There are many other situations in physics where it is natural to consider a given function, even though it does not necessarily describe an oscillation, as the sum of an infinite trigonometric series of the form (21). Such a case arises, for example, in connection with the vibrating string itself. The exact law for the subsequent oscillation of a string, to which at the beginning of the experiment we have given a specific initial displacement (for example, as illustrated in figure 12) is easy to calculate, provided we know the expansion in a trigonometric series $f(x) = \sum_1^\infty a_k \sin (k\pi/l)x$, (a particular case of the series (21)), of the function $f(x)$ describing the initial position.

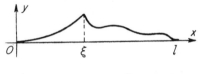

FIG. 12.

Expansion of functions in a trigonometric series. On the basis of what has been said there arises the fundamental question: Which functions of period $2\pi/\alpha$ can be represented as the sum of a trigonometric series of the form (21)? This question was raised in the 18th century by Euler and Bernoulli in connection with Bernoulli's study of the vibrating string. Here Bernoulli took the point of view suggested by physical considerations that a very wide class of continuous functions, including in particular all graphs drawn by hand, can be expanded in a trigonometric series. This opinion received harsh treatment from many of Bernoulli's contemporaries. They held tenaciously to the idea prevalent at the time that if a function is represented as an analytic expression (such as a trigonometric series) then it must have good differentiability properties. But the function illustrated in figure 12 does not even have a derivative at the point ξ; in such a case, how can it be defined by one and the same analytic expression on the whole interval $[0, l]$?

We know now that the physical point of view of Bernoulli was quite right. But to put an end to the controversy it was necessary to wait an entire century, since a full answer to these questions required first of all that the concepts of a limit and of the sum of a series be put on an exact basis.

The fundamental mathematical investigations confirming the physical point of view but based on the older ideas concerning the foundations of analysis were completed in 1807-1822 by the French mathematician Fourier.

Finally, in 1829, the German mathematician Dirichlet showed, with all the rigor with which it would be done in present-day mathematics, that every continuous function of period $2\pi/\alpha$,* which for any one period has a finite number of maxima and minima, can be expanded in a unique trigonometric Fourier series, uniformly convergent† to the function.

Figure 13 illustrates a function satisfying Dirichlet's conditions. Its graph is continuous and periodic, with period 2π, and has one maximum and one minimum in the period $0 \leqslant x \leqslant 2\pi$.

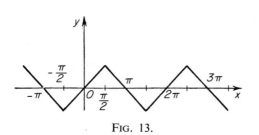

FIG. 13.

Fourier coefficients. In what follows we will consider functions of period 2π, which will simplify the formulas. We consider any continuous function $f(x)$ of period 2π satisfying Dirichlet's condition. By Dirichlet's theorem it may be expanded into a trigonometric series

$$f(x) = \frac{a_0}{2} + \sum_{k=1}^{\infty} (a_k \cos kx + b_k \sin kx), \qquad (22)$$

which is uniformly convergent to it. The fact that the first term is written as $a_0/2$ rather than a_0 has no real significance but is purely a matter of convenience, as we shall see later.

We pose the problem: to compute the coefficients a_k and b_k of the series for a given function $f(x)$.

---

* The function $f(x)$ has period ω if it satisfies the equation $f(x + \omega) = f(x)$.

† In fact, Dirichlet's theorem also applies to a certain class of discontinuous functions, the so-called functions of bounded variation. For discontinuous functions, of course, the corresponding series is nonuniformly convergent.

To this end we note the following equation:

$$\int_{-\pi}^{\pi} \cos kx \cos lx \, dx = 0 \quad (k \neq l; \; k, l = 0, 1, \cdots),$$

$$\int_{-\pi}^{\pi} \sin kx \sin lx \, dx = 0 \quad (k \neq l; \; k, l = 0, 1, \cdots),$$

$$\int_{-\pi}^{\pi} \sin kx \cos lx \, dx = 0 \quad (k, l = 0, 1, 2, \cdots), \tag{23}$$

$$\int_{-\pi}^{\pi} \cos^2 kx \, dx = \pi \quad (k = 1, 2, \cdots),$$

$$\int_{-\pi}^{\pi} \sin^2 kx \, dx = \pi \quad (k = 1, 2, \cdots),$$

which the reader may verify. These integrals are easy to compute by reducing the products of the various trigonometric functions to their sums and differences and their squares to expressions containing the corresponding trigonometric functions of double the angle. The first equation states that the integral, over a period of the function, of the product of two different functions from the sequence 1, $\cos x$, $\sin x$, $\cos 2x$, $\sin 2x$, $\cdots$ is equal to zero (the so-called orthogonality property of the trigonometric functions). On the other hand, the integral of the square of each of the functions of this sequence is equal to π. The first function, identically equal to one, forms an exception, since the integral of its square over the period is equal to 2π. It is this fact which makes it convenient to write the first term of the series (22) in the form $a_0/2$.

Now we can easily solve our problem. To compute the coefficient a_m, we multiply the left side and each term on the right side of the series (22) by $\cos mx$ and integrate term by term over a period 2π, as is permissible since the series obtained after multiplication by $\cos mx$ is uniformly convergent. By (23) all integrals on the right side, with the exception of the integral corresponding to $\cos mx$, will be zero, so that obviously

$$\int_{-\pi}^{\pi} f(x) \cos mx \, dx = a_m \pi,$$

hence

$$a_m = \frac{1}{\pi} \int_{-\pi}^{\pi} f(x) \cos mx \, dx \quad (m = 0, 1, 2, \cdots). \tag{24}$$

Similarly, multiplying the left and right sides of (22) by $\cdot \sin mx$ and integrating over the period, we get an expression for the coefficients

$$b_m = \frac{1}{\pi} \int_{-\pi}^{\pi} f(x) \sin mx \, dx \quad (m = 1, 2, \cdots), \tag{25}$$

and we have solved our problem. The numbers a_m and b_m computed by formulas (24) and (25) are called the *Fourier coefficients* of the function $f(x)$.

Let us take an example the function $f(x)$ of period 2π illustrated in figure 13. Obviously this function is continuous and satisfies Dirichlet's condition, so that its Fourier series converges uniformly to it.

It is easy to see that this function also satisfies the condition $f(-x) = -f(x)$. The same condition also clearly holds for the function $F_1(x) = f(x) \cos mx$, which means that the graph of $F_1(x)$ is symmetric with respect to the origin. From geometric arguments it is clear that $\int_{-\pi}^{\pi} F_1(x)\, dx = 0$, so that $a_m = 0$ $(m = 0, 1, 2, \cdots)$. Further, it is not difficult to see that the functions $F_2(x) = f(x) \sin mx$ has a graph which is symmetric with respect to the axis Oy so that

$$b_m = \frac{1}{\pi} \int_{-\pi}^{\pi} F_2(x)\, dx = \frac{2}{\pi} \int_0^{\pi} F_2(x)\, dx.$$

But for even m this graph is symmetric with respect to the center $\pi/2$ of the segment $[0, \pi]$, so that $b_m = 0$ for even m. For odd $m = 2l + 1$ $(l = 0, 1, 2, \cdots)$ the graph of $F_2(x)$ is symmetric with respect to the straight line $x = \pi/2$, so that

$$b_{2l+1} = \frac{4}{\pi} \int_0^{\pi/2} F_2(x)\, dx.$$

But, as can be seen from the sketch, on the segment $[0, \pi/2]$ we have simply $f(x) = x$, so that by integration by parts, we get

$$b_{2l+1} = \frac{4}{\pi} \int_0^{\pi/2} x \sin (2l + 1)x \, dx = \frac{4(-1)^l}{\pi(2l + 1)^2} ,$$

and consequently

$$f(x) = \frac{4}{\pi} \sum_{l=1}^{\infty} \frac{(-1)^l \sin (2l + 1)x}{(2l + 1)^2} .$$

Thus we have found the expansion of our function in a Fourier series.

Convergence of the Fourier partial sums to the generating function. In applications it is customary to take as an approximation to the function $f(x)$ of period 2π the sum

$$S_n = \frac{a_0}{2} + \sum_1^n (a_k \cos kx + b_k \sin kx)$$

of the first n terms of its Fourier series, and then there arises the question of the error of the approximation. If the function $f(x)$ of period 2π has a derivative $f^{(r)}(x)$ of order r which for all x satisfies the inequality $|f^{(r)}(x)| \leqslant K$, then the error of the approximation may be estimated as follows:

$$|f(x) - S_n(x)| \leqslant \frac{c_r K \ln n}{n^r},$$

where c_r is a constant depending only on r. We see that the error converges to zero with increasing n, the convergence being the more rapid the more derivatives the function has.

For a function which is analytic on the whole real axis there is an even better estimate, as follows:

$$|f(x) - S_n(x)| < cq^n, \tag{26}$$

where c and q are positive constants depending on f and $q < 1$. It is remarkable that the converse is also true, namely that if the inequality (26) holds for a given function, then the function is necessarily analytic. This fact, which was discovered at the beginning of the present century, in a certain sense reconciles the controversy between D. Bernoulli and his contemporaries. We can now state: If a function is expandable in a Fourier series which converges to it, this fact in itself is far from implying that the function is analytic; however, it will be analytic, if its deviation from the sum of the first n terms of the Fourier series decreases more rapidly than the terms of some decreasing geometric progression.

A comparison of the estimates of the approximations provided by the Fourier sums with the corresponding estimates for the best approximations of the same functions by trigonometric polynomials shows that for smooth functions the Fourier sums give very good approximations, which are in fact, close to the best approximations. But for nonsmooth continuous functions the situation is worse: Among these, for example, occur some functions whose Fourier series diverges on the set of all rational points.

It remains to note that in the theory of Fourier series there is a question which was raised long ago and has not yet been answered: Does there exist a continuous periodic function $f(x)$ whose Fourier series fails for all x to converge to the function as $n = \infty$? The best result in this direction is due to A. N. Kolmogorov, who proved in 1926 that there exists a periodic Lebesgue-integrable function whose Fourier series does not converge to it at any point. But a Lebesgue-integrable function may be discontinuous, as is the case with the function constructed by Kolmogorov. The problem still awaits its final solution.

To provide approximations by trigonometric polynomials to arbitrary continuous periodic functions, the methods of the so-called summation of Fourier series are in use at the present time. In place of the Fourier sums as an approximation to a given function we consider certain modifications of them. A very simple method of this sort was proposed by the Hungarian mathematician Fejér. For a continuous periodic function we first, in a purely formal way, construct its Fourier series, which may be divergent, and then form the arithmetic means of the first n partial sums

$$\sigma_n(x) = \frac{S_0(x) + S_1(x) + \cdots + S_n(x)}{n + 1}. \tag{27}$$

This is called the *Fejér sum* of order n corresponding to the given function $f(x)$. Fejér proved that as $n = \infty$ this sum converges uniformly to $f(x)$.

§8. Approximation in the Sense of the Mean Square

Let us return to the problem of the oscillating string. We assume that at a certain moment t_0 the string has the form $y = f(x)$. We can prove that its potential energy W, i.e., the work made available as it moves from the given position to its position of equilibrium, is equal (for small deviations of the string) to the integral $W = \int_0^l f'^2(x)\, dx$, at least up to a constant factor. Suppose now that we wish to approximate the function $f(x)$ by another function $\phi(x)$. Together with the given string, we will consider a string whose shape is defined by $\phi(x)$, and still a third string, defined by the function $f(x) - \phi(x)$. It may be proved that if the energy

$$\int_0^l [f'(x) - \phi'(x)]^2\, dx \tag{28}$$

of the third string is small, then the difference between the energy of the first two strings will also be small.* Thus, if it is important that the second string have an energy which differs little from the first, we must

---

* In fact, if

$$\int_0^l f'^2\, dx \leqslant M^2 \quad \text{and} \quad \int_0^l \phi'^2\, dx \leqslant M^2,$$

then

$$\left| \int_0^l f'^2\, dx - \int_0^l \phi'^2\, dx \right|$$

$$\leqslant \left(\sqrt{\int_0^l f'^2\, dx} + \sqrt{\int_0^l \phi'^2\, dx} \right) \left| \sqrt{\int_0^l f'^2\, dx} - \sqrt{\int_0^l \phi'^2\, dx} \right| \leqslant 2M \sqrt{\int_0^l (f' - \phi')^2\, dx}.$$

try to find a function $\phi'(x)$ for which the integral (28) will be as small as possible. We are thus led to the problem of approximation to a function (in this case $f'(x)$) in the sense of the mean square.

Here is how this problem is to be stated in the general case. On the interval $[a, b]$ we are given the function $F(x)$, and also the function

$$\Phi(x; \alpha_0, \alpha_1, \cdots, \alpha_n), \tag{29}$$

depending not only on x but also on the parameters $\alpha_0, \alpha_1, \cdots, \alpha_n$. It is required to choose these parameters in such a way as to minimize the integral

$$\int_a^b [F(x) - \Phi(x; \alpha_0, \alpha_1, \cdots, \alpha_n)]^2 \, dx. \tag{30}$$

This problem is very similar in idea to Čebyšev's problem. Here also the idea is to find the best approximation of the function $F(x)$ by functions of the family (29), but only in the sense of the mean square. It is now unimportant for us whether or not the difference $F - \Phi$ is small for all values of x on the interval $[a, b]$; on a small part of the interval the difference $F - \Phi$ may even be large provided only that the integral (30) is small, as is the case, for example, for the two graphs illustrated in figure 14. The smallness of the quantity (30) shows that the functions F and Φ are close to each other on by far the greater part on the interval.* As to the choice in practice of one method of approxi-

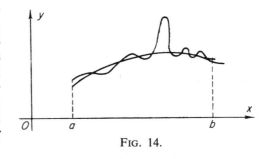

FIG. 14.

mation or another, everything depends on the purpose in view. In the earlier example of the string, it is natural to approximate the function $f'(x)$ in the sense of the mean square. On the other hand, the method of mean squares was unsatisfactory for Čebyšev in solving his problems in the construction of mechanisms, since a machine component projecting beyond the limits of tolerance, even if only over a very small part of the machine, would be quite intolerable: One such projection would spoil the whole machine. Thus Čebyšev had to develop a new mathematical method corresponding to the problem which confronted him.

---

* In Chapter XIX we will see that there is a profound analogy between the closeness of the functions in the sense of the mean square and the distance between points in ordinary space.

We should state that from the computational point of view the method of the mean square is more convenient, since it can be reduced to the application of well-developed methods of general analysis.

As an example let us consider the following characteristic problem.

We wish to make the best approximation in the sense of the mean square to a given continuous function $f(x)$ on the interval $[a, b]$ by sums of the form

$$\sum_{1}^{n} \alpha_k \phi_k(x),$$

where the α_k are constants and the functions $\phi_k(x)$ are continuous and form an orthogonal and normal system.

This last means that we have the following equations:

$$\int_a^b \phi_k \phi_l \, dx = 0 \quad k - l \quad (k, l = 1, 2, ..., n),$$

$$\int_a^b \phi_k^2 \, dx = 1 \quad (k = 1, 2, ..., n).$$

Let us introduce the numbers

$$a_k = \int_a^b f(x) \, \phi_k(x) \, dx \quad (k = 1, ..., n).$$

These numbers a_k are called the Fourier coefficients of f with respect to the ϕ_k.

For arbitrary coefficients α_k, on the basis of the properties of orthogonality and normality of ϕ_k, we have the equation

$$\int_a^b \left(f - \sum_1^n \alpha_k \phi_k \right)^2 dx = \int_a^b f^2 dx + \sum_1^n \alpha_k^2 - 2 \sum_1^n \alpha_k a_k$$

$$= \left(\int_a^b f^2 \, dx - \sum_1^n a_k^2 \right) + \sum_1^n (\alpha_k - a_k)^2.$$

The first term on the right side of the derived equation does not depend on the numbers α_k. Thus the right side will be smallest for those α_k which make the second term itself small, and obviously this can happen only if the numbers α_k are equal to the corresponding Fourier coefficients a_k.

Thus we have reached the following important result. If the functions ϕ_k form an orthogonal and normal system on the interval $[a, b]$, then the sum $\sum_1^n \alpha_k \phi_k(x)$ will be the best approximation, in the sense of the mean square, to the function $f(x)$ on this interval if and only if the numbers α_k are the Fourier coefficients of the function f with respect to $\phi_k(x)$.

On the basis of equation (23) it is easily established that the functions

$$\frac{1}{\sqrt{2\pi}}, \frac{\cos x}{\sqrt{\pi}}, \frac{\sin x}{\sqrt{\pi}}, \frac{\cos 2x}{\sqrt{\pi}}, \ \ldots$$

form an orthogonal and normal system on the interval $[0, 2\pi]$. Thus the stated proposition, as applied to the trigonometric functions, will have the following form.

The Fourier sum $S_n(x)$, computed for a given continuous function $f(x)$ of period 2π, is the best approximation, in the sense of the mean square, to the function $f(x)$ on the interval $[0, 2\pi]$, among all trigonometric polynomials

$$t_n(x) = \alpha_0 + \sum_1^n (\alpha_k \cos kx + \beta_k \sin kx)$$

of order n.

From this result and from Fejér's theorem, formulated in §7, we are led to another remarkable fact.

Let $f(x)$ be a continuous function of period 2π and $\sigma_n(x)$ be its Fejér sum of order n, defined in §7 by equation (27).

We introduce the notation

$$\max |f(x) - \sigma_n(x)| = \eta_n .$$

Since the Fourier sums $S_k(x)$ $(k = 0, 1, \ldots, n)$ are trigonometric polynomials of order $k \leqslant n$, it is obvious that $\sigma_n(x)$ is a trigonometric polynomial of order n. Thus from the minimal property of the sum $S_n(x)$ shown previously, we have the inequality

$$\int_{-\pi}^{\pi} [f(x) - S_n(x)]^2 \, dx \leqslant \int_{-\pi}^{\pi} [f(x) - \sigma_n(x)]^2 \, dx \leqslant \int_{-\pi}^{\pi} \eta_n^2 \, dx = 2\pi\eta_n^2 .$$

Since, by Fejér's theorem, the quantity η_n converges to zero for $n \to \infty$ we obtain the following important result.

For any continuous function of period 2π we have the equation

$$\lim_{n \to \infty} \int_{-\pi}^{\pi} [f(x) - S_n(x)]^2 \, dx = 0.$$

In this case we say that the Fourier sum of order n of a continuous function $f(x)$ converges to $f(x)$ in the sense of the mean square, as n increases beyond all bounds.

In fact, this statement is true for a wider class of functions, namely those which are integrable, together with their square, in the sense of Lebesgue.

We will stop here and will not present other interesting facts from the theory of Fourier series and orthogonal functions, based on approximation in the sense of the mean square. Important physical applications of orthogonal systems of functions have already been introduced in Chapter VI. Finally, we note that these questions are also discussed from a somewhat different point of view in Chapter XIX.

Suggested Reading

N. I. Ahiezer, *Theory of approximation*, Frederick Ungar, New York, 1956.

D. Jackson, *The theory of approximation*, American Mathematical Society, Providence, R. I., 1930.

J. L. Walsh, *Interpolation and approximation by rational functions in the complex domain*, 2nd ed., American Mathematical Society, Providence, R. I., 1956.

CHAPTER XIII

APPROXIMATION METHODS AND COMPUTING TECHNIQUES

§1. Approximation and Numerical Methods

Characteristic peculiarities of approximation methods. In many cases the application of mathematics to the study of events in the outside world is based on the fact that the laws governing these events have a quantitative character and can be described by certain formulas, equations, or inequaltities. This allows us to investigate the events numerically and to make the calculations which are so necessary in practical life.

As soon as a quantitative law has been found, purely mathematical methods may be used to investigate it. For definiteness, let us take some law which is described by an equation. This may be the law of motion of a body in Newtonian mechanics, the law of heat conduction or the propagation of electromagnetic oscillations, and so forth. Such equations are discussed in detail in Chapters V and VI. Usually the equation has adjoined to it certain conditions which its solution must satisfy (in Chapters V and VI these are the boundary and initial conditions) and which define a unique solution.

The first and most important mathematical tasks here will be the following:

1. To establish the existence of a solution. Even if it seems obvious from the physical point of view that the problem has a solution, a mathematical proof of the solvability of a rigorously formulated problem is usually considered as the necessary evidence that the mathematical formulation of the problem is a satisfactory one. In a wide class of problems it is possible to establish mathematically the existence of a solution.

2. To attempt to find an explicit expression or *formula* for the quantity

which characterizes the event under consideration. Usually such an expression can be found only in the simplest cases. It often happens that the explicit expression obtained is so complicated that to make use of it for the desired numerical results is very difficult or even impossible.

3. To find a procedure for constructing an *approximation formula*, which gives a solution with any desired degree of accuracy. This can be done in many cases.

4. But very often it will be possible to find one or more methods for direct *numerical calculation* of the solution.

The development of such numerical methods (many of which are approximate) of solving problems of science and technology has produced a particular branch of mathematics that at the present time is usually called mathematics of computation.

The methods of computational mathematics are naturally approximative, since every quantity is computed only to a certain number of significant figures; for example, to five, six, etc., decimal places.

For applications this is sufficient, since knowing the exact value of any quantity is often unnecessary. In technical questions, for example, the desired quantity usually serves to define the dimensions or other parameters of a manufactured article. Every manufacturing process is only approximate, so that technical computations with an exactness which goes beyond the allowed "tolerances" are obviously valueless.

So for computational purposes there is no need of exact formulas or of exact solutions of equations. Exact formulas and equations may be replaced by others that are admittedly inexact, provided they are close enough to the original ones that the error produced by such a change does not exceed given bounds.

Later we shall return to this question of replacing one problem by another. At the moment, however, we merely wish to emphasize the first characteristic feature of computational methods, namely that by their very nature they can, as a rule, produce only approximate results; but then only such results are needed in practice.

We now turn our attention to a second aspect of computational methods in mathematics. In any computation we can operate with only a finite number of digits and obtain all the results after a finite number of arithmetic operations. If we perform the computations according to some formula, then the latter must first have been transformed in such a way that it involves only a finite number of terms with a finite number of parameters. It is known, for example, that many functions may be represented as the sum of a power series

$$f(x) = c_0 + c_1 x + c_2 x^2 + \cdots . \tag{1}$$

Thus, the function sin x, where x is the radian measure of an angle, may be expanded in the power series

$$\sin x = \frac{x}{1!} - \frac{x^3}{3!} + \frac{x^5}{5!} - \cdots .$$

To find the exact value of $f(x)$, we would need to sum up "all" the terms of the series (1), but generally speaking, this is impossible. To find $f(x)$ approximately, it is sufficient to take only a certain finite number of terms of the series. For example, it may be proved that to compute sin x with an accuracy of 10^{-5} for an angle from zero to half a right angle it is sufficient to take the terms through x^5, so that sin x is replaced by the polynomial

$$\frac{x}{1!} - \frac{x^3}{3!} + \frac{x^5}{5!} .$$

For the numerical solution of a problem of mathematical analysis that consists of determining some function, we must by one means or another replace this problem by the problem of finding certain numerical parameters, the knowledge of which enables us to make an approximate computation of the unknown function. We will illustrate this by an example.

Let it be required to solve, on the interval $a \leqslant x \leqslant b$, the boundary-value problem for the differential equation

$$L(y) - f(x) = y'' + p(x)\,y' + q(x)\,y - f(x) = 0 \qquad (2)$$

with boundary conditions $y(a) = 0$, $y(b) = 0$. In one of the possible methods of solution, namely Galerkin's method, we start with a system of linearly independent functions $\omega_1(x)$, $\omega_2(x)$, $\cdots$, which satisfy the boundary conditions (Chapter VI, §5). This system is so chosen as to be "complete" in the sense that a function which is integrable on $[a, b]$ and is orthogonal to all the ω_k $(k = 1, 2, \cdots)$ will be equal to zero at all (more exactly, at "almost all") points of the interval. The condition that $y(x)$ satisfies the differential equation (2) may be described in the form of an orthogonality requirement

$$\int_a^b [L(y) - f]\omega_k\,dx = 0 \qquad (k = 1, 2, \cdots). \qquad (3)$$

Let us assume that the solution of the problem may be expanded in a series in the ω_k

$$y(x) = a_1\omega_1(x) + a_2\omega_2(x) + \cdots . \qquad (4)$$

We now seek to determine the conditions that must be satisfied by the coefficients a_k. For arbitrary a_k the sum of the series (4) will satisfy the boundary conditions. It remains to choose the a_k in such a way that equations (3) are satisfied. The coefficients a_k form an infinite set, and to compute all of them is generally speaking impossible. For simplification we retain only a finite number of terms on the right side of (4) and so obtain the expression

$$y(x) \approx a_1\omega_1(x) + \cdots + a_n\omega_n(x). \tag{5}$$

We cannot hope to satisfy equation (3) for all ω_k $(k = 1, 2, \cdots)$ since we have only n arbitrary parameters a_k $(k = 1, 2, \cdots, n)$. Thus we are forced to give up an exact solution of the differential equation (2). But it is natural to expect that the sum (5) will satisfy this differential equation with a small error if n is taken sufficiently large and condition (3) is satisfied for the first n of the functions ω_k. This leads to the equations of Galerkin's method

$$\int_a^b \left[L\left(\sum_{k=1}^n a_k\omega_k \right) - f \right] \omega_i \, dx = 0 \qquad (i = 1, 2, \cdots, n).$$

After finding the a_k from these equations, we construct an approximate expression for the function (5).

A similar simplified formula holds for the solution of variational problems by the Ritz method, in approximate harmonic analysis of functions and in many other questions.

We give another example of simplification of an equation. Let it be required to find a function y of one or several arguments by solving some functional equation, for example, a differential or an integral equation. As parameters defining the function y let us choose its values $y_1, y_2, \cdots, y_n$ at some system of points (on a net).

The functional equation must then be changed to a system of numerical equations containing n unknown quantities y_k $(k = 1, \cdots, n)$. Such a replacement may, as a rule, be made in many ways. Here it is always necessary to take pains that the solution of the numerical system differs sufficiently little from the solution of the functional equation.

We give several examples of this sort of replacement. When we solve a differential equation of the first order $y' = f(x, y)$ by Euler's method, we replace this equation by a recursive numerical scheme which enables us to make an approximate calculation of each succeeding value of the unknown function from the previous value (Chapter V, §5):

$$y_{n+1} = y_n + (x_{n+1} - x_n)f(x_n, y_n).$$

For an approximate solution of the Laplace equation

$$\Delta u = \frac{\partial^2 u}{\partial x^2} + \frac{\partial^2 u}{\partial y^2} = 0$$

by the net method, we replace this equation by a linear algebraic system (Chapter VI, §5)

$$u(x + h, y) + u(x, y + h) + u(x - h, y) + u(x, y - h) - 4u(x, y) = 0.$$

Let us consider one more example of such a kind. Let it be required to solve numerically the integral equation

$$y(x) = f(x) + \int_a^b K(x, s)\, y(s)\, ds. \tag{6}$$

The points at which we wish to find the values of the unknown function $y(x)$ will be denoted by $x_1, x_2, \cdots, x_n$. In order to set up the system of numerical equations replacing (6), we require that equation (6) be satisfied not for all the x on the interval $a \leqslant x \leqslant b$ but only at the points x_i $(i = 1, 2, \cdots, n)$

$$y(x_i) = f(x_i) + \int_a^b K(x_i, s)\, y(s)\, ds.$$

Then we replace the integral by any approximate quadrature (by the trapezoidal rule, Simpson's rule, or some other)* with the points of division $x_1, \cdots, x_n$

$$\int_a^b K(x_i, s)\, y(s)\, ds \approx \sum_{j=1}^{n} A_{ij} K(x_i, x_j)\, y(x_j).$$

To determine the desired values of $y(x_i)$, we have the system of linear algebraic equations

$$y(x_i) = f(x_i) + \sum_{j=1}^{n} A_{ij} K(x_i, y_j)\, y(x_j) \qquad (i = 1, 2, \cdots, n). \tag{7}$$

We note that all the methods considered of seeking an unknown function have involved determining certain parameters which define it

---

* Cf. Chapter XII, §3.

approximately. Thus the exactness of these methods depends on how well the function is defined by this system of parameters; for example, how well it may be approximated by an expression of the form (7) or represented by its values at a certain system of points. Questions of this kind constitute a particular branch of mathematics, called the theory of approximation of functions (Chapter XII). From this it can be seen that the theory of approximation has very great value for applied mathematics.

Convergence of approximate methods and an estimate of error.   Let us examine in more detail the requirements for a computational method. The simplest and most basic of these requirements is the possibility of finding the desired quantity with any chosen degree of accuracy.

The required exactness of a computation may change greatly from one problem to another. For certain rough technical computations, two or three decimal places will be sufficiently exact. Most engineering computations are carried out to three or four decimal places. But considerably greater exactness is often required in scientific calculations. Generally speaking, the need for greater accuracy has increased with the passage of time.

Particularly important, therefore, are the approximation methods and processes that allow one to get results with as great a degree of accuracy as desired. Such methods are called *convergent*. Since they are encountered most often in practice and since the requirements they must satisfy are typical, we will keep them in mind in what follows.

Let x be the exact value of a desired quantity. For every such method we may construct a sequence of approximations, $x_1, x_2, \cdots, x_n, \cdots$ to the solution x.

After showing how the approximations are constructed, the first problem in the theory of the method is to establish the convergence of the approximations to the solution $x_n \to x$, and if the method is not always convergent, to set out the conditions under which it will converge.

After the convergence is established there arises the more difficult and subtle problem of an estimate of the *rapidity of convergence*, i.e., an estimate of how rapidly x_n converges to the solution x for $n \to \infty$. Every convergent method theoretically guarantees the possibility of finding the solution with any desired degree of accuracy, if we take an approximation x_n with sufficiently large index n. But, as a rule, the larger the n, the greater the labor required to calculate x_n. Thus, if x_n converges slowly to x, then to get the needed accuracy it may be necessary to make enormous computations.

In mathematics itself, and especially in its applications, many cases are known of a convergent process for finding the solution x, which would require more computational work than can be carried out even on present-day high-speed computers.*

Insufficiently fast convergence is one of the criteria by which the disadvantages of a given method are judged. But this criterion is, of course, not the only one and in comparing methods one must consider many other sides of the question, in particular the convenience of making the computations on machines. Of two methods we sometimes prefer to use the one with somewhat slower convergence, if the computations by this method are easier to carry out on a computing machine.

The error produced by replacing x with its approximate value x_n is equal to the difference $x - x_n$. Its exact value is unknown, and in order to estimate the rapidity of convergence, we must find an upper bound for the absolute value of this difference, i.e., a quantity A_n, such that

$$| x - x_n | \leqslant A_n ,$$

which we call an *error estimate*. Later we give examples of estimates A_n. Consequently, the usual method of judging the rapidity of convergence of a method is to examine how fast the estimate A_n decreases with increasing n. In order that the estimate reflects the actual degree of nearness of x_n to x, it is necessary that A_n differ little from $| x - x_n |$. Also the estimate A_n must be effective, i.e., be such that it can itself be found, otherwise it cannot be used.

Let x be a numerical variable whose value we wish to determine from some equation. We assume that our equation reduces to the form

$$x = \phi(x). \tag{8}$$

---

* Let us mention some simple examples of slowly converging computational processes. It is known that the series

$$\frac{1}{1} - \frac{1}{2} + \frac{1}{3} - \frac{1}{4} + \cdots$$

converges to the natural logarithm of the number 2. We can find ln 2 approximately by means of this series, by computing the sum

$$s_n = \frac{1}{1} - \frac{1}{2} + \cdots \pm \frac{1}{n}$$

of the first n terms for sufficiently large n. But it may be shown that to compute ln 2 with an error less than half of the fifth significant figure, we must take more than 100,000 terms of the series. To find the sum of such a number of terms, if we are using, for example, only a desk computer, would be very laborious. Another familiar example is the series

$$\frac{1}{\sqrt{2}} = 1 - \frac{1}{2 \cdot 1!} + \frac{1 \cdot 3}{2^2 \cdot 2!} - \frac{1 \cdot 3 \cdot 5}{2^4 \cdot 3!} + \frac{1 \cdot 3 \cdot 5 \cdot 7}{2^4 \cdot 4!} - \cdots.$$

Its convergence is so slow that to compute $1/\sqrt{2}$ with accuracy of 10^{-5}, we would need to take about 10^{10} terms, which is difficult even with high-speed machines.

To this equation we apply the *method of iteration*, which is also often called the *method of successive approximations*. To explain the method itself and the estimates connected with it, we will examine the case of one numerical equation, although the method also applies to systems of numerical equations, to differential equations, integral equations, and many other cases. The application of the method to ordinary differential equations has already been illustrated in Chapter V, §5.

We will assume that we have somehow found an approximate value x_0 for a root of the equation. If x_0 were an exact solution of equation (8), then after substituting it in the right side $\phi(x)$ of the equation we would get a result equal to x_0. But since x_0, generally speaking, is not an exact solution, the result of the substitution will differ from x_0. Let us denote it by $x_1 = \phi(x_0)$.

In order to establish in which cases x_1 will be nearer to the exact solution than x_0, we turn to a geometric interpretation of our problem. Let us consider the function

$$y = \phi(x). \tag{9}$$

We choose a numerical axis and represent the numbers x and y by points of this axis. Equation (9) assigns to every point x a corresponding point y on the same axis. It may be regarded as a rule that produces a point transformation of the numerical axis into itself.

Consider the segment $[x_1, x_2]$ on the numerical axis. By the transformation (9) the points x_1 and x_2 will be transformed into the points

$$y_1 = \phi(x_1) \text{ and } y_2 = \phi(x_2).$$

The segment $[x_1, x_2]$ is transformed into the segment $[y_1, y_2]$. The ratio

$$k = \frac{|y_2 - y_1|}{|x_2 - x_1|}$$

is called the "coefficient of dilation" of the segment under the transformation. If $k < 1$, we will have a contraction of the segment.

We return to equation (8). It says that the desired point x must be transformed into itself under the transformation (9). Thus solving equation (8) is equivalent to finding a point on the numerical axis which is transformed into itself under the transformation (9), i.e., remains fixed.

We now consider the segment $[x, x_0]$, one end of which lies at the fixed point x and the other at the point x_0. Under the given transformation x_0 goes into x_1 and the segment $[x, x_0]$ into the segment $[x, x_1]$. If the function ϕ has the property that under transformation (9) every segment is contracted, then x_1 will certainly be closer than x_0 to the root of equation (8).

Since we wish to obtain approximations which converge to the exact solution of (8), we make the same transformation many times in succession on the right side of (8) and construct the sequence of numbers

$$x_1 = \phi(x_0), \quad x_2 = \phi(x_1), \cdots, x_{n+1} = \phi(x_n), \cdots. \tag{10}$$

Here we will prove that the sequence of approximations (10) converges.*

Let us assume that the function $\phi(x)$ is defined on a certain segment $[a, b]$ and that equation (9) gives a transformation of $[a, b]$ into itself, i.e., for every x belonging to $[a, b]$, $y = \phi(x)$ will also belong to $[a, b]$. We will also assume that the initial approximation x_0 is in $[a, b]$; all the successive approximations (10) will then also lie in $[a, b]$. Under these conditions the following theorem is true. If $\phi(x)$ has a derivative ϕ' satisfying the condition

$$|\phi'| \leqslant q < 1$$

on $[a, b]$, then the following proposition holds. Equation (8) has a root x^* in the segment $[a, b]$. The sequence (10) converges to this root, and the rapidity of convergence is characterized by the estimate

$$|x^* - x_n| \leqslant \frac{m}{1 - q} q^n,$$

where $m = |x_0 - \phi(x_0)| = |x_0 - x_1|$. Equation (8) has a unique root in $[a, b]$.

To prove these statements, we estimate the difference $x_2 - x_1$. If Taylor's formula is applicable (Chapter II, §9, (26)), we obtain, for $n = 0$

$$x_2 - x_1 = \phi(x_1) - \phi(x_0) = \phi'(\xi_0)(x_1 - x_0).$$

Then ξ_0 lies between x_1 and x_0 and so belongs to the segment $[a, b]$. Thus $|\phi'(\xi_0)| \leqslant q$ and

$$|x_2 - x_1| \leqslant q |x_1 - x_0| = mq.$$

Similarly

$$|x_3 - x_2| = |\phi(x_2) - \phi(x_1)| = |\phi'(\xi_1)(x_2 - x_1)| \leqslant q |x_2 - x_1| \leqslant mq^2.$$

Continuing these estimates, we have, for every value of n, the inequality

$$|x_{n+1} - x_n| \leqslant mq^n. \tag{11}$$

---

* Because of the geometric interpretation, this theorem and others like it are often called contraction theorems.

We now establish the convergence of the sequence x_n. To this end we consider the auxiliary series

$$x_0 + (x_1 - x_0) + (x_2 - x_1) + \cdots + (x_n - x_{n-1}) + \cdots . \tag{12}$$

The partial sum of the first $n + 1$ of its terms is equal to

$$s_{n+1} = x_0 + (x_1 - x_0) + \cdots + (x_n - x_{n-1}) = x_n .$$

Thus $\lim_{n \to \infty} s_{n+1} = \lim_{n \to \infty} x_n$ and the existence of a finite limit for x_n is equivalent to the convergence of the series (12). We compare the series (12) with the series

$$|x_0| + m + mq + \cdots + mq^{n-1} + \cdots .$$

From the estimate (11) the terms of the series (12) are not greater in absolute value than the corresponding terms in the latter series. But this series, except for its first term $|x_0|$, is a geometric progression with common ratio q, and since $q < 1$, the series converges. Series (12) is thus also convergent, and the sequence (10) is convergent to some finite limit x^*

$$\lim_{n \to \infty} x_n = x^*.$$

Obviously x^* belongs to the segment $[a, b]$, since all the x_n belong to it.

If in the equation $x_{n+1} = \phi(x_n)$ we pass to the limit as $n \to \infty$, then in the limit we get the equation $x^* = \phi(x^*)$, which shows that x^* actually satisfies equation (8). We now estimate how close x_n is to x^*. We choose x_n and any following approximation x_{n+p}

$$|x_{n+p} - x_n| = |(x_{n+p} - x_{n+p-1}) + (x_{n+p-1} - x_{n+p-2}) + \cdots + (x_{n+1} - x_n)|$$

$$\leqslant mq^{n+p-1} + mq^{n+p-2} + \cdots + mq^n$$

$$= \frac{mq^n - mq^{p+n}}{1 - q} .$$

Hence, for $p \to \infty$, from $x_{n+p} \to x^*$ and $q^{n+p} \to 0$ it follows that

$$|x^* - x_n| \leqslant \frac{m}{1 - q} q^n.$$

It remains to prove the statement on uniqueness. Let x' be any solution of the equation on $[a, b]$. We estimate the difference $x' - x^*$

$$|x' - x^*| = |\phi(x') - \phi(x^*)| = |\phi'(\xi)(x' - x^*)| \leqslant q |x' - x^*|,$$

from which

$$(1 - q)| \, x' - x^* \, | \leqslant 0.$$

Since $1 - q > 0$, this inequality is possible only for $| \, x' - x^* \, | = 0$, which means that x' is identical with x^*.

The theorem not only exhibits sufficient conditions for the convergence of the method of iteration but also allows us to estimate the necessary number of steps in the computation, i.e., how large n must be taken to obtain the required accuracy when the exact solution x^* is replaced by x_n. Such an estimate is effective, since the quantities m and q appearing in the inequality $| \, x^* - x_n \, | \leqslant (m/1 - q)q^n$ may in fact be found by investigating the function ϕ.

As an example let us consider the equation $x = k \tan x$, which has many practical applications. For definiteness, we consider the case $k = 0.5$. Let it be required to find the smallest positive root of the equation $x = \frac{1}{2} \tan x$. It must lie near the point 1 and be somewhat larger than 1, as can be easily established from any table or graph of the function $\tan x$.

To secure the condition $| \, \phi' \, | \leqslant q < 1$, which enters into the theorem on the convergence of the method of iteration, we invert the function $\tan x$ and consider the equation $x = \arctan 2x$, which is equivalent to the given one.

We give here the results of the computation. For the original approximation we have taken the value $x_0 = 1$. The following approximations are computed from a table of the function $\arctan x$, from which one finds the following numerical values

$$
\begin{aligned}
x_1 &= \arctan 2 &&= 1.10715, \\
x_2 &= \arctan 2.21430 &&= 1.14660, \\
x_3 &= \arctan 2.29320 &&= 1.15959, \\
x_4 &= \arctan 2.31918 &&= 1.16370, \\
x_5 &= \arctan 2.32740 &&= 1.16498, \\
x_6 &= \arctan 2.32996 &&= 1.16538, \\
x_7 &= \arctan 2.33076 &&= 1.16550, \\
x_8 &= \arctan 2.33100 &&= 1.16554, \\
x_9 &= \arctan 2.33108 &&= 1.16555, \\
x_{10} &= \arctan 2.33110 &&= 1.16556, \\
x_{11} &= \arctan 2.33112 &&= 1.16556.
\end{aligned}
$$

The computation may be stopped here, since further iterations will repeat the value of the root

$$x^* = 1.16556.$$

A geometric illustration of the approximations to the root is given in figure 1. Here x_n tends to x^* so rapidly that x_4 is already indistinguishable from x^* in the diagram.

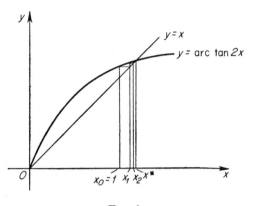

Let us give one more example of the method of iteration. We solve numerically the integral equation

$$y(x) = \frac{1}{6} \int_0^1 e^{xt} y(t) \, dt + e^x$$

$$- \frac{1}{6} \frac{1}{x+1} (e^{x+1} - 1). \quad (13)$$

FIG. 1.

Its exact solution is $y = e^x$.

First we replace the integral equation by a system of linear algebraic equations. To this end the interval of integration $[0, 1]$ is divided into four equal parts at the points $t = 0, \frac{1}{4}, \frac{1}{2}, \frac{3}{4}, 1$. The values of the unknown function y at these points will be denoted by y_0, y_1, y_2, y_3, y_4, respectively. If we require that the equation be satisfied for $x_0 = 0, \frac{1}{4}, \frac{1}{2}, \frac{3}{4}, 1$, when the integral is replaced by Simpson's sum for four partial intervals (Chapter XII, §3, (6)), we have the following system of equations for y_k:

$$y_0 = \frac{1}{6} (0.083333 y_0 + 0.333333 y_1 + 0.166667 y_2$$
$$+ 0.333333 y_3 + 0.083333 y_4) + 0.713619,$$

$$y_1 = \frac{1}{6} (0.083333 y_0 + 0.354831 y_1 + 0.188858 y_2$$
$$+ 0.402077 y_3 + 0.107002 y_4) + 0.951980,$$

$$y_2 = \frac{1}{6} (0.083333 y_0 + 0.377716 y_1 + 0.214004 y_2$$
$$+ 0.484997 y_3 + 0.137393 y_4) + 1.261867,$$

$$y_3 = \frac{1}{6} (0.083333 y_0 + 0.402077 y_1 + 0.242499 y_2$$
$$+ 0.585018 y_3 + 0.176417 y_4) + 1.664181,$$

$$y_4 = \frac{1}{6} (0.083333 y_0 + 0.428008 y_1 + 0.274787 y_2$$
$$+ 0.705667 y_3 + 0.226523 y_4) + 2.185861.$$

This system is solved by the method of iteration. As our initial approximation to y_k ($k = 0, 1, 2, 3, 4$) we will take the constant terms of the corresponding equations: $y_0^{(0)} = 0.713619$, $y_1^{(0)} = 0.951980$, $\cdots$. The values found for the successive approximations are given in Table 1:

Table 1.

Number of Approximation	y_0	y_1	y_2	y_3	y_4
1	0.93428	1.20841	1.56129	2.01542	2.59972
2	0.98517	1.26699	1.62905	2.09419	2.69173
3	0.99667	1.28021	1.64433	2.11194	2.71245
4	0.99926	1.28319	1.64778	2.11595	2.71713
5	0.99985	1.28386	1.64856	2.11685	2.71818
6	0.99998	1.28402	1.64873	2.11705	2.71842
7	1.00001	1.28405	1.64877	2.11710	2.71847
Value of the exact solution	1.00000	1.28403	1.64872	2.11700	2.71828

At the end of Table 1 the value of the exact solution is given for comparison. Further approximations would not improve the values of y_k. The divergence in the last digits in the y_k comes from the error introduced by replacing the integral by Simpson's sum.

Stability of approximate methods. The needs of practical computation impose on approximative methods another general requirement that must be kept in mind because of its great importance. This is the requirement of the *stability* of the computational process. The essence of the matter is as follows: Every approximative method leads to some computational scheme, and it often turns out that to produce all the required numbers, we must carry out a long series of computational steps in accordance with the scheme. At each step the computation is not carried out exactly but only to some specific number of significant figures, and thus at each step we introduce a small error. All such errors will have their influence on the final results.

The computational scheme adopted may sometimes turn out to be so unsatisfactory that small errors made at the beginning may have a greater and greater influence as the calculations are carried further and may produce in the final stages a wide deviation from the exact values.

Let us consider the numerical solution of a differential equation

$$y' = f(x, y)$$

with the initial condition $y(x_0) = y_0$, where we are required to find the values of $y(x)$ for equally spaced values $x_k = x_0 + kh$ ($k = 0, 1, \cdots$).

We assume that the computation has begun and has been carried out to step n with the results shown in Table 2.

Table 2.

x	y	$y' = f$
x_0	y_0	y'_0
x_1	y_1	y'_1
...	...	...
x_{n-1}	y_{n-1}	y'_{n-1}
x_n	y_n	y'_n

We must now find y_{n+1}. By the Euler method of broken lines we make the approximation

$$y_{n+1} = y_n + hy'_n. \tag{14}$$

Here y_{n+1} is calculated only from the numbers y_n and y'_n which occur in the last line of Table 2. Suppose we wish to increase the accuracy and for this purpose make use of all the quantities appearing in the last two lines. Then we may construct the computational formula

$$y_{n+1} = -4y_n + 5y_{n-1} + h(4y'_n + 2y'_{n-1}). \tag{15}$$

We note that if the computation is absolutely exact, i.e., with an infinite number of significant digits, then formula (14) will give the exact result whenever y is a linear polynomial, and formula (15) will be exact for every polynomial of degree through the third. It would seem at first glance that the results produced by applying formula (15) must be more exact than those found by the method of broken lines. However, it can easily be seen that formula (15) is inappropriate for computation, since its application may produce a rapid increase in the error.

The values of the derivative y'_n and y'_{n-1} contain a small multiplier h, so that the errors in these values have less influence than the errors in y_n and y_{n-1}. For simplicity we will assume that the values of y' are found exactly so that we do not need to take them into account in the following attempt to estimate the error in general in the above two cases. Let us suppose that in finding y_{n-1}, we make an error of $+ \epsilon$, and in finding y_n an error of $- \epsilon$. Then, as equation (15) shows, in y_{n+1} we will make an error of the magnitude of $+ 9\epsilon$. In y_{n+2} the error will be $- 41\epsilon$ and will grow rapidly as we continue. Formula (15) leads to a computational process that is unstable with respect to errors and must be discarded.

The example given shows how badly the results may be distorted by an unstable computational scheme. Here we have solved the differential equation $y' = y$ with the initial condition $y_0 = 1$. The exact solution is

$y + e^x$. For the numerical solution we took equally spaced values of the independent variable x with steps $h = 0.01$, i.e., $x_k = 0.01\,k$. An approximate solution was computed in two ways: by the method of broken lines (14) and by formula (15). For comparison, Table 3 gives the value of the exact solution to seven decimal places.

The approximate values of the solution found by formula (15) are more exact for the first few steps than the results given by the method of broken lines. But after a small number of steps the instability of formula (15) begins to distort the approximate values of y_k quite strongly and leads to numbers which are very different from the true values of y_k.

Table 3.

x	Values of the Exact Solution	Values of the Approximation Solutions Computed	
		by Formula (14)	by Formula (15)
0.00	1.0000000	1.0000000	1.0000000
0.01	1.0100502	1.0100000	1.0100502
0.02	1.0202013	1.0201000	1.0202012
0.03	1.0304545	1.0303010	1.0304553
0.04	1.0408108	1.0406040	1.0408070
0.05	1.0512711	1.0510100	1.0512899
0.06	1.0618365	1.0615201	1.0617431
0.07	1.0725082	1.0721353	1.0729726
0.08	1.0832871	1.0828567	1.0809789
0.09	1.0941743	1.0936853	1.1056460
0.10	1.1051709	1.1046222	1.0481559
0.11	1.1162781	1.1156684	1.3996456
0.12	1.1274969	1.1268250	-0.2808540

Choice of computational methods. Every computation may in the final analysis be reduced to the four arithmetic operations of addition, subtraction, multiplication, and division. Describing a method of computation consists of stating the initial data with which one begins and then prescribing which arithmetical operations, and in which order, are to be performed in order to get the desired results. Let us show by a very simple example how much depends in the organization of the calculations on the experience and knowledge of the mathematician responsible for setting up the computational scheme and what excellent results can be obtained by a suitable choice of methods especially adapted to the situation.

Let it be required to solve the system of n equations in n unknowns $x_1, x_2, \cdots, x_n$

$$
\begin{aligned}
a_{11}x_1 + a_{12}x_2 + \cdots + a_{1n}x_n &= b_1, \\
a_{21}x_1 + a_{22}x_2 + \cdots + a_{2n}x_n &= b_2, \\
&\cdots\cdots\cdots\cdots\cdots\cdots\cdots\cdots\cdots\cdots \\
a_{n1}x_1 + a_{n2}x_2 + \cdots + a_{nn}x_n &= b_n.
\end{aligned}
$$

From the theory of algebraic systems (Chapter XVI, §3) we have an explicit expression for the values of the unknowns by means of determinants

$$
x_j = \frac{\Delta_j}{\Delta} \qquad (j = 1, 2, \cdots, n). \tag{16}
$$

Here Δ is the determinant of the system

$$
\Delta = \begin{vmatrix}
a_{11} & a_{12} & \cdots & a_{1n} \\
a_{21} & a_{22} & \cdots & a_{2n} \\
\multicolumn{4}{c}{\cdots\cdots\cdots\cdots\cdots} \\
a_{n1} & a_{n2} & \cdots & a_{nn}
\end{vmatrix},
$$

and Δ_j is the determinant obtained from Δ by replacing its jth column by the column of constant terms in the system.

Let us assume that we wish to make use of formula (16) to solve the system and that we have begun to compute the determinants on the basis of their usual definition, without recourse to any simplifications. How many multiplications and divisions will be necessary? (Addition and subtraction will not be taken into account, since they are relatively simple operations.) We face the prospect of computing $n + 1$ determinants of order n. Each of them consists of $n!$ terms, each term being the product of n factors and consequently requiring $n - 1$ multiplications. For the computation of all the determinants, we must carry out $(n + 1)n!$ $\times (n - 1)$ multiplications. The total number of multiplications and divisions will be equal to $(n^2 - 1)n! + n$.

We now choose another method of solving the system, namely successive elimination of the unknowns. The scheme of computation corresponding to this method is associated with the name of Gauss. We find x_1 from the first equation of the system

$$
x_1 = \frac{b_1}{a_{11}} - \frac{a_{12}}{a_{11}}x_2 - \cdots - \frac{a_{1n}}{a_{11}}x_n.
$$

For this we need n divisions. Substituting x_1 in each of the following $n - 1$ equations requires n multiplications. The elimination of x_1 and the setting up of $n - 1$ equations in the unknowns $x_2, \cdots, x_n$ will then require n^2

multiplications and divisions. Continuing in this way, we find that to compute all the values of x_j ($j = 1, \cdots, n$) the elimination method requires $n/6\,(2n^2 + 9n - 5)$ multiplications and divisions. Let us compare these two results. For the solution of a system of five equations in the first case we would need 2,885 multiplications and divisions, and in the second case 75.

For a system of ten equations the number of operations will be $(10^2 - 1)\,10! + 10 \approx 360{,}000{,}000$ and $10/6\,(2 \cdot 10^2 + 9 \cdot 10 - 5) = 475$, respectively. So we see that the amount of computational labor depends very strongly on the choice of the method of computing. In organizing the scheme of computation, it is often possible by a rational choice of the method to reduce the necessary amount of work very greatly.

§2. The Simplest Auxiliary Means of Computation*

Tables.   The oldest auxiliary means of computation consists of tables. The simplest tables, e.g. the multiplication table and tables of logarithms or of the trigonometric functions, are certainly well known to the reader. The range of problems that are solvable in practical affairs is being continuously extended. New problems are often solved by the application of new formulas or may lead to new functions, so that the number of tables required is constantly increasing.

Every table, regardless of how it is constructed, contains the results of earlier computations and therefore represents a sort of mathematical memory. Printed or written tables are intended to be read by human beings. But we might also consider tables formed in some special manner, for example by holes punched in some special manner in cards, which are intended to be read by computing machines. But such tables are considerably rare and we will not discuss them here.

The tables in widest use are those of the values of functions. If a function y depends on only one argument x, then the simplest table corresponding to it has the form

x	y
x_1	y_1
x_2	y_2
$\cdots$	$\cdots$
x_n	y_n

(17)

---

* In this section we give a description only of the simplest auxiliary equipment and machines. The description of contemporary rapid computing machines is given in Chapter XIV. For lack of space we have also omitted graphical methods.

This is called a single-entry table.* From it we may take without further effort only the values corresponding to tabulated values of x. Values corresponding to x not in the table must be found by interpolation of various kinds, as described in Chapter XII.† Consequently the tables often contain, in addition to the values of the functions, certain auxiliary quantities which make the interpolation easier. Usually these are values of the first or second differences. More specialized tables require specially devised interpolation formulas for which they include the corresponding data.

In a table of a function of two arguments $u = f(x, y)$ the values of the function are distributed in a double-entry table of the following form

x ＼ y	y_1	y_2	...	y_m	
x_1	u_{11}	u_{12}	...	u_{1m}	
x_2	u_{21}	u_{22}	...	u_{2m}	(17')
...	...	...	...	...	
x_n	u_{n1}	u_{n2}	...	u_{nm}	

Each column of such a table is itself a single-entry table, so that (17') is a collection of many tables of the form (17). The size of a table for a function of two arguments is, as a rule, much greater than for a function of one argument with the same interval for the independent variables. In view of this, functions of two arguments are much less often tabulated than functions of one argument.

How quickly the size of a table can grow with an increase in the number of arguments is shown by the following simple example. Let it be required to tabulate a function of four arguments $f(x, y, z, t)$ for 100 values of each of the arguments. Let us assume that the function does not need to be computed very exactly, only to three significant figures. If under such conditions we tabulate a function of one argument, the whole table of values will consist of a hundred three-digit numbers and may easily be put on one page.

---

* Such a column may be very long and may therefore be broken up into many smaller columns for convenience of printing. But of course it is still called a single-entry table.

† Interpolation, as a rule, is more complicated if the tabulated values x_i are farther apart and simpler if they are closer together. Moreover, the requirement concerning rapidity of interpolation may vary widely. In tables designed for artillery use, interpolation must be done almost instantly, "at sight." But in tables of higher accuracy, designed for use in the sciences, we may allow interpolations which require a whole series of operations.

But in a four-entry table for the function $f(x, y, z, t)$, we will have 100^4 combinations of the values of x, y, z, t and as many values of f, from which it is easy to calculate that the table would fill more than 300 volumes.

Because such tables are so unwieldy, functions of many arguments are seldom tabulated and then only in particularly simple cases. In the last few years there has begun a systematic study of classes of functions of many variables for which tables may be formed with a number of entries less than the number of arguments. At the same time studies have been begun on the simplest possible construction of such tables.

We give a simple example of such a function.

Let it be required to tabulate the function u of three arguments x, y, z with the following structure

$$u = f[\phi(x, y), z].$$

It is perfectly clear that here one may restrict oneself to two double-entry tables if we introduce the auxiliary variable $t = \phi(x, y)$ and consider u as the composite function

$$u = f(t, z),$$
$$t = \phi(x, y).$$

For convenience in the use of these tables, we may combine them in the following manner. We consider the function $t = \phi(x, y)$ and solve this equation with respect to y

$$y = \Phi(x, t).$$

In theory it makes no difference which of the functions $t = \phi(x, y)$ or $y = \Phi(x, t)$ is tabulated, but it will be more convenient for us to tabulate the second of them. We construct two double-entry tables for the functions $y = \Phi(x, t)$ and $u = f(t, z)$ and combine them in the manner shown in Table 4.

Table 4.

x_1	x_2	$\cdots$	x_i	$\cdots$	t	z_1	z_2	$\cdots$	z_k	$\cdots$
					t_1					
					t_2					
					$\vdots$					
$\cdots$	$\cdots$	$\cdots$	y_j	$\cdots$	t_j	$\cdots$	$\cdots$	$\cdots$	u_{jk}	$\cdots$

The value of u which corresponds to given values x_i, y_j, z_k is found as follows: We find the column headed by x_i and running down it, pick out the value y_j (or one near it). In the horizontal row through it will be the corresponding value of t. Moving further along this horizontal row we find in column z_k the required value $u = f(x_i, y_j, z_k)$.

In this example we see that, rather than make a triple-entry table, we may restrict ourselves to two double-entry tables with a simple rule for operating with them.

The use of various possible methods of shortening tables allows us in certain cases to decrease the size of the tables by a factor of ten, a hundred, or even a thousand in comparison with tables in which the number of entries is equal to the number of independent arguments.

Desk computers. Almost as old as tables as an aid to computation are various computing devices. Some of them were used even in ancient Greece.

The first models of calculating machines were constructed in the 17th century by Pascal, Moreland, and Leibnitz. From that time on the machines were repeatedly changed and improved and were in wide use by the end of the last century and especially at the beginning of the present one.

We will only look at certain forms of machines and will consider the possibility of speeding up the computations which they perform. We begin with the small, so-called universal desk computers. Each of these, independently of its construction, is designed to perform the four arithmetic operations, with multiplication and division being done by repeated series of additions and subtractions.

A typical early model of such a machine is the wheeled arithmometer of Odner. Entering a number into the adjustable mechanism is accomplished by moving a lever the necessary number of notches corresponding to each digit of the number. In the process of addition each summand is entered into the adjustable mechanism and then, by one rotation of the handle, is transferred to the accumulator, where it is automatically added to the number already there. Subtraction corresponds to a rotation of the handle in the opposite direction. Multiplication is carried out by entering the multiplicand into the adjustable mechanism and then repeatedly adding it to itself for each digit of the multiplier. For example, to multiply by 45 corresponds to five repeated additions of the multiplicand and then four repeated additions of the same number moved over one place.

For division the dividend is placed in the accumulator and the quotient is found by repeated subtraction of the divisor, digit by digit. The result is determined by the number of rotations of the handle needed in each digit place to remove the number from the accumulator.

We have given this brief description of the computations here only in order to make clear the direction of further improvements in desk calculators. Some of these improvements have merely made the machines more convenient without changing the basic scheme of their construction. An improvement of this kind is the introduction of electricity, which accelerates the action of the machine and frees the operator from having to turn the handle.

To accelerate and simplify the entering of numbers into the adjusting mechanism, keys for receiving instructions were introduced. The entering of given digits is carried out, not by rotating a lever for the specific number of notches, but simply by punching the corresponding key. Calculators were invented on which it is sufficient for the operator to enter the number on which it is desired to perform a given operation and then to punch the key which tells which of the four operations is to be performed. The machine will carry on from there without further human intervention. The improvement of desk computers also brought about a remarkable increase in their rapidity, so that in the latest models the result of a multiplication is obtained within one second after punching the keys. Further acceleration in the action of such machines is obviously superfluous, since it takes considerably longer than that for the operator merely to punch the keys and record the results.

Digital (punched card) machines and relay machines. Digital machines were invented for statistical computations and for financial and industrial use. They are designed to carry out a large number of uncomplicated computations of the same kind. They are less convenient for technical and scientific calculations because of their very small operating "memory" and the restricted possibility of establishing computational programs for them. In spite of these deficiencies, digital machines, up to the appearance of fast-acting electronic machines, were quite widely used in complicated and large-scale calculations when the whole process could be reduced to a fairly short sequence of operations to be carried out on a massive scale (for example, in preparing tables).

The numbers with which the digital machine operates are entered on punched cards (figure 2). The digits and symbols are entered on the card by means of a punch in specific places. The card is introduced into the machine through a system of brushes. A brush under which a hole is passing closes an electrical circuit and sets in operation a given phase of the machine.

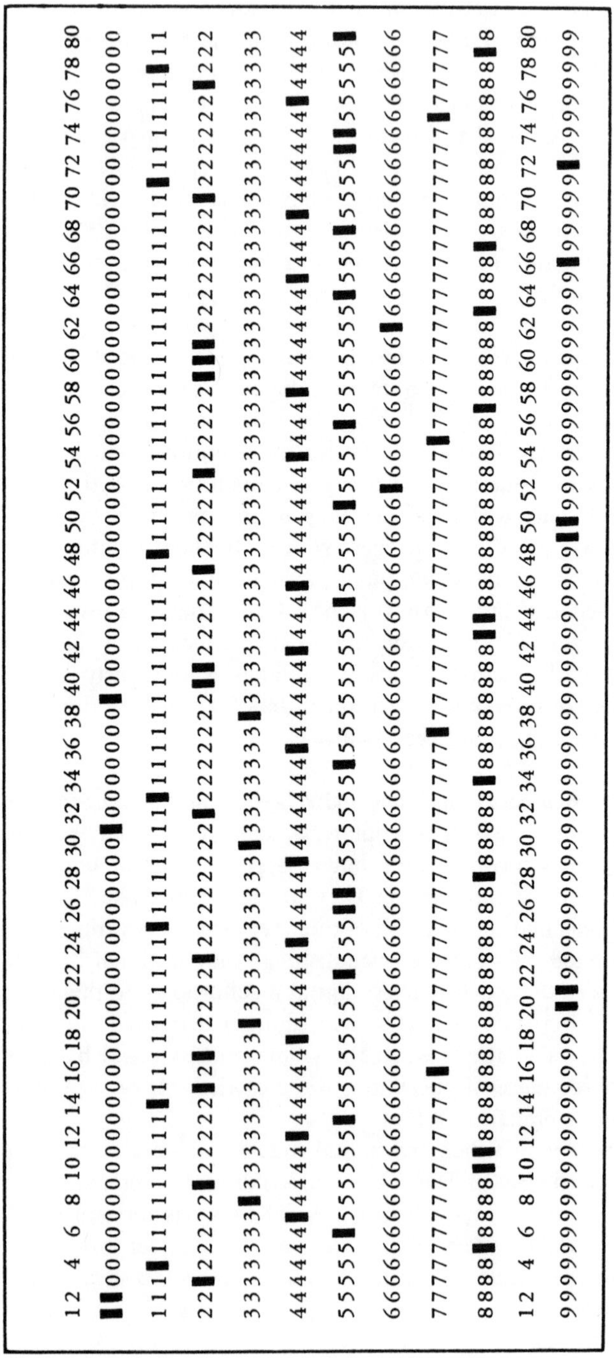

FIG. 2.

The different types of digital machines are designed to work in sets, each set containing at least the following machines:

A *card-punch* serves to punch the holes in the cards. The machine has a keyboard operated by hand and works at the speed of a typewriter.

A *sorter* is designed to arrange the cards in the order in which they are to be introduced into the calculating machines. The speed of the work is 450-650 cards per minute.

A *reproducing punch* or *reproducer* transfers punches from one card to another, compares two sets of cards, and selects from them cards with specific perforations. The speed of working is around 100 cards per minute.

A *tabulator* performs the operations of addition and subtraction and also prints out the results. It may handle 6,000 to 9,000 cards an hour.

A *multiplying punch* (*multiplier*) adds, subtracts, and multiplies numbers. The results are given in the form of punches on the cards. In working with numbers of 6 or 7 digits it may perform 700-1,000 multiplications an hour.

Digital machines work rather slowly. As a rough estimate of the amount of work they can perform, we may say that the above set of machines can replace 12 to 18 desk computers. The first attempts to create faster machines led to the construction of relay machines based on the application of electromechanical relays. The rate of work of such machines turned out to be about ten times as great as the speed of the simple digital machines. But the gains in other respects were remarkable: Relay machines carry out complicated computational programs and have a flexible control system that greatly extended the range of technical and scientific problems solvable on machines. However, the appearance of these machines almost coincided in time with the creation of the first models of electronic machines with programmed control, and these led to a further sharp increase in the working speed. As an indication of the great increases in speed which have been made possible by the invention of electronic machines, we may point out that the time required for a change of state in an electronic tube is measured in millionths of a second.

Mathematical machines with continuous action (analogue machines). Mathematical machines with continuous action are made up of physical systems (mechanical apparatus, electrical circuits, and so forth), constructed in such a manner that the same numerical interrelations occur among the continuously changing parameters of the system (displacements, angles of rotation, currents, voltages, and so forth) as among the corresponding magnitudes in the mathematical problem to be solved. Such machines are often called *simulating* (or *analogue*) *machines*.

Every machine with continuous action is especially designed for the solution of some narrow class of problems.

The accuracy with which the machine gives the solution depends on the quality of manufacture of the component parts, the assembling and calibration of the machine, the inertial errors in its operation, and so forth. On the basis of lengthy experience in using the machines, it has been established that as a rule they are capable of an accuracy of two or three significant digits. In this respect simulating machines are notably inferior to digital machines, whose accuracy is theoretically unlimited.

An important characteristic of machines with continuous action is that they are suitable for the solution of a large number of problems of one type. In addition, they often produce the solution with considerably greater rapidity than a digital machine. Their principal advantage consists of the fact that in many cases it is more convenient to introduce the initial data of the problem into them, and also the results are often obtained in a more convenient form.

There are many different types of simulating machines. It is possible to create machines, or parts of machines, that are models of various mathematical operations: addition, multiplication, integration, differentiation, and so forth. We may also simulate various formulas used in computation; for example, we can construct machines to compute the values of polynomials or the Fourier coefficients in harmonic analysis of functions. We may also simulate numerical or functional equations. The many analogies that exist between problems from completely different branches of science lead to the same differential equations. Identity of the equations involved allows us for example, to simulate heat phenomena by electrical means and to solve problems in heat engineering by means of electrical measurements, a procedure that is certainly convenient, since electrical measurements are more exact than measurements of heat and are much easier to make.

In view of the large number of simulating machines, it is impossible to describe in a few words the machines themselves or even the principles of their construction. To give the reader at least some idea of how mathematical problems may be simulated, let us give a short description of two simple mathematical machines, one of which is designed for integration of functions and the other for approximate solution of the Laplace equation.

The *friction integrator* (figure 3) is designed, as the name indicates, to integrate functions. It works by friction. The basic idea of its construction is shown in figure 4, where the component 1 is the base of the integrator, 2 is a horizontal friction disc with a vertical shaft, 3 is a friction roller, i.e., a roller with a smooth rim which can not only roll along the disc but also move in the plane perpendicular to the plane of rolling. Components 4 and 5 constitute a screw mechanism in which the screw 4 is connected with the carriage bearing the roller. If the pitch of the screw is denoted by h, then rotation of the screw through angle γ will transfer the roller over a distance $\rho = h\gamma$ in the plane of the drawing.

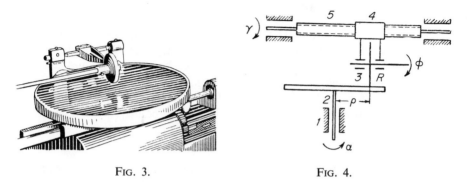

FIG. 3.   FIG. 4.

Let the shaft of the disc be rotated through angle $d\alpha$. The point of contact of the roller will then move through an arc of length $\rho\, d\alpha$. If the roller moves over the disc without slipping, the angle of rotation of the roller will be equal to

$$d\phi = \frac{\rho}{R}\, d\alpha = \frac{h}{R}\, \gamma\, d\alpha.$$

We assume that the rotation of the shaft of the disc began with angle α_0 and the initial angle of rotation of the roller was ϕ_0. From this equation we obtain by integration

$$\phi - \phi_0 = \frac{h}{R} \int_{\alpha_0}^{\alpha} \gamma\, d\alpha.$$

By suitable choice of the relation between the angles γ and α, we can use the friction integrator to compute a desired integral in a wide variety of cases. By means of integrating mechanisms it is possible to obtain a mechanical solution of many differential equations.

We turn to the second example. Let a domain Ω be given in the plane, bounded by a curve l. It is required to find a function u which inside the domain satisfies the Laplace equation

$$\Delta u = \frac{\partial^2 u}{\partial x^2} + \frac{\partial^2 u}{\partial y^2} = 0$$

and on the contour *l* takes given values

$$u \mid_l = f.$$

We introduce a square net of points

$$x_k = x_0 + kh, \ y_k = y_0 + kh, \ k = 0, \pm 1, \pm 2, \cdots,$$

and replace the domain Ω itself by a polygon composed of squares. Corresponding to the contour *l* we have a broken line. We transfer the boundary values of *f* on *l* to this broken line. The value of the unknown function *u* at a node (x_j, y_k) is denoted by u_{jk}. To secure an approximate solution of the Laplace equation in Ω, we replace it by an algebraic system, which must be satisfied for all interior points of the domain:

$$u_{jk} = \tfrac{1}{4}(u_{j+1,k} + u_{j,k+1} + u_{j-1,k} + u_{j,k-1}).$$

For a solution of this algebraic system, we may construct the following electrical model. We introduce in the plane a two-dimensional conduction net, the scheme of which is illustrated in figure 5. The resistance between two nodes is assumed to be everywhere the same. At the boundary nodes of the net, we now apply voltages equal to the boundary values of *u* at these nodes. These voltages will determine the voltage at all interior points of the net. We denote by $U_{j,k}$ the voltage at the node (x_j, y_k). If we apply Kirchhoff's law to the node (x_j, y_k), it is clear that at this node the following equation will be satisfied

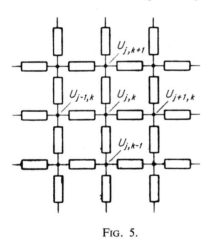

FIG. 5.

$$\frac{1}{R} [(U_{j+1,k} - U_{j,k}) + (U_{j,k+1} - U_{j,k})$$
$$+ (U_{j-1,k} - U_{j,k}) + (U_{j,k-1} - U_{j,k})] = 0,$$

which differs only in notation from the previous equation for our algebraic system. At the nodes of the net the values u_{jk} of the solution of the algebraic system must agree with the voltages U_{jk}, which can be obtained from the model by the usual electrical measurements.

Suggested Reading

V. N. Faddeeva, *Computational methods of linear algebra*, Dover, New York, 1959.

D. R. Hartree, *Numerical analysis*, 2nd ed., Oxford University Press, New York, 1958.

F. B. Hildebrand, *Introduction to numerical analysis*, McGraw-Hill, New York, 1956.

A. S. Householder, *Principles of numerical analysis*, McGraw-Hill, New York, 1953.

W. J. Karplus and W. W. Soroka, *Analog methods: computation and simulation*, 2nd ed., McGraw-Hill, New York, 1959.

W. E. Milne, *Numerical calculus: approximations, interpolation, finite differences, numerical integration and curve fitting*, Princeton University Press, Princeton, N. J., 1949.

——, *Numerical solution of differential equations*, Wiley, New York, 1953.

A. M. Ostrowski, *Solution of equations and systems of equations*, Academic Press, New York, 1960.

J. B. Scarborough, *Numerical mathematical analysis*, 5th ed., Johns Hopkins Press, Baltimore, Md., 1962.

R. G. Stanton, *Numerical methods for science and engineering*, Prentice-Hall, Englewood Cliffs, N. J., 1961.

CHAPTER XIV

ELECTRONIC
COMPUTING MACHINES

§1. Purposes and Basic Principles of the Operation of Electronic Computers

Mathematical methods are widely used in science and technology, but the solution of many important problems involves such a large amount of computation that with an ordinary desk calculator they are practically unsolvable. The advent of electronic computing machines, which perform computations with a rapidity previously unknown has completely revolutionized the application of mathematics to the most important problems of physics, mechanics, astronomy, chemistry, and so forth.

A contemporary universal electronic computing machine performs thousands and even tens of thousands of arithmetic and logical operations in one second and takes the place of several hundred thousand human computers. Such rapidity of computation allows us, for example, to compute the trajectory of a flying missile more rapidly than the missile itself flies.

In addition to their great rapidity in performing arithmetic and logical operations, universal electronic computing machines enable us to solve the most diverse problems on one and the same machine. These machines represent a qualitatively new method which, besides an enormously increased production of standard results, makes it possible to solve problems previously considered quite inaccessible.

In many cases the computations must be carried out with great rapidity if the results are to have any value. This is particularly obvious in the example of predicting the weather for the following day. With hand calculators the computations involved in a reliable weather forecast for the next day may themselves require several days, in which case they naturally lose all practical value. The use of electronic computing machines for this purpose makes it possible to secure the complete results in plenty of time.

The high-speed electronic computing machine. The high-speed electronic computing machine (BESM) which was constructed in the Institute for Exact Mechanics and Computing Technology of the Academy of Sciences of the USSR is an example of such a machine. In one second the machine performs between 8,000 and 10,000 arithmetic operations. We scarcely need to remind the reader that on a desk calculator an experienced operator can carry out only about 2,000 such operations in one working day. Consequently, the electronic computer can perform in a few hours computations that the experienced operator could not perform in his whole lifetime. One such machine would replace a colossal army of tens of thousands of such operators. Merely to give them a place to stand would take up several hundred thousand square yards.

These electronic machines have been used to solve a large number of problems from various domains of science and technology. As a result economies have been achieved amounting to hundreds of millions of dollars. We give several examples.

For the international astronomical calendar the orbits of approximately seven hundred asteriods were computed in the course of a few days, account being taken of the influence on them of Jupiter and Saturn. Their coordinates were determined for ten years ahead and their exact positions were given for every forty days. Up till now such computations would have required many months of labor by a large computing office.

In making maps from the data provided by a geodetic survey of a given locality, it is necessary to solve a system of algebraic equations with a large number of unknowns. Problems with 800 equations, requiring up to 250 million arithmetic operations, were solved on the electronic machine in less than twenty hours.

On the same machine tables were calculated to determine the steepest possible slope for which the banks of a canal would not crumble, and in this way large savings of time and material were effected in the construction of hydroelectric power stations. In previous attempts fifteen human computers had worked without success for several months in an effort to solve this problem for only one special case. On the electronic machine the computations for ten cases took less than three hours.

On the machine one may rapidly test many different solutions for given problems and choose the most appropriate. Thus one may determine, for example, the most appropriate mechanical construction of a bridge, the best shape for the wing of an airplane, or for the nozzle of a jet motor, the blade of a turbine, and so forth.

The practically infinite accuracy of the computations makes it possible to construct very rapidly all kinds of tables for the needs of science and technology. On the BESM the construction of a table containing 50,000 values of the Fresnel integral required only one hour.

Applications of electronic computing machines to problems of logic. In addition to handling mathematical problems, we may also solve logical problems on an electronic computing machine; for example, we may translate given texts from one language into another. In this case, instead of storing numbers in the machine, we store the words and numbers that take the place of a dictionary.

Comparing the words in the text with the words in the "dictionary," the machine finds the necessary words in the desired language. Then by means of grammatical and syntactical rules, which are described in the form of a program, the machine "processes" these words, changing them in case, number or tense, and setting them in the right order in a sentence. The translated text is printed on paper. For a successful translation a very large amount of painstaking work on the part of philologists and mathematicians is needed to set up the programs.

Experimental dictionaries and programs for the translation of a scientific-technical text from English into Russian were set up at the Academy of Sciences of the USSR, and at the end of 1955 the first experimental translation was produced on the BESM machine, even though this machine is not especially adapted for translation.

By way of experiment complicated logical problems were successfully solved on the BESM; for example, chess problems. A complete analysis of chess is not possible on present-day electronic machines in view of the enormous number of possible combinations. As an approximate method the relative values of the various pieces are estimated; for example, ten thousand points for the king, one hundred for the queen, fifty for a rook. Various positional advantages are also estimated to be worth a certain number of points; i.e., open files, passed pawns, and so forth. By a series of trials the machine chooses the course of action that after a specified number of moves produces the greatest number of points for all possible answers on the part of the opponent. However, in view of the enormous number of possible combinations the solution is necessarily restricted to trying a comparatively small number of moves, which excludes the study of strategic plans of play.

Basic principles of the operation of electronic computing machines.
A present-day electronic computing machine consists of a complicated complex of elements of electronic automation: electron tubes, germanium crystal elements, magnetic elements, photoelements, resistors, condensers, and other elements of radio technology.

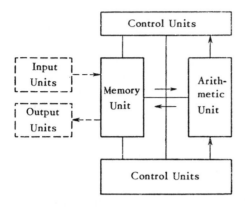

Arithmetic operations are performed with colossal rapidity by electronic computing devices, which are assembled in the arithmetic unit (figure 1).

But to guarantee high speed for computations it is not enough just to perform rapid arithmetic operations on numbers. In the machine the whole computational process must be completely automatic. Access to the required numbers and establishment of a specific sequence of operations on them are set up automatically.

Fig. 1. Diagram of the basic units of an electronic digital computer.

The numbers on which the operations are to be performed and also the results of intermediate calculations must be stored in the machine. An entire mechanism, the so-called "memory unit" is designed for this purpose; it allows access to any required number and also stores the result of the computation. The capacity of the memory unit, i.e., the number of numbers that may be stored in it, to a great extent determines the flexibility of the machine for the solution of various problems.

In present-day electronic machines the capacity of the memory unit is from 1,000 to 4,000 numbers.

The extraction of the required numbers from the memory unit, the operation that must be performed on these numbers, the storing of the result in the memory unit and the passage to the next operation are all guided in the electronic computing machine by a control unit. After the computing program and the initial data are introduced into the machine the control unit guarantees the fully automatic character of the computational process.

To introduce the initial data and the computational program into the machine, and also to print the results on paper, is the purpose of special input and output units.

When we are using the machine for making computations, we must have confidence in the correctness of the results produced; i.e., we must have some means of checking them. Verification of the correctness of the computations is effected either by means of special verification mechanisms or by the usual methods of logical or mathematical verification embodied in a special program. The simplest example of such a verification is the "duplication check" (the so-called "calculation on both hands"), which consists of computing twice and collating the results.

Before proceeding to the solution of a particular problem, we must first of all, on the basis of the physical process under investigation, state the problem in terms of algebraic formulas, or of differential or integral equations, or other mathematical relations. Then by applying well-developed methods of numerical analysis, we can almost always reduce the solution of such a problem to a specific sequence of arithmetic operations. In this way the most complicated problems are solved by means of the four operations of arithmetic.

To perform any arithmetic operation by hand computation it is necessary to take two numbers, perform the given arithmetic operation on them, and write down the result produced. This result may be necessary for further computations or may itself be the desired answer.

The same operations are also carried out in electronic computing machines. The memory unit of the machine consists of a series of locations or cells. The locations are all enumerated in order, and to select a number for calculation, we must give the location in which it "is stored."

To perform any one arithmetic operation on two numbers, we must give the locations in the memory unit from which the two numbers are to be taken, the operation to be performed on them, and the location in which the result is to be placed in the memory. Such information, presented in a specific code, is called an "instruction."

The solution of a problem consists of performing a sequence of instructions. These instructions constitute the program for the computation and usually they are also stored in the memory unit.

A computing program, i.e., a set of instructions effecting the sequence of arithmetic operations necessary for the solution of the problem, is prepared by mathematicians in advance.

Many problems require for their solution several hundred million arithmetic operations. So in electronic machines we use methods which allow a comparatively small number of initial instructions to govern a large number of arithmetic operations.

Together with the instructions governing arithmetic operations, electronic computers also provide for instructions governing logical operations; such a logical operation may consist, for example, of the comparison of two numbers with the purpose of choosing one of two possible further courses for the computation, depending on which of the two numbers is the larger.

The instructions of a program and also the initial data are written in terms of a prearranged code. Usually the description of the instruction is recorded on perforated cards or tape in the form of punched holes or else on magnetic tape in the form of pulses. Then these codes are introduced into the machine and placed in the memory unit, after which the machine automatically carries out the given program.

The results of the computation are again recorded, for example in the form of pulses on a magnetic tape. Special decoding and printing units translate the magnetic tape code into ordinary digits and print them in the form of a table.

The speed with which computers perform the most complicated calculations has produced a saving of mental labor which can only be compared with the saving in physical labor made possible by modern machinery. Of course, an electronic machine only carries out a program set up by its operator; it does not itself have any creative possibilities and cannot be expected to replace a human being.

The wide use of electronic computing machines in institutes of science and technology, in construction offices, and in planning organizations has opened up limitless possibilities in the solution of problems in the national economy. Engineers and mathematicians have before them rewarding prospects for further development in the operation and construction of computing machines and also in their application and exploitation.

Electronic computing machines are powerful tools in human hands. The significance of these machines for the national economy can hardly be overestimated.

§2. Programming and Coding for High-Speed Electronic Machines

The basic principles of programming; 1. Euler's method for differential equations. For computations on electronic machines the mathematical method selected for approximating the solution of a problem necessarily consists of a sequence of arithmetic operations. The execution of these operations by the machine is guaranteed by the program, which as we have said, consists of a sequence of instructions. Of course, if we were required to give a separate instruction for each one of the arithmetical operations, the program would be very lengthy and even to describe it would take about as much time as performing the operations themselves by hand. Thus in programming we must try to make a small number of instructions suffice for a large number of arithmetic operations.

To clarify the structure of a sequence of instructions and the methods of setting up a program, let us first examine the operations that must be performed when a very simple problem is solved by hand.

We will take as an example the solution by Euler's method of the following differential equation of the first order with the given initial conditions

$$\frac{dy}{dx} = ay, \qquad y\mid_{x_0} = y_0 . \tag{1}$$

In this method the range of values of x is divided up into a sequence of intervals of equal length $\Delta x = h$, and within each interval the derivative dy/dx is regarded as a constant, equal to its value at the beginning of the interval.* With these assumptions the computation for the kth interval is given by the formulas

$$\left(\frac{dy}{dx}\right)_k = ay_k ,$$

$$\Delta y_k = \left(\frac{dy}{dx}\right)_k h = (ah)y_k ,$$

$$y_{k+1} = y_k + \Delta y_k ,$$

$$x_{k+1} = x_k + h.$$

After carrying out the calculation for the kth interval, we go on to the $(k+1)$th interval. The computation begins with the given initial values x_0 and y_0. The sequence of operations is shown in Table 1.

In hand computations only the first three operations are performed, the others being understood but not written down; this is true, for example, of the instruction to begin over again for the following interval, to end the computation, and so forth. In machine computation all these operations must be exactly formulated (operations 4-7). Consequently, in the machine, in addition to the arithmetic operations, we must also arrange in advance for the control operations (operations 4-7). The control operations have either a completely definite character (for example, operations 4 and 5) or a conditional character, which depends on the result just produced (for example, operations 6 and 7). Since the last two operations are mutually exclusive (we must perform either one or the other of them), these two operations are combined in the machine into one (a comparison operation), which is formulated in the following way: "If x is less than x_n, repeat the operations beginning with number 1; but if x is equal to or greater than x_n, stop the computation." In this

---

* In practice the solution of an ordinary differential equation is usually calculated by a more complicated and exact formula.

Table 1. Operations Necessary for the Solution of Equation (1) by Euler's Method

Number of the Operation	Quantity Defined	Formula	Computations*
1	Δy_k	$(ah)y_k$	$(ah)(2)_{k-1}$
2	y_{k-1}	$y_k + \Delta y_k$	$(2)_{k-1} + (1)_k$
3	x_{k+1}	$x_k + h$	$(3)_{k-1} + h$
4			Print the value found for x_{k+1}.
5			Print the value found for y_{k+1}.
6			Repeat the computation, beginning with operation no. 1 for the new values of x and y.
7			When x reaches the value x_n, stop the computation.

way, the sequence of further computations depends on the magnitude of the x already produced in the process of computing.

2. The three-address system. A glance at Table 1 shows that to perform any arithmetic operation it is necessary to indicate: First, which operation (addition, multiplication, etc.) is to be performed; second, which numbers is it to be performed on; and third, where to put the result, since it is to be used in further computation.

The code expressions for the numbers are stored in the memory unit of the machine; consequently the indexes of the corresponding locations in the memory must be given: namely, where the numbers are to be taken from and where the result is to be placed. This leads to the most natural "three-address system of instructions."

In the three-address system, a specific set of locations in the code is assigned to defining the operations; i.e., to stating which operation is to be performed on the given two numbers (the code of operations). The remaining locations in the instruction code are divided into three equal groups, called "instruction addresses" (figure 2). The code in the

---

* The digits (with subscripts) in parentheses in the column "Computations" indicate the operation whose result is to be used in the computation. For example, in the first operation (the first row) we have to multiply the quantity (ah) by the quantity found as a result of performing the second operation (the second row for the preceding interval $(2)_{k-1}$; in the second operation we have to add the quantity resulting from the operation for the preceding interval $(2)_{k-1}$ to the quantity resulting from the first operation for the present interval $(1)_k$.

At the beginning of the computation the initial data x_0 and y_0 are placed in the column "Quantity Defined" for operations 2 and 3.

first address shows the index of the location in the memory unit from which the first number is to be taken, the second address code is the index of the location from which the second number is to be taken, and

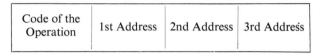

| Code of the Operation | 1st Address | 2nd Address | 3rd Address |

FIG. 2.   The structure of a three-address system of instructions.

the third address code is the index of the location of the memory unit in which the result is to be placed.

Code expressions for instructions referring to the control unit may also be put into the three-address system. Thus, the instruction "transfer a number to the print-out unit" must be represented in the code of operations by the number assigned to this operation; in the first address will appear the index of the location in the memory unit where the number to be printed is stored and in the third address the index of the printing unit (in the second address the code is blank). An instruction that either one course or another is to be followed is called a "comparison instruction." The code of operations of such an instruction states that it is necessary to compare two numbers, namely the ones indicated in the first and second addresses of the instruction. If the first number is smaller than the second, we must pass to the instruction indicated in the third address of the comparison command. But if the first number is greater than or equal to the second, then the given instruction consists simply of the command to pass to the next instruction.

Instruction codes, as well as number codes, are stored in the memory unit and follow one after the other in the order in which they are numbered provided there is no change indicated in the course of the computations (for example, by a comparison operation).

Let us consider how the program will look in the previous example. We set up the following distribution of number codes in the locations of the memory unit:

> The quantity ah is in the 11th location
> The quantity h is in the 12th location
> The quantity x_n is in the 13th location
> The quantity x is in the 14th location
> The quantity y is in the 15th location
> The operative location* is the 16th.

---

* A location in which intermediate values found in the course of the computation are placed is called operative.

Corresponding to the preceding table we get the following program (Table 2).

Table 2. Program for the Solution of Equation (1) by Euler's Method

Number of the Instruction	Instruction Code				Remarks
	Code of the Operation	1st Address	2nd Address	3rd Address	
1	Multiplication	11	15	16	$\Delta y_k = (ah)y_k$
2	Addition	15	16	15	$y_{k+1} = y_k + \Delta y_k$
3	Addition	14	12	14	$x_{k+1} = x_k + h$
4	Print	14	—	1	Print x_{k+1} in the first printing unit
5	Print	15	—	2	Print y_{k+1} in the second printing unit
6	Compare	14	13	1	If $x < x_k$, return to instruction no. 1; if $x \geqslant x_k$, pass to the following instruction, i.e., to instruction no. 7.
7	Stop	—	—	—	End of the computation.

The instruction code is placed in the memory unit (in Table 2, in the 1st through 7th locations). In the control unit we then place the instruction found in the first location of the memory unit. In obedience to this instruction the number in the 11th location is multiplied by the number in the 15th; i.e., the quantity $\Delta y_k = (ah)y_k$ is computed. The result is placed in the operative 16th location. With the completion of this operation the instruction from the next location of the memory unit, i.e., from the second location, enters the control unit. By this instruction the quantity $y_{k+1} = y_k + \Delta y_k$ is found, and is placed in the 15th memory location; i.e., it replaces the previous value of y. Similarly, by the third instruction the new value of x is found; the 4th and 5th instructions cause the printing of the newly found values of x and y; the 6th instruction defines the further course of the computational process. This instruction produces a comparison of the number found in the 14th memory location with the number in the 13th location, i.e., a comparison of the value x_{k+1} which has been produced with the final value x_n. If $x_{k+1} < x_n$, the computation must be repeated for the next interval; i.e., in the given example we must return to the first instruction. The index of this instruction, to which we must pass if the first number is less than the second, is shown in the third address of the comparison instruction. But if the computation has produced a value $x_{k+1} \geqslant x_n$, the comparison instruction causes passage to the next instruction, i.e., to the 7th, which stops the computing process.

Before beginning the computation, we must introduce in the memory unit the instruction codes (in locations 1-7), the code expressions for the constants (locations 11-13) and also the initial data, i.e., the values x_0 and y_0 (in locations 14 and 15).

After completion of the computation for the first interval, the 14th and 15th memory locations will contain, in place of x_0 and y_0, the quantities x_1 and y_1, i.e., the values of the variables for the beginning of the next interval. In this manner, the computations for the next interval will be produced by repetition of the same instruction program.

The example considered shows that, by carrying out a cyclical repetition of a series of instructions, we may carry out a large amount of computation with a comparatively small program. The method of cyclical repetition of separate parts of a program is widely used in programming the solution of problems.

3. Change of address of instructions. A second widely used method that allows one to make essential reductions in the size of a program consists of automatically changing the addresses of certain instructions. To explain the essence of this method, we take the example of computation of the values of a polynomial.

Let it be required to compute the value of the polynomial

$$y = a_0 x^6 + a_1 x^5 + a_2 x^4 + a_3 x^3 + a_4 x^2 + a_5 x + a_6 .$$

For machine computation this polynomial is more conveniently represented in the form

$$y = (((((a_0 x + a_1)x + a_2)x + a_3)x + a_4)x + a_5)x + a_6 .$$

Let the values of the coefficients $a_0, \cdots, a_6$ be placed in memory locations 20-26, and the value of x in the 31st location of the memory unit. The program is very easy to construct and is given in Table 3.

As can be seen, in this program the operations of multiplication and addition occur alternately. All the multiplication instructions, with the exception of the 1st, are completely alike: we have to multiply the number found in the 27th location by the number found in the 31st and put the result in the 27th. All the addition instructions have the same 1st and

Table 3. Program for Computing a Polynomial

Number of the Instruction	Code of the Operation	Instruction Code			Remarks
		1st Address	2nd Address	3rd Address	
1	Multiplication	20	31	27	$a_0 x$
2	Addition	27	21	27	$a_0 x + a_1$
3	Multiplication	27	31	27	$(a_0 x + a_1)x$
4	Addition	27	22	27	$(a_0 x + a_1)x + a_2$
5	Multiplication	27	31	27	$((a_0 x + a_1)x + a_2)x$
6	Addition	27	23	27	$((a_0 x + a_1)x + a_2)x + a_3$
7	Multiplication	27	31	27	$(((a_0 x + a_1)x + a_2)x + a_3)x$
8	Addition	27	24	27	$(((a_0 x + a_1)x + a_2)x + a_3)x + a_4$
9	Multiplication	27	31	27	$((((a_0 x + a_1)x + a_2)x + a_3)x + a_4)x$
10	Addition	27	25	27	$((((a_0 x + a_1)x + a_2)x + a_3)x + a_4)x + a_5$
11	Multiplication	27	31	27	$(((((a_0 x + a_1)x + a_2)x + a_3)x + a_4)x + a_5)x$
12	Addition	27	26	27	$y. = (((((a_0 x + a_1)x + a_2)x + a_3)x + a_4)x + a_5)x + a_6$

3rd address. But the index of the location in the second address, in changing from one instruction of addition to the next, is increased each time by one: in the second instruction the number is found in the 21st location, in the fourth instruction in the 22nd, and so forth.

The computing program may be essentially shortened, if we arrange for an automatic change in the indexes (giving the memory location) in the second address of the addition instruction. The instruction codes are stored in the corresponding locations and they may themselves be considered as certain numbers. By the addition of suitable numbers to them, we can make an automatic change in the instruction addresses. In such a method the program for computing the values of a polynomial will have the form given in Table 4.

Table 4.   Program for Computing a Polynomial

Number of the Instruction	Instruction Code			
	Code of the Operation	1st Address	2nd Address	3rd Address
1	Addition	20	—	27
2	Multiplication	27	31	27
3	Addition	27	21	27
4	Addition	3	28	3
5	Comparison	3	29	2
6	Stop			

The first instruction serves to transfer the number from the 20th location to the 27th in order to have the multiplication instruction in standard form. In performing the 2nd and 3rd instructions, we get the values of $a_0 x + a_1$. For further computation it is necessary as a preliminary to change by 1 the second address in the addition instruction (the 3rd instruction), and this change is made by the 4th instruction. According to this instruction we take the number found in the 3rd location, i.e., the addition instruction in question (the 3rd instruction) and add to it the quantity found in the 28th location. In order to change by 1 the 2nd address of the 3rd instruction, the 28th memory location must contain the following:

Code of the Operation	1st Address	2nd Address	3rd Address
—	—	1	—

After performing the instruction in this way, we have put the 3rd instruction into the following form:

Code of the Operation	1st Address	2nd Address	3rd Address
Addition	27	22	27

This new form is stored in the 3rd memory location in place of the previous form of the addition instruction.

Having obtained this new form by the addition instruction, we may repeat the computations, beginning with the multiplication instruction, i.e., with the 2nd instruction. The 5th comparison serves for this purpose. This instruction compares the newly found instruction in the 3rd location with the quantity stored in the 29th location. In the 29th location is stored the following:

Code of the Operation	1st Address	2nd Address	3rd Address
Addition	27	27	27

This comparison initially tells us that the first quantity (in the third location) is less than the second (in the 29th location), and so the process of computation passes to the 2nd instruction, shown in the 3rd address of the comparison instruction. Thus the multiplication instruction (the 2nd instruction) and the addition instruction (the 3rd instruction) will be automatically repeated, and each time the number of the location in the 2nd address of the addition instruction will be changed by one (as arranged for by the 4th instruction).

Repetition of the cycle will continue until the 2nd address of the addition instruction (the 3rd instruction) reaches the magnitude 27, which happens after six repetitions of the cycle. Here the 3rd instruction will have the form:

Code of the Operation	1st Address	2nd Address	3rd Address
Addition	27	27	27

i.e., the instruction code will be the same as in the 29th location. The comparison instruction (the 5th instruction) takes note at this stage of the equality of the quantities found in the 3rd and 29th location, so that the process of computation passes to the next instruction, i.e., the 6th, and herewith the computation of the polynomial is finished.

The method of automatically changing, as part of the program itself, the number of the location in the addresses of certain instructions is widely applied for the solution of many different problems. Together with the method of cyclic repetitions, it enables us to perform a very large volume of computations with a small number of instructions.

4. The one-address system. In addition to the three-address system of instructions that we have considered, in many machines a one-address system is used. In a one-address system each instruction contains, in addition to the code of operation, only one address. Performing an arithmetic operation with two numbers and placing the result in the memory unit calls for three instructions: The first instruction puts one of the numbers of the memory unit into the arithmetic unit, the second puts in the second number and performs the given operation with the numbers, the third places the result in the memory unit. In the course of any computation, the result produced is often used only to perform the next following arithmetic operation. In these cases one does not need to put the result obtained into the memory unit, and for the performance of the following operation one does not need to recall the first number. Thus the number of instructions in a program with a one-address system is found to be roughly only twice as large as for a three-address system. Since a one-address instruction needs a smaller number of locations than a three-address system, the amount of space taken up in the memory unit by the program will be about the same for both systems of instructions (usually in a one-address system of instructions each location of the memory unit will contain two instructions). The differences in the two different systems of instructions must be taken into account in making a comparison of the rapidity of working of the machines. For the same rapidity of performing an operation, a one-address machine will perform computations about twice as slowly as a three-address machine.

In addition to these systems, certain machines have a two-address or a four-address system of instructions.

5. Subroutines. Usually the solution of a problem is carried out in several stages. Many of these stages are common to a series of problems. Examples of such stages are: computing the value of an elementary function for a given argument, or determining the definite integral of a function already computed.

Naturally it is desirable for such typical stages to have standard subroutines worked out once and for all. If in the course of the solution of a problem we are required to carry out standard computations, we should transfer the computation at the appropriate moment to one of the standard subroutines. Then at the end of the computations involved in the subroutine, it is necessary to return to the basic program at the place where it was interrupted.

The existence of standard programs makes the task of the programmer considerably easier. With a library of such subroutines, recorded either on punched cards or on magnetic tape, the programming of many problems consists simply of setting up some short parts of the basic program linking together a sequence of standard subroutines.

6. Verification of results.   On electronic computing machines problems are solved that require several million arithmetic operations. An error in even one of the operations may lead to incorrect results. Of course, it is practically impossible to set up a check system by hand over such a large number of computations. Thus the checks and verifications must be carried out by the machine itself. Apparatus exists that will verify the correctness of the machine's operations and bring it to an automatic stop if an error is discovered. However, this apparatus involves a considerable increase in the size and complexity of the machine and usually does not act on all its parts. More promising are the methods of verification that are included in advance in the program itself.

One such method of verification consists simply of repetition of the computation, as is so common in hand computation under the name of "duplication check." If an independent repetition of the computation produces the same results, we may be sure that there are no random errors but this method will naturally fail to reveal the presence of systematic errors. To exclude the latter we must carry out in advance some control computations with previously known answers, and these computations must involve all parts of the machine. Correctness of the results produced in the control computations serves to guarantee the absence of systematic errors.

In addition to this "duplication check," we may apply more complicated methods of verification, depending on the type of problem. For example, in calculating the trajectory of a projectile, we may first solve the system of differential equations for the two components of the velocity and then subsequently solve the single differential equation for the total velocity and at each step of the integration verify the formula:

$$v^2 = v_x^2 + v_y^2 \, .$$

For the solution of ordinary differential equations, in addition to the computation with steps of integration h, we may carry out a second computation with steps $h/2$. This will not only guarantee the absence of random errors in the computation but also will give an estimate of the validity of the choice of step size. In computing a table by a recurrence formula, we may sometimes compute certain key values by other methods. A correct result for the key values is a sufficient guarantee of the correctness of all intermediate values. In some cases verification may consist of noting the differences between the results produced.

In constructing a program it is necessary to provide in advance for some form of logical verification of the results obtained.

Coding of numbers and instructions. Numbers and instructions are placed in machines in the form of codes. In most cases the binary system of notation is used instead of the ordinary decimal system.

In the decimal system the number 10 is taken as the base. The digits in each position may take one of the ten values from 0 through 9. The unit in each successive position is ten times as large as the unit in the preceding position. Consequently, an integer in the decimal system may be written

$$N_{10} = k_0 10^0 + k_1 10^1 + k_2 10^2 + \cdots + k_n 10^n,$$

where $k_0, k_1, \cdots, k_n$ may take the values from 0 through 9.

In the binary system the number 2 is taken as the base. The digits in each position may take only the two values 0 and 1. A unit in each successive position is twice as large as a unit in the preceding position. Consequently, an integer in the binary system may be written

$$N_2 = k_0 2^0 + k_1 2^1 + \cdots + k_p 2^p,$$

where $k_0, k_1, \cdots, k_p$ may take the values 0 or 1.

The first few natural numbers in the binary and the decimal system are written,

Binary system	0	1	10	11	100	101	110	111	1000	1001	1010	1011 etc.
Decimal system	0	1	2	3	4	5	6	7	8	9	10	11 etc.

A noninteger is written analogously in terms of negative powers of the base. For example, $3\frac{1}{8}$ is written in the binary system as

$$11.001.$$

The transfer of numbers from one system of notation to another involves specific arithmetic operations that are usually carried out in the electronic computing machine itself by special programs.

Arithmetic operations on numbers in the binary system are carried out in exactly the same way as in the decimal system. Here the addition of two units in any position produces zero in the given position and carries one to the following position. For example,

$$1010 + 111 = 10001.$$

Multiplication and division in the binary system are simpler than in the decimal system, since the multiplication table is replaced by the rules for multiplying by 0 and 1. For example,

$$
\begin{array}{r}
1010\ (10) \\
\times\ \ 101\ \ (5) \\
\hline
1010 \\
0000 \\
1010 \\
\hline
110010\ (50)
\end{array}
$$

The choice of the binary system of notation in the majority of electronic computing machines is because the arithmetic unit is thereby greatly simplified (generally at the expense of brevity in the operations of multiplication and division) and also the digits in each position are conveniently represented, for example, by open or closed relays, the presence or absence of a signal in a circuit, and so forth (in the binary system the digits in each position can only have the two values: 0 or 1).

Every digit of a binary number may be represented in the form of the presence or absence of a signal in its circuit, or in the state of a relay. In this case it is necessary that every digit have its own circuit or relay (figure 3) and the number of such circuits will be equal to the number of digits (parallel system). A binary number may also be represented in the form of a time-pulse code. In this case each digit of a number is represented at specific intervals of time on one circuit (series system). The time intervals for each digit are created by synchronizing pulses, common to the entire machine.

Corresponding to these two principles, the methods of coding a number for an electronic computing machine fall into two categories: one for a machine with parallel operation and the other for a machine with series operation. In a machine with parallel operation all the digits of a number are transmitted at the same time and each digit requires its own circuit.

In a machine with series operation the number is transmitted by one circuit, but the time of the transmission is proportional to the number of digits. Thus machines with parallel operation are faster than machines with series operation, but they also require more apparatus.

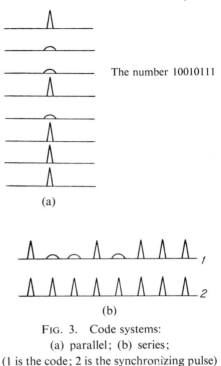

The number 10010111

(a)

(b)

Fig. 3. Code systems:
(a) parallel; (b) series;
(1 is the code; 2 is the synchronizing pulse)

Every electronic computing machine has a specific number of places for digits. All numbers to be dealt with in a computation must be included in that number of places, and the position of the decimal point, separating the integer part from the fractional, must naturally be included.

In certain machines the position of the decimal point is rigidly fixed; these are the so-called "fixed-point" machines. Usually the decimal point is put before the first place; i.e., all the numbers for the computation must be less than one, which is guaranteed by the choice of a suitable scale. For complicated computations it is difficult to determine in advance the range of the results to be expected, and thus we have to choose the scale so as to have something in reserve, a procedure which lowers the accuracy, or else we must arrange in the program itself for an automatic change of scale, which complicates the programming.

In certain machines the position of the decimal point is indicated for each number; these are machines which keep track of the exponents and they are usually called "floating-point" machines. Indicating the position of the decimal point is equivalent to representing the number in the form of its sequence of digits and its exponent, i.e.,

$$N_{10} = 10^k N'_{10} \text{ in the decimal system,}$$

$$N_2 = 2^p N'_2 \text{ in the binary system.}$$

Thus the number 97.35 may be represented as $10^2 \cdot 0.9735$. To represent the number in a machine we must indicate both its exponent (p or k)

and its sequence of digits. Thus all the digits in the number are made use of independently of its size; i.e., every number is represented by its entire set of significant digits with the same relative error. This increases the accuracy of the computation, especially for multiplication, so that in most cases one can dispense with a special choice of scale.

Increased accuracy and simplified programming in the floating-point machines are attained at the expense of some complication in the arithmetic unit, particularly in the operations of addition and subtraction. Since numbers may initially have different exponents, it is necessary to provide them with the same exponents before adding or subtracting them, in which process the final digits of the smaller number are discarded, thus:

$$10^2 \cdot 0.7587 + 10^0 \cdot 0.3743 = 10^2 \cdot 0.7587 + 10^2 \cdot 0.0037 = 10^2 \cdot 0.7624.$$

The code for a number in the binary system for a fixed-point machine consists simply of its sequences of digits (the number is assumed to be less than one); for example:

$$.00110110000000 = \frac{27}{128}.$$

In floating-point machines a specific part of the code describes the exponent, which is also coded in the binary system. An example of the way in which a number is expressed in such a code is

$$6\frac{3}{4} = 2^3 \cdot \frac{27}{32} = 0011.11011000000.$$

In addition, it is customary to reserve two places for the algebraic sign (for example, "+" in the form 0 or "—" in the form 1), one for the sign of the exponent and one for the sign of the number itself.

Instructions are coded the same way as numbers are, a specific part of the code being allotted to expressing the index (in the binary system) of the operation and another to the indexes of the memory location of each address.

§3. Technical Principles of the Various Units of a High-Speed Computing Machine

The order of performing the operations in electronic computing machines. The performance of each arithmetic operation in a machine in accordance with a given list of instructions may be reduced to the following successive steps (it is understood that we are talking about a three-address system of instructions).

1. Transfer of the first number from the memory unit to the arithmetic unit (the location of this number in the memory unit is given in the first address of the instruction code).

2. Transfer of the second number from the memory unit to the arithmetic unit (its location is given in the second address of the instruction code).

3. Performance by the arithmetic unit of the given operation on these numbers in accordance with the operation code.

4. Transfer of the result from the arithmetic unit to the corresponding location in the memory unit (the index of this location is given in the third address of the instruction code).

5. Selection from the memory unit of the next instruction, whereupon the machine begins to carry out the next operation.

In the machine the instruction code is accepted in the "instruction memory block" (IMB, figure 4). An electronic commutator (EC) trans-

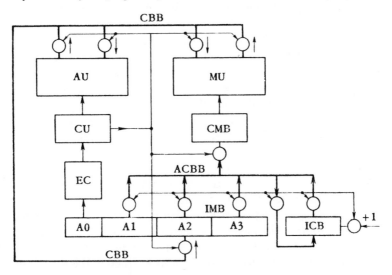

FIG. 4.   Structural diagram of an electronic digital computer.

forms the binary number of the operation code into an activating voltage in one of its output circuits corresponding to the given arithmetic operation. This voltage through the control unit (CU) prepares the circuits of the machine to perform the required operation.

In order to select the first number, the first address code of the instruction (A1), is transferred via the address code bus bars (ACBB) from the instruction memory block (IMB) to the control memory block (CMB). The signal for the transfer of this code is given by the control unit (CU) of the machine. From the location in the memory unit (MU) which corresponds to the code number transmitted the first number is selected and via the code bus bars (CBB) is placed in the arithmetic unit (AU). The opening of the input circuits in the arithmetic unit is effected by a corresponding signal from the control unit (CU) of the machine.

The second number is selected in a similar manner. A signal from the control unit (CU) of the machine transfers the code of the second instruction address (A2) from the instruction memory block (IMB) to the control memory block (CMB). The second number, taken in this way from the memory unit (MU), is transferred via the code bus bars (CBB) into the arithmetic unit (AU).

The arithmetic unit (AU) performs the given operation with the numbers in accordance with the operation code inserted in it previously.

In order to effect the transfer of the result thus obtained into the memory unit the third address code of the instruction (A3) is transferred via the address code bus bars (ACBB) from the instruction memory block (IMB) to the control memory block (CMB). The signal for the transfer of this code is given by the control unit (CU) of the machine. The memory location corresponding to the number thus obtained is then selected and its input circuits are opened. The rules for the selection or insertion of numbers are given by signals from the control unit (CU) of the machine. The signal from the control unit (CU) of the machine transfers the result obtained from the arithmetic unit (AU) to the code bus bars (CBB), via which the number is placed in the chosen location of the memory unit.

The instruction control block (ICB) is provided for the selection of the instructions. In this block is given the number of the chosen instruction. Usually the instructions go in numerical order so that, to give the number of the following instruction, it is necessary that the number found in the instruction control block (ICB) be increased by one. This is done by the control unit of the machine (circuit + 1). The instructions are stored in the memory unit. For selection of the next instruction the newly obtained number is transferred via the address code bus bars (ACBB) from the instruction control block (ICB) to the control memory block (CMB). The signal for this transfer comes from the control unit of the machine (CU). The new instruction taken from the memory unit (MU) is transferred via the code bus bars (CBB) into the instruction memory block (IMB), the output circuits of which are opened by a signal from the control block of the machine. This concludes one cycle of the operation of the machine. In the next cycle the machine performs the newly received instructions. The normal succession of instructions in numerical order may be altered by performing a control operation; for example, a comparison instruction. This instruction does not call for any arithmetic operation but specifies the course of the computational process. If the first number is less than the second, then it is necessary to go over to the instruction whose number is shown in the third address. But if the first number is greater than or equal to the second, then we pass on to the next instruction.

In transferring the comparison instruction code to the instruction memory block (IMB) an electronic commutator (EC) transforms the binary number of the operation code to an activating voltage in that one of its output circuits which corresponds to this operation. This voltage prepares the circuits of the machine for performing the operation of comparison.

The selection from the memory unit of the two numbers whose locations are given in the first and second addresses of the comparison instruction is carried out in exactly the same way as an arithmetic operation. The comparison of the numbers in the arithmetic unit (AU) may be carried out by subtracting the second number from the first. Depending on the sign of the result the control unit (CU) either transfers the code number of the next command from the third address (A3) via the address code bus bar (ACBB) to the instruction control block (ICB), or adds one to the number which is found in this block (circuit $+ 1$), exactly as in performing an arithmetic operation. After the number of the next command has been placed in the instruction control block (ICB), its selection from the memory unit is effected in the same way as in an arithmetic operation.

The arithmetic unit and the control unit. Electronic computing machines make use of present-day devices for electronic automatization. Basically the units of the machine work on the crude principle of "yes" or "no"; i.e., essentially there either is a signal or the signal is absent. Consequently, we may vary the parameters of an electronic circuit rather widely without affecting the operation of the machine.

One of the most widely used elements applied in electronic machines is the flip-flop or trigger cell. The simplest flip-flop (figure 5) consists of two amplifiers with plate resistors R_a, connected by the divider resistors R_1 and R_2. The bias established (O_B) is chosen so that one of the tubes operates and the other does not. Since the two halves of the circuit are symmetric, either tube may be closed; i.e., the circuit has two stable positions of equilibrium. In fact, if the left tube is closed, and the right one is open, then on the plate of the left tube (O_1) there will be a high voltage, and on the plate of the right tube (O_0) a low voltage (because of the voltage drop on the plate resistance R_a from the current through the tube. These voltages are transferred through the divider resistors R_1

and R_2 to the grids of the opposite tube, and consequently there will be a small voltage on the grid of the left tube and a high voltage on the grid of the right tube. With a proper choice of the parameters of the circuit, these grid voltages will keep the tubes in the given state.

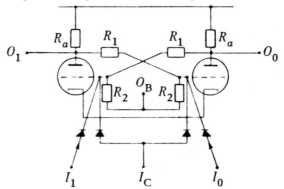

FIG. 5.   The circuit of a flip-flop.

Similarly, if the left tube is open and the right one closed, there will be low voltages on the plate of the left tube and on the grid of the right tube and high voltages on the plate of the right tube and on the grid of the left tube.

The flipping of a flip-flop from one state to the other may be brought about by negative pulses placed on the grids of the tubes through diodes. If we place a negative pulse on the grid of the left tube, then the left tube is closed, and its plate voltage will increase. This produces a higher voltage on the grid of the right tube, which opens the right tube. In this manner, the trigger assumes the first position of equilibrium (high voltage on the plate of the left tube). But if a negative pulse is placed on the grid of the right tube, the flip-flop assumes the second stable equilibrium position (a high voltage on the plate of the right tube). If a negative pulse is placed

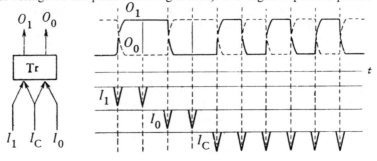

FIG. 6.   The operation of a flip-flop.

simultaneously on the grids of both tubes, then each such pulse will cause the flip-flop to move from one state of equilibrium to the other.

If we consider the circuits by which pulses are placed on the grids of the tubes as inputs of the system and the plate voltages as outputs, we have the diagram in figure 6 for the operation of a flip-flop.

The properties of flip-flops make them convenient for use in the various units of an electronic computing machine. To one equilibrium state of the flip-flop we may assign the code value "0," for example, to high voltage on the right output (O_0)—and to the other the code value "1," high voltage at the left output (O_1). Correspondingly, the inputs may be denoted by I_0, I_1, and I_C (the counting input).

Flip-flops are used in electronic machines for the temporary storage of codes (receiving registers) (figure 7). Initially all the flip-flops are set

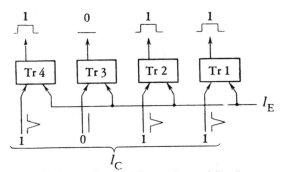

FIG. 7. Diagram of a receiving register of flip-flops.

in the code position "0" by means of negative pulses (I_E) on the zero inputs of all cells. The code of a number or of an instruction is placed on the unit inputs of the flip-flops in the form of negative pulses. In those positions in which there are code pulses the flip-flops pass to the code position "1" and hold this position until they receive an extinguishing pulse (I_E). Receiving registers are used in the arithmetic units for storing the code of an instruction, for giving the number of a required location of the memory unit, and so forth.

A second realm of application of flip-flops is in addition circuits. Here use is made of the property of a flip-flop that it changes its state of equilibrium every time a negative pulse is applied to the counting input (simultaneously to both inputs). If the flip-flop starts in the code position "0," then the application of a pulse moves it into code position "1." But if the flip-flop starts in code position "1," then the application of a pulse moves it to code position "0." In the absence of a pulse the flip-flop remains in its previous position. The initial position of the flip-flop may be considered as a code for a given digit of the first position of the second number. Here it is easy to see that the behavior of the flip-flop exactly corresponds to the rules of addition of binary numbers for one digit $(0 + 0 = 0; 0 + 1 = 1; 1 + 0 = 1; 1 + 1 = 10$, i.e., "0" in the given position and the carrying of "1" to the next position). In order that the addition circuit may work for several binary digits, it is necessary to guarantee the carry from one digital position to the next. A carry in the original position is caused by the addition of two units, i.e., by the passage of the flip-flop from the code position "1" to the code position "0." In this passage the voltage on the left output of the trigger is changed from high to low. If this voltage is passed through a circuit containing a condenser and a resistor, then in leaving the circuit it causes a negative pulse. Through a delay line this carry pulse may be directed into the counting input of the next position.

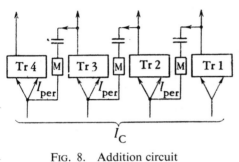

Fig. 8. Addition circuit with flip-flops.

Figure 8 represents the simplest addition circuit with flip-flops. Initially all the flip-flops are set in the code position "0" by a pulse I_0 placed on their zero inputs. On reception of the code of the first number, which appears in the form of negative pulses on the counting inputs, the flip-flops assume a position corresponding to the code of the first number. On reception of the code of the second number, there occurs digit-by-digit addition of the binary numbers, and in those positions where the addition has produced two ones, there arise carry pulses that after a time delay t_d are applied to the counting inputs of the flip-flops in the higher positions. These carry pulses may move the flip-flops from the code position "1" to the code position "0." In this case there arises a carry pulse to the next higher position. In the worst case, when in the addition of the codes all the positions are set in the code position "1," and the lowest position passes from code position "1" to code position "0," the carry pulse arises successively in each position after a time delay t_d. In this manner, the total time required for the passage of the carry pulses will be equal to one time delay multiplied by the number of positions. More complicated electronic circuits of flip-flops allow the elimination of such step-by-step carries with consequent shortening of the time required for addition.

For multiplication of numbers an arithmetic unit of flip-flops (figure 9)

has two receiving registers for storage of the multiplicand and the multiplier (R_1, R_2) and with them an adder (Add). Multiplication is carried out in the follow-
ing manner. The code of the multiplier is shifted one place to the right. If in the lowest place the multiplier has the code "1," then in the right output of the register of the multiplier there arises a pulse that is applied to the circuits governing the application of the code in the multiplicand register to the adder (the circuit + N). After this has been done the partial product

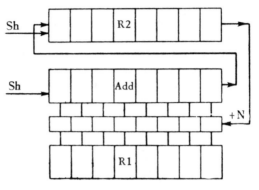

Fig. 9. Multiplication circuit with flip-flops.

in the adder is moved one place to the right and the operations are repeated. In this manner the sum of the partial products is accumulated in the adder. These operations are repeated as many times as there are digit positions in the number codes. In the multiplication of two numbers each of which takes up "n" positions, the product will take up "$2n$" positions. The highest "n" positions of the product are distributed in the adder, and the lowest "n" positions of the product may be entered one after the other, as the shifts to the right successively set free the positions in the register of the multiplier. With the completion of the multiplication, the lowest "n" digits of the product are placed in the multiplier register. The time required for multiplication is roughly equal to the time required for addition multiplied by the number of digit positions in the number code.

A code shift with flip-flops is produced by the circuit illustrated in figure 10. Applying the shift pulse (I_{sh}) to the zero inputs of all the flip-flops places them in code position "0." From these flip-flops which are in the code position "1," carry pulses arise which put the adjacent flip-

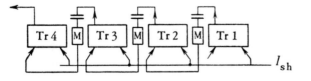

Fig. 10. Circuit for shifting a code with flip-flops.

flops into code position "1" with a time delay t_d. In this way, every application of a carry pulse moves the code one place.

An arithmetic unit with flip-flops which consists of two receiving registers and an adder also enables us to divide one number by another.

Usually an arithmetic unit with flip-flops is constructed so as to serve in a universal way for all the arithmetic and logical operations.

Flip-flops are also used in electronic machines for counting pulses, which is necessary in a number of different control arrangements. The circuit for an electronic counter (figure 11) differs from the circuit for

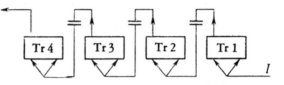

FIG. 11.   Circuit of an electronic computer
with flip-flops.

an elementary adder (figure 8) only in the omission of the delay line in the carry pulse links. A counter of this sort can count up to 2^n pulses (n is the number of places in the counter), after which the position of the counter is repeated. At the cost of some complication in the system it is possible to construct an electronic counter for an arbitrary number of pulses (not equal to 2^n).

For the realization of logical operations and control circuits in electronic computing machines, we make use of coincidence units (the so-called "AND" elements), of inverters, and of divider diode links ("OR" elements).

The AND elements work on the logical principle of "both—and" ("one and also the other"); i.e., at the output of such a unit a signal will occur only in case there are signals at all inputs. Inverters work on the logical principle of "yes—no"; i.e., if there is a signal on an input, then there will be no signal at the output, and conversely, when there is no signal on the input, then there is an output signal. The OR elements obey the logical law "either—or"; i.e., at the output there will be a signal in the case when there is a signal at any one input.

AND elements are widely used for "channeling" electric signals in a machine, i.e., for directing signals to the required circuits. For example, figure 12 illustrates a code bus bar for one of the digits of a number. This code bus bar is joined through an AND element to the inputs and outputs of the locations of the memory unit, to the inputs of two receiving registers of the arithmetic organ and to the output of an adder. Applying a control signal to the output of an AND element of any location of the memory unit, we thereby put the code stored in this location onto the code bus bar. If we simultaneously put a control signal on the input AND elements of the first receiving register, for example, then the code on the bus bar is entered into the first register. Similarly, if we put a control signal on the output AND units of the adder, then the code which is produced in the adder is transferred to the code bus bar. If here we place a control on the AND-circuit inputs of any location of the memory unit, then the codes being transferred by the code bus bars will be received in this location. Of course, before receiving codes in locations of the memory unit or in the receiving registers of the arithmetic unit, it is necessary to clear the codes which were in them previously.

This example does not exhaust all the various applications of AND elements for channelling electric signals in an electronic computing machine. They also are widely applied in the

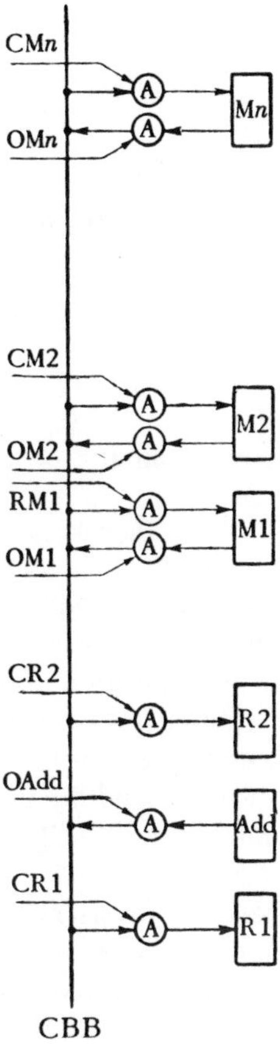

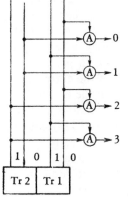

FIG. 12. Channeling of signals by an AND element.

FIG. 13. Circuit of an electronic commutator with four output links.

memory unit, in the arithmetic unit, and in the control unit of the machine.

In addition to solving problems of channelling signals, AND elements perform more complicated functions. For example, when we are having access to the location of the memory unit, there often arises the problem of converting the number of the location (given in binary form) to a control voltage placed on this location. This problem is handled by the electronic commutator, constructed from AND elements. Figure 13 illustrates a circuit for an electronic commutator with four output links. The number of the location is given in the form of a binary code on two flip-flops. All four possible combinations of the state of these locations are given in Table 5.

Table 5.

Code	2nd Trigger		1st Trigger	
	Left Output	Right Output	Left Output	Right Output
"00"	L	H	L	H
"01"	L	H	H	L
"10"	H	L	L	H
"11"	H	L	H	L

L = Low voltage at ouput,   H = High voltage at output

If in an AND element the high voltage is controlling, then to get a signal on the zero-output link it is necessary that the inputs of the AND elements be connected to the right outputs of the first and second flip-flops. In this case on the output of this AND element, there will be a signal only when the flip-flops are found in the code position "00." Similarly, to get a signal on the first output link (the code "01"), the inputs of the corresponding AND element must be connected to the left output of the first flip-flop and to the right output of the second flip-flop. The connections of the AND elements for the second (code "10") and third (code "11") links will also be made on the same principle.

In a number of cases the AND elements together with inverters and OR elements are used in the construction of the arithmetic units. For digit-by-digit addition of numbers with two binary digits, we have the four possible combinations in Table 6.

Table 6.

No.	Value of the Addends		Value of the sum	Transfer to the next Higher Order
	1st	2nd		
1	0	0	0	0
2	0	1	1	0
3	1	0	1	0
4	1	1	0	1

These relations may be realized, for example, by the circuit shown in figure 14. Such circuits are called "semiadders." The carry signal for the higher of the two positions is produced by an AND element (combination 4). To get the signal of the sum (combinations 2 and 3), it is sufficient to have a signal on one of the two outputs with the absence of an output carry signal, which may be done by an AND element, an inverter, and a diode link unifier. For addition of numbers it is necessary to consider not only the digits in a given position but also the carry from the preceding position. The

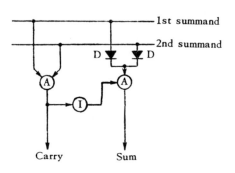

Fig. 14. Circuit for a one-place semiadder.

carry may be taken as repeated addition to the result produced by carrying from the previous position. In this manner, the union in series of two semiadders fully guarantees the addition of one position in two binary numbers.

The circuit of an adder for one position may also be realized directly by considering the possible combinations and taking account of carrying from the preceding lower position.

It is most effective to use adder circuits in AND elements in machines with sequential code distribution. In this case the code of a number is transferred by one of the code bus bars. The digits of the number follow one after another at strictly determined intervals of time. In this case for the addition of numbers, we may use a one-place adder (figure 15).

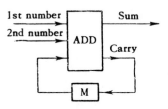

Fig. 15. Circuit for a series adder with AND elements.

The codes of both numbers are placed in advance in the lowest positions on the two basic inputs of the one-place adder. The carry output is run through a delay line to the third input of the adder. The time of the delay is taken equal to the interval between pulses. In this manner, if in the addition of any digit of the numbers there occurs a carry pulse, it is placed in the input of the adder at exactly the same time as the occurrence of the pulses in the next higher position. The time required for addition of two numbers is equal to the time required for the passage of the code of one number.

Multiplication of two numbers in a series code may also be done with a one-place adder, and here it is necessary to put the numbers through the adder a number of times equal to the number of positions occupied by the number code, i.e., the time required for multiplication is "n" times as long as the time for addition.

Memory units. The possibilities of a machine are to a great extent determined by the capacity of its memory unit, i.e., by the number of numbers that can be stored in the machine. For contemporary universal electronic computing machines this capacity is usually 500-4,000 numbers.

For code storage it is possible to use flip-flops. However, the amount of apparatus here turns out to be so large that this form of memory unit is almost never used.

For machines with series operation, widespread application has been found for memory units consisting of electroacoustic mercury tubes (figure 16). An electric signal in the form of a pulse is placed on a quartz

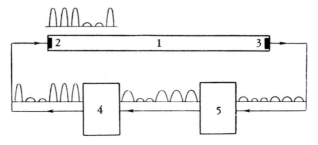

Fig. 16.   Basic circuit for dynamic storage of a code
in an electroacoustic tube:
(1) mercury tube;   (2) transmitting quartz crystal;
(3) receiving quartz crystal;   (4) transmitted form
of the pulse;   (5) received form of the pulse.

crystal at the input of the tube. The quartz crystal has the property of transforming an electrical pulse into a mechanical oscillation, and conversely. In this manner the entering electrical signal is transformed into a mechanical (ultrasonic) vibration, which is propagated along the tube with a specific velocity. When the signal reaches the end of the tube, it falls on a receiving quartz crystal and is transformed again into an electrical pulse. After being amplified and put into its original form, the signal is again directed toward the input of the tube. In this manner, the codes of the numbers introduced in the form of pulses in the mercury tube are circulated indefinitely in the tube. To introduce the numbers into the tube, a code from the machine is placed on the input of the tube, and simultaneously the circuit for the return of pulses from the end of the tube is broken for the same period of time. For the selection of numbers in the corresponding instant of time, when the required code reaches the end of the tube, the output links are opened, thereby transmitting the code to the other units of the machine. The entry and removal of the numbers is accomplished automatically by appropriate electronic circuits. Usually, with the goal of simplifying the apparatus, several numbers are stored in each mercury tube. Thus for access to a number, it is necessary to wait while the required code goes to the end of the tube. The more numbers there are stored in the tube, the greater the time required to find a required number.

Series machines with memory units composed of electroacoustic mercury tubes operate at a rate of 1,000-2,000 operations per second.

For memory units one often applies the principle of magnetic recording of electrical signals, similar to the recording of sound. The record may be made either on a magnetic tape or on a continuously revolving drum covered with a ferromagnetic material (figure 17). Along the generator of the drum there are placed magnetic heads. If at a specific instant of time current pulses are passed through the windings of the magnetic heads, then in the corresponding places on the surface of the drum the signals will be recorded in the form of residual magnetization. With the

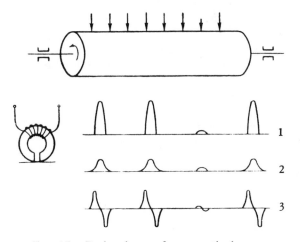

Fig. 17. Basic scheme of a magnetic drum:
(1) current through the coil; (2) residual magnetization;
(3) emf in the coil in read-out.

rotation of the drum the field resulting from the residual magnetization, passing under the heads, causes in them electric signals, which are amplified and transmitted to the other units of the machine.

A magnetic drum may be used both for a series system and for a parallel system of transmitting codes. However, the drawback of electroacoustic mercury tubes, namely the delay in access to numbers, is even more characteristic of the magnetic drum. Thus memory units with magnetic drums are used for machines of comparatively low speed (of the order of several hundred operations per second). On the other hand, a magnetic drum allows a marked increase in the capacity of the memory unit with only a tolerable increase in the amount of apparatus. Thus the magnetic drum and the magnetic tape are often used in universal machines as complementary (exterior) memory units in addition to fast-acting (operative) memory units.

In high-speed electronic computing machines with parallel operation, cathode-ray tubes are often used for the memory unit (figure 18). If the electron beam is directed at any point of the screen, then at this point there is accumulated an electric charge. The charge will be preserved for a considerable time, so that it is possible to record number codes on the screen. In the process of making a computation, a beam of electrons is again directed to the required point. If the given element has not been charged, it now receives a charge, and through the signal plate and the output amplifier there emerges a code pulse. But if the element is charged, the signal does not emerge. In this way we can determine whether a signal has been recorded at a given point or not. After access to the code we must re-establish the previous state of the given element, which is done automatically by a special circuit. In exactly the same way it is necessary to renew the code recordings periodically, in order to avoid an essential change in the charge by stray electrons and leakage through the dielectric.

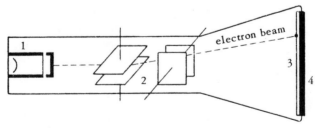

Fig. 18.   Basic scheme of a cathode-ray tube:
(1) source of electrons;   (2) deflection plates;
(3) screen;   (4) signal plate.

Usually there are 1,024 (32 × 32) or 2,048 (32 × 64) points distributed over the screen. The direction of the beam of electrons to the required point is accomplished by appropriate voltages on two pairs of deflecting plates.

In machines with parallel operation, every digit of a binary number requires its own cathode-ray tube and access to the number is made simultaneously for all tubes. The access time, including the entire operation of the element, may be reduced to a few microsèconds.

Recently use has been made of memory units with magnetic elements that have rectangular hysteresis loops (figure 19). If we put a positive signal through the coil, then the core is positively magnetized and for a negative signal it will be negatively magnetized.

With the removal of the signal, the core remains magnetized either positively or negatively. Thus, the state of the core characterizes the signal recorded. In the computing process, there passes through the coil a signal of specific polarity, for example, a positive one. If in this case the core was magnetized negatively, then a remagnetization will occur (a change in the magnetic flux),

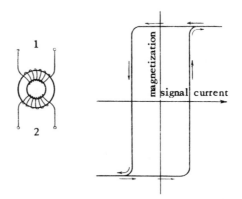

FIG. 19.   Basic scheme of a memory element with a rectangular hysteresis loop:
(1) input coils;   (2) output coils.

and in the output coil there will be induced an electromotive force, which is fed into an amplifier. But if the core was magnetized positively, then a change in its state will not take place, and no signal will arise in the output coil. In this way it is possible to distinguish which signal has been placed on a given element. Of course, after access has been had to the code, it is necessary to restore the original state of the core, which is done by a special circuit.

§4. Prospects for the Development and Use of Electronic Computing Machines

The use of electronic computing machines will inevitably have a great influence on the development of many fields in contemporary science and technology, especially in the physical and mathematical sciences. Thus it is appropriate for us to indicate the basic prospects for further application of computing machines and their significance for mathematics.

Further extension of the areas of application of mathematical machines; 1. Improved machines. At the present time there is continuous and intensive technological progress going on in the production of high-speed computing machines, in further improvement of their construction, and in the use of new physical principles and of combinations of new types. Thus we may expect better technical properties for these machines (speed, capacity of the memory, regularity, and reliability of operation), and also a notable simplification in their construction and use which will guarantee their widespread distribution.

The diversity of the types of the machines will be another factor ensuring their widespread use. Along with powerful machines of enormous capacity there will be the small-gauge machines that are simple to use and are within the purchasing power of any scientific or planning institute or of a factory; in addition to the universal ones, there are simpler special machines, intended for some specific range of problems; besides the purely digital machines other types have been invented, which accept data from certain devices, perform digital calculations on them, and then give out the results again continuously in the form of curves or of values of parameters controlling various units of the machine.

2. Better programming. A second path to new effectiveness in the use of these machines is further improvement in methods of programming. The construction of programs in the usual manner, described in §2, is easy for comparatively simple mathematical problems; in actual problems of any magnitude, it involves very complicated and detailed labor. This work may be lightened to a certain extent by the use of a "library" of standard subroutines, set up permanently for the calculation of basic functions and for performing certain necessary mathematical operations, such as inversion of a matrix or numerical integration. In spite of this, the fitting of subroutines into the basic program, addressing and re-addressing the results, and testing and rearranging the program is a quite complicated and detailed task calling for definite skill. This fact may essentially delay the setting up of new problems for electronic machines.

There are two possibilities for further development in this direction. One of them consists of constructing the program automatically by using the machine itself for this purpose, i.e., by converting the basic formulas and the logical structure of the problem, placed in the machine in coded form, into the desired program through the operation of the machine in accordance with a special "programming program."

The second direction consists of having the machine operate on a certain special universal program, which immediately examines and performs the operations in accordance with a general plan of computation introduced into the machine; this general plan would contain a number of important problems (for example, the solution of a system of equations) and, without setting up the detailed working of the program, would guarantee that the correct results were worked out and assigned to each particular problem.

3. More intellectual tasks. Further progress in the application of computing machines in mathematics is connected with the use of the machines for the performance not only of numerical calculations but also of the standard calculations of analysis.

Basically such a possibility is, in well-known cases, altogether practicable. For example, if we describe a polynomial by its set of coefficients, then such operations as multiplication and division of polynomials consist of arithmetic operations on sequences of coefficients, which are easily programmed on machines. By the use of specific coding in describing a function, it is completely possible to construct a program which gives the derivative of an elementary function (described in the same code), i.e., which allows one to perform the analytic process of differentiation. All these facts ensure the possibility in the future of solving problems by a specific method (for example, of solving a system of differential equations by means of power series), with complete carrying out of all the analytic and numerical calculations. In this manner, computing machines may be used for performing quite subtle and typically intellectual tasks (but only of a standard character), just as the present machines of the everyday world have replaced the physical labor not only of the stevedore but also of the seamstress.

The influence of high-speed machines on numerical and approximative methods. The means and instruments used in any task naturally influence the methods of the work itself. For example, trigonometric formulas computed by using logarithms are unsuitable for use on computing machines, on which only multiplication and division can be carried out directly. The use of a desk machine calls for entirely different computational schemes in approximation methods (for example, nondifference schemes in differential equations).

The fundamental changes in computational instruments and the possibilities that have been opened up by the use of electronic computing machines have naturally brought about a change of attitude not only toward the methods of computational analysis but also, to a great extent, toward the problems of mathematics in general and their applications.

Let us consider a few questions where the changes are most evident.

Mathematical tables and other ways of introducing functions into the computation. First of all, electronic machines made a fundamental change in our powers of computing tables. In place of a single table of functions, we witness an annual output of hundreds of tables, including complete and exact tables for all the basic special functions, not only for one but for several variables. But at the same time an essential change must be made in the structure of the tables. For use in high-speed machines, compact tables are appropriate, containing widely spread basic values and designed for interpolation of a high order.

In many cases, in place of tables, it is convenient to use other methods of introducing functions into the machines, namely polynomials of best approximation over subintervals, expansions in continued fractions, approximating formulas based on numerical calculation of an integral which represents the function, and so forth; all of these may profitably be introduced, in various cases, into the program of computation of a given function.

Special functions and partial analytic solutions. The special functions themselves and the solutions of problems in finite analytic form still retain their significance for qualitative investigation of a problem and for clearing up the character of its singularities, both of which are important for a numerical solution. In certain large-scale problems, the use of such special functions may provide the most economical means of finding the solution numerically. Nevertheless, the construction in many particular cases of an exact or approximate solution, by means of complicated apparatus or of the special functions that were formerly introduced for greater ease of computation, has turned out to be a mistaken policy. For machine calculations it is much simpler and shorter to find the solution by general numerical methods without making use of any of the analytic representations discussed earlier.

Thus the very considerable efforts that have been made to put into complicated analytic form the solutions of various particular problems in technology and mechanics have in many cases turned out to be wasted.

The choice of computational methods. It is incorrect to say that, because of the high productivity of electronic machines, there is no need to develop approximating methods further and that we may always use the most primitive methods. In reality, only for the simplest one-dimensional problems where, independently of the choice of method, the calculation will not run to more than a few thousand steps, can the solution be found on the machine in a few seconds or minutes.

For the systematic solution of newer, more complicated problems the number of steps may well amount to several hundred million, so that a proper choice of methods to decrease this number is quite essential. Consequently, it is a matter of great practical importance to work out effective methods of approximation, especially for multidimensional problems such as interpolation of functions of many variables, computation of multiple integrals, solution of systems of nonlinear algebraic or transcendental equations, solution of three-dimensional integral equations, systems of partial differential equations, and so forth.

At the same time there has been a considerable change in our attitude of mind in estimating the value of approximative methods; they must be judged by the ease with which they can be carried out on the machine or by their universality, that is, by the extent of their applicability to massive problems. Methods lose a great deal in value if they depend on special peculiarities of the problem or on the skill of the person who is directing the computation

The greatest value must be attached to universal methods that apply to a wide range of problems: difference methods, variational methods, the gradient method, iterative methods, linearization, and so forth.

Of course, in choosing a computational method and the manner of carrying it out, one must remember that the method is in fact carried out on the machine, so that in some cases one ought to take into account the peculiarities of construction of the given machine. In particular, one must consider maximal use of the operative memory, minimization of the data introduced from outside, the possibility of introducing intermediate checks, and the convenience of programming the problem.

But one must not think that the machine can carry out only the simplest methods, based on one kind of operation. The wide possibilities in programming and the latest improvements in its methods allow us to carry out very complicated computational programs with many different branches, so that we can change the course of the computation according to the results obtained, which is hard to do even with hand computations. The only essential requirement is that all these possibilities be completely provided for in advance.

Also one must not think that no methods can be carried out which require algebraic operations. As mentioned above, it is also completely possible to carry out some of the operations of analysis.

Significance of the estimates of error. In estimates of error for approximation methods, greater significance must be attached to those of an asymptotic character, since large values of n (for example, the number of equations replacing an integral equation by an algebraic system), small steps in difference methods, and so forth, are fully realizable on high-speed machines. In any comparison of the value of various approximative methods, primary consideration must be given to asymptotic estimates describing the rapidity of convergence of the method.

To increase the usefulness of machine methods, greater attention must be paid to *a posteriori* estimates of the error; that is, estimates made on the basis of the solution already computed. Such estimates may be included in the program and will then help to determine the future course of the computation. For example, if it is seen that the error is unacceptably large, the computation may be automatically repeated with steps decreased by half. In this connection *a posteriori* estimates may turn out to be more convenient and practical than *a priori* ones, which are inevitably too high and considerably more complicated.

The possibility of theoretical analysis of the problem. There is still another possible use for the information obtained in the numerical solution of a problem. In fact, by applying the methods of functional analysis to the approximation obtained, we may judge the existence and uniqueness of the solution, and also establish the range of the solution. Since the investigation of such questions by purely theoretical methods is sometimes extremely complicated and lengthy, and in many cases altogether impracticable, the possibility of making use for this purpose of numerical calculations produced on the machine is undoubtedly of interest.

New problems in numerical methods. The sharp increase in computational possibilities and the accumulation of skill in their use has given rise to an entirely new range of problems in the investigation of numerical methods. Instead of being used in isolated cases as in the past, the solution of systems of linear equations with a large number of unknowns has now become established as a fixed element in the solution of mathematical problems. This fact has given great practical importance to the following question: How important for the accuracy of our determination of the unknowns is the influence of rounding off, not only of the coefficients but also of various processes in the course of the solution? This question has led to a series of interesting investigations.

The possibility of numerical integration on the machine of a system of differential equations over a large interval with small steps has given acute importance to the question of stability of the process of numerical integration. Experimental analysis of this question and subsequent theoretical investigation have produced a considerable change in our estimates of the value of various methods of numerical integration of differential equations.

Questions of stability have primary significance also for the application of difference methods to partial differential equations.

New methods. The possibility of using machines had led to the appearance of completely new types of approximative and numerical methods or on the other hand has made it quite possible and convenient to employ the older methods in cases where up to now they had seemed completely impracticable. A characteristic example is the method of random sampling or, as it is often called, the "Monte-Carlo method." This method consists of finding a probability problem whose solution (probability, mathematical expectation) is identical with the desired quantity. In this probability problem the solution is found experimentally, by random sampling, as the mean value in a series of experiments. For example, to find the area of a figure defined by the inequality $F(x, y) \geqslant 0$ and contained in the square $(0, 1; 0, 1)$, we make as long a sequence as we like of random choices of pairs of numbers (x, y) contained in this square and then determine what fraction of these pairs satisfy the given inequality. Of course, such a method will be very ineffective if the trials are made by hand, but if they are done on a machine, then it is fully practicable. The trials themselves may be carried out by means of a table of random numbers. For certain problems, e.g., for calculating a multiple integral without great exactness, such a method may even be more effective than any other.

A similar method may also be used for the problem of inverting a matrix, if we apply it to samples forming a Markov chain, and also for the solution of partial differential equations, if we have found a stochastic (probabilistic) process connected with it.

The significance of high-speed machines for mathematical analysis, mechanics, and physics. In mathematical analysis great interest and practical importance is attached to investigations of multidimensional problems leading to the integral equations and boundary-value problems of mathematical physics. These investigations and the resulting methods of solution are no longer impracticable but will now be put into effect as a result of the new computing techniques, especially since the solution of such problems is of urgent importance at the present time.

Of course, the value of these newly developed methods must be judged by the ease with which it is possible to put them into practice.

On the other hand the possibility, thanks to machines, of carrying out with sufficient exactness a computation involving a large number of trials has led to an enormous extension in the range of application of "mathematical experiments" for the preliminary investigation of a mathematical problem and to a great increase in their effectiveness. This fact has made it important to work out applications of this Monte-Carlo method not only in general but also for particular problems; for example, the qualitative investigation of differential equations.

It is interesting also to note that the machines may be used in problems of analysis not only in applications but also for purely theoretical questions. Thus machine computation may prove necessary to increase the accuracy of the constants in certain inequalities and estimates in functional analysis; applications of this sort occur not only in analysis but also in the theory of numbers.

Finally, machines may be used for testing the correctness of formulas of mathematical logic, and since many mathematical propositions and proofs can be written by means of the symbols of mathematical logic, it becomes theoretically possible to test on high-speed machines the logical correctness of certain mathematical deductions.

As for mechanics and physics, we must first of all emphasize the vast increase in the application of mathematics in these sciences. Up to the present time the application of mathematics to concrete problems of mathematical physics was restricted by the enormous volume and complicated character of the necessary computations. In the problems arising in actual practice, this volume was usually such that the computation for one problem required several months and in some cases even several years of computational work. Thus, in spite of the fact that general mathematical formulations of many problems were known in mechanics and theoretical physics, and methods of their solution had been worked out in theory, in actual fact mathematical solutions, exact or numerical, had been obtained only for a few idealized and highly simplified cases, such as plane or axially symmetric problems, especially simple boundaries, or an airplane wing of infinite length.

As a result the mathematical solutions were used not so much for finding the necessary numerical values as for a qualitative and tentative investigation of the problem, which in practice had to be supplemented by costly experiments.

On the other hand, the application of new computing methods opens up the possibility of large-scale solutions of problems of mechanics and physics with all their actual complications (space problems, problems with complicated boundary contours, and nonlinear partial differential equations).

Of course, the actual carrying out of this possibility requires further development of the methods of numerical analysis and of machine solution for these problems. However, the practicability of treating such problems in this way has been strikingly demonstrated by successful experience with solution on high-speed machines of systems of partial differential equations in meteorology, in gas dynamics, in the equations of friable materials, and in other questions.

The application of theoretical mathematical analysis to problems of mechanics and physics with a close approximation to the actual physical problems and the increase in rapidity and flexibility resulting from the use of high-speed machines has made it possible in many cases to replace physical experiments by mathematical ones. This possibility will lead to further improvement in the methods of investigating problems in physics and mechanics and will increase the role played in them by theoretical and computational methods.

The significance of electronic machines for technology and industry. The rapidity and effectiveness of numerical solutions of problems of mathematical analysis also allow us to make much greater use in the various branches of technology (structural mechanics, electrical engineering and radiotechnology, the exploitation of water power, and so forth) of theoretical methods and consequently to produce much more accurate and practical results. It is now possible to apply mathematical analysis to many technical problems where it has not been used before.

In addition to the numerical solution of problems of mathematical analysis encountered in technology, a completely different application of mathematical machines to technology has been discovered. It will be possible to apply mathematical machines, for example in technical planning, to the choice of various possibilities for the construction or distribution of various objects. In questions of the organization of an industry many solutions are possible to the problem of distributing the various tasks and determining their proper sequence. The choice of the best, the most productive, and the most economical solution presents great difficulty. Here also one may find applications of machines; if it is possible to program a systematic examination of various solutions that takes account of the features of interest to us, then with the help of the machines we may compare several hundred thousand variants, which would be impossible by usual methods.

In particular, a series of relay-contact circuits allows us to analyze and verify these solutions by the methods of mathematical logic, which may be carried out on high-speed machines. In this way it is possible to select a set of such variants on the basis of any desired criteria and then to choose the best one among this selected set.

Of great promise is the use of machines in the automatic control of industry, if such machines are used in conjuction with servomechanisms and transmission devices. For example, if geometric data concerning a manufactured article are introduced into the machine, together with a specific program for the purpose, it will determine and transmit parameters that will govern the motion of a power press and make necessary changes in the article. Because of its high speed, the same electronic machine may be used for simultaneous control of the work of several presses. It is also easy to see the significance of such machines for automatic guidance of moving objects, for example interplanetary rocket projectiles, since the guidance program can take into account not only the data originally introduced but also the changes in position indicated by various recording devices.

In this way, the construction and analysis of computing machines and the possibilities of their application present a wide field of activity for mathematicians. The use of mathematical machines in the coming years will undoubtedly play a great role in the development of our technology and culture.

Suggested Reading

F. L. Alt, *Electronic digital computers: their use in science and engineering*, Academic Press, New York, 1958.

A. D. Booth and K. H. V. Booth, *Automatic digital calculators*, Academic Press, New York, 1953.

P. von Handel (Editor), *Electronic computers: fundamentals, systems and applications*, Prentice-Hall, Englewood Cliffs, N. J., 1961.

G. N. Lance, *Numerical methods for high-speed computers*, Iliffe and Sons, London, 1960.

D. D. McCracken, *Digital computer programming*, Wiley, New York, 1957.

J. J. Murray, *Mathematical machines*, I, *Digital computers*, II, *Analog devices*, Columbia University Press, New York, 1961.

J. von Neumann, *The computer and the brain*, Yale University Press, New Haven, Conn., 1958.

R. K. Richards, *Arithmetic operations in digital computers*, Van Nostrand, New York, 1955.

G. R. Stibitz and J. A. Larrivee, *Mathematics and computers*, McGraw-Hill, New York, 1957.

M. V. Wilkes, *Automatic digital computers*, Wiley, New York, 1956.

INDEX

This revised, enlarged index was prepared
through the generous efforts of Stanley Gerr.

375

CONTENTS OF THE SERIES

VOLUME ONE

PART 1

PART 2

CONTENTS

CONTENTS OF THE SERIES

VOLUME THREE

PART 5

PART 6

CONTENTS